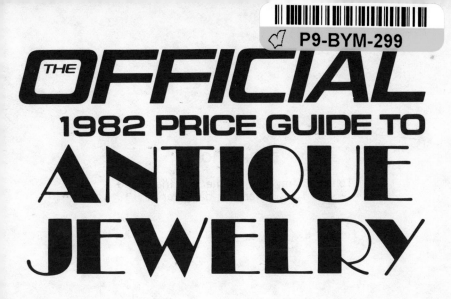

THE OFFICIAL
1982 PRICE GUIDE TO
ANTIQUE JEWELRY

BY
ARTHUR GUY KAPLAN

EDITOR
THOMAS E. HUDGEONS III

FIRST EDITION

THE HOUSE OF COLLECTIBLES, INC., ORLANDO, FLORIDA 32809

P9-BYM-299

DEDICATION

To Robin - my wife, partner and friend and
To Jennifer - our daughter

Published by: The House of Collectibles, Inc.
                Orlando Central Park
                1900 Premier Row
                Orlando, FL 32809
                Phone: (305) 857-9095

Printed in the United States of America

Library of Congress Catalog Card Number: 78-72035

ISBN: 0-87637-341-4 / Paperback

ACKNOWLEDGEMENTS

This book involved the cooperation and assistance of a countless number of individuals and firms, many of which are mentioned under the Photographic Recognition list. Thanks are due to Jean R. Butler of Robert W. Skinner, Inc., Raizel Halpin of Ares Antiques, Ian Harris of N. Bloom & Son (Antiques) Limited, M. K. Harwood of James Robinson, Inc., Kathy Mitzel, typist, Maggie Nimkin of PB Eighty-Four, Roy Perry, photographer, M. Douglas Schmidt, photographer, Jonathan W. Snellenburg of Christie's East, The Victorian Society in America, the Surrat Society, Clinton, Maryland, and Duane Suter, photographer. My family also deserves recognition for their sacrifies during the two years it took to prepare this book.

Dozens of private individuals have supplied photographs or lent their collection to me to have photographed, with the sole express direction that their name not be included. Without this assistance it would have been impossible to collect the number and range of photographs included in the book. A special thanks to each of you.

PHOTOGRAPHIC RECOGNITION

The following numbers indicate the page and item number of each individual piece of jewelry: 12-5 (page 12, item 5); Color-6 (entire color page 6); Color-6-2 (color page 6, item 2)

Loaned by Ares Incorporated, New York, New York - 92-3, 92-6, 96-24, 362-1, 367-29, 378-95, 382-2, 383-8.

Courtesy of Ashland, Buffalo, New York - 548-4, 548-5, 549-6, 550-12, 551-16, 552-17, 553-21, 555-28, 559-42, 560-45, 561-49, 570-21, 577-45.

Courtesy of Auktionshaus Peter Sneichen, Zurich, Switzerland - 26-112, 60-98, 232-15 to 17, 242-40, 549-7, 549-8, 550-9 to 11, 551-13, 551-15, 553-22, 555-29, 557-36 to 38, 561-48, 581-1 to 7, 582-8 to 23, 583-24 to 36.

Courtesy of N. Bloom & Son (Antiques) Limited, London, England - color 1, color 2, color 3, color 6, 67-6, 68-7, 69-18, 70-19, 70-20-23, 71-27, 72-31, 73-36, 73-37, 79-66, 79-67, 100-40, 136-51, 157-1 (bottom), 159-10, 225-4, 247-2, 251-9, 256-47, 262-4, 277-17, 323-7, 326-6, 336-23, 338-30, 344-51, 364-13, 372-64, 375-79, 380-107.

Courtesy of Christie's, 1979 - 29-2 (clasp), 30-3 to 8, 291-1, 293-12, 294-13 to 16, 295-17 to 20, 296-21 to 25, 297-26 to 31, 298-32 to 36, 299-37 to 41, 300-42 to 46.

Courtesy of Christie's, 1980 - 39-5, 39-6, 126-15, 127-21, 168-7, 258-56, 345-55.

Courtesy of Christie's East, 1979 - 87-42, 107-5, 108-12, 109-14, 119-58, 332-13, 335-20, 335-22, 342-43, 396-20, 398-33, 398-34, 434-218, 434-219, 439-255, 522-27.

Courtesy of Peter Delfino, Jr. - 279-29.

Courtesy of S.L. Emmet - 354-13.

Courtesy of G and M Antiques, Washington, D.C. - 23-99, 111-26, 120-63, 270-16, 365-19.

Copyright Hart Publishing Company, Inc. - 11-4, 12-13, 12-14, 13-15 to 22, 14-23 to 28, 15-32 to 35, 16-44, 16-45, 18-55, 19-60, 19-63, 20-72, 20-73, 21-75, 21-76, 22-88, 27-5, 28-8, 29-1 (bracelet), 29-2 (bracelet), 36-1, 37-7, 38-2, 38-3, 41-12, 42-17, 44-25, 45-27, 51-60, 53-66 to 68, 54-69, 54-70, 55-75, 57-86, 158-2, 171-31, 172-34, 181-4, 186-27, 209-6, 210-8, 214-31, 216-47, 219-63, 237-28, 241-36, 242-38, 244-9, 246-19, 255-38, 255-39, 255-41, 255-42, 258-54, 260-70, 261-1 to 3, 262-5 to 8, 263-17 to 20, 264-21 to 25, 267-1, 268-9, 270-20, 270-21, 311-38, 311-39, 332-12, 336-25, 339-33, 350-72, 352-5, 352-6, 372-63, 580-54.

Courtesy of Heirloom Jewels Ltd. - 17-52, 18-53, 97-28, 125-11, 143-89, 144-93, 311-37, 331-8.

Reproduced by permission of the Director, Institute of Geological Sciences, Crown Copyright reserved, London, England - gemplate 1 and 2

Courtesy of Barbara B. Jackson - 99-37, 101-43, 101-44, 102-45, 164-5, 164-7, 165-8, 165-11, 166-12, 166-13, 383-12 to 14, 495-22.

Courtesy of Trina Kearney - 127-24, 308-20, 347-62.

Courtesy of Ceceile Klein - 212-21, 212-22, 217-50, 250-18, 254-37, 419-93.

Used with permission 1896 Marshall Field Jewelry and Fashion Catalogue, Copyright by DBI Books, Inc. - 80-9, 81-15, 81-17, 82-4, 84-16, 84-19, 88-45, 91-65, 136-47, 167-1, 167-5, 167-6, 169-17 to 22, 170-23, 170-25 to 27, 170-29, 171-30, 172-37 to 40, 173-2, 174-9, 175-10, 175-11, 177-20, 178-21 to 23, 179-28, 179-29, 189-3 to 6, 190-7 to 10, 191-11 to 14, 220-1 to 6, 221-7 to 12, 222-13 to 18, 223-19 to 24, 224-25, 224-26, 226-1, 226-2, 230-10, 243-2, 248-10, 249-11, 252-11 to 13, 254-30, 260-80, 267-2 to 5, 268-6 to 8, 269-10 to 15, 271-22 to 27, 272-28, 272-29, 273-1, 273-2, 273-4, 273-5, 274-6 to 8, 274-1 to 3, 275-4 to 6, 276-13 to 16, 277-21, 278-24, 278-25, 283-48, 283-49, 283-52, 284-54 to 58, 285-59, 285-60, 285-62 to 64, 286-67 to 70, 287-71, 287-72, 287-75, 287-76, 303-2, 314-53, 315-1, 316-2, 382-121, 384-1 to 3, 384-8, 385-9 to 21, 386-22 to 28, 386-2, 386-3, 388-15 to 17, 389-25, 409-1 to 4, 409-7, 409-10, 415-53 to 57, 417-76, 420-97, 420-103, 420-104, 421-107 to 112, 422-121 to 123, 423-124 to 127, 426-151 to 156, 426-158, 429-183 to 185, 430-186 to 194, 431-195 to 201, 435-225 to 232, 436-233 to 235, 439-259, 440-266 to 268, 446-1, 448-8, 454-1, 456-15, 459-31, 461-45, 464-61 to 67, 465-1 to 3, 466-9, 467-17, 468-23, 469-24, 469-28, 472-14, 472-15, 473-19, 473-21, 473-22, 481-48, 482-49, 483-57, 484-65 to 67, 485-68 to 72, 486-75 to 77, 497-1, 497-2, 499-13, 499-15, 499-16, 500-17, 500-19 to 21, 501-22 to 24, 502-28 to 31, 503-2 to 4, 503-6, 503-7, 505-15 to 17, 506-19, 506-22, 508-28, 509-31 to 34, 547-1, 547-3, 551-14, 552-19, 552-20, 554-24, 554-26, 555-27, 555-30, 556-34, 557-35, 561-47, 561-50, 565-4, 565-6, 567-13, 568-16, 569-19, 569-20, 572-28, 572-29, 574-36, 578-47, 578-48, 579-51, 579-52, 580-56.

Used with permission 1894-95 Montgomery Ward & Co. Catalogue, Copyright by DBI Books, Inc. - 36-2, 80-1 to 8, 81-10 to 14, 81-16, 81-2, 82-6, 82-7, 83-12, 84-15, 84-17, 84-18, 85-28, 85-29, 86-30, 86-33, 87-38, 87-39, 90-57, 90-60, 91-66, 132-25, 132-26, 136-48, 140-73, 141-80, 141-81, 145-100 to 103, 146-104, 146-105, 167-2, 167-3, 168-12, 168-13, 169-16, 170-24, 171-32, 172-35, 172-36, 192-2, 192-3, 193-4 to 8, 194-9, 194-10, 194-12, 195-13, 195-14, 195-16, 196-17 to 19, 197-1 to 6, 198-7 to 12, 199-13 to 18, 200-19 to 24, 201-25 to 30, 202-31 to 36, 203-37 to 43, 204-44 to 46, 205-49 to 54, 206-55 to 60, 207-61 to 65, 209-1, 209-4, 209-5, 210-7, 210-9 to 12, 211-13, 211-14, 212-18, 212-20, 213-24, 213-27 to 29, 214-30, 214-34, 215-37, 215-38, 215-40, 215-41, 216-48, 216-49, 217-54, 218-56, 218-57, 219-65 to 67, 219-71, 251-3 to 6, 252-15 to 18, 253-21, 253-23, 253-24, 254-28, 254-29, 254-31 to 36, 255-44, 258-55, 258-58, 258-59, 259-61 to 68, 260-71 to 79, 262-9 to 12, 263-13 to 16, 362-4, 363-9, 363-10, 365-17, 365-20 to 22, 368-34 to 36, 370-48 to 51, 371-56, 372-61, 377-87, 377-89, 379-100 to 105, 380-108, 380-110, 380-111, 384-1 to 6 (top), 384-4 to 7 (bottom), 386-29, 386-1, 386-4, 387-6, 387-8 to 10, 387-12, 387-13, 388-18, 388-19, 388-21, 389-24, 389-26, 403-64 to 71, 404-72 to 78, 405-79-86, 409-8, 409-9, 415-58 to 60, 416-61 to 66, 417-77-81, 420-98 to 101, 421-113, 421-114, 426-157, 426-159 to 161, 427-162, 427-163, 427-166 to 170, 431-202, 432-203, 436-236 to 239, 439-260, 440-269, 440-270, 447-2, 448-7, 455-7 to 9, 456-13, 456-14, 458-28, 459-33, 459-34, 460-40, 462-50, 462-51, 463-57, 463-58, 465-4 to 6, 466-8, 466-12, 468-18, 468-19, 468-22, 469-25 to 27, 469-29 to 33, 472-13, 472-16, 472-17, 473-23, 474-24 to 27, 476-38, 481-42 to 45, 482-50 to 52, 482-54, 482-55, 483-56, 483-61, 484-62, 487-78, 487-80 to 85, 492-1 to 4, 493-13, 496-26, 505-12 to 14.

Courtesy of Munderly Antique Shows - 339-34, 343-49, 578-46.
Courtesy of M. McAleer, London, England - 163-1, 164-4, 165-9, 165-10, 166-14, 255-40, 255-43.
Courtesy of James Robinson, Inc., New York, New York - 74-42, 344-50, 518-17, 521-26.
Courtesy of E. A. Show Antiques - (color 8 bottom), 58-87, 125-10, 134-39, 188-33, 192-15, 245-14, 276-11, 280-34, 293-10, 293-11, 378-93, 411-20, 411-21, 411-23, 413-32, 422-117, 448-3 to 5, 458-29, 459-32, 462-49, 471-9, 486-73, 486-74, 494-14, 494-15, 511-2, 533-12, 547-2.
Courtesy of Robert W. Skinner Inc. - 44-24, 67-4, 289-6, 333-16, 500-18, 534-14.
Copyright Sotheby Parke Bernet, Inc., 1979 - 12-11, 14-29 to 31, 15-36 to 38, 16-40, 16-41, 17-47, 20-68, 21-77, 22-86, 22-87, 22-89, 23-94, 23-95, 24-103, 25-108, 31-1 to 3, 31-5, 32-7 to 9, 33-10 to 13, 34-15 to 18, 35-19 to 22, 39-7, 40-11, 42-16, 42-18, 44-22, 45-29, 47-39, 48-40, 48-41, 49-52, 50-56, 51-58, 52-64, 54-71, 55-74, 55-76, 56-80 to 83, 59-92, 59-95, 67-1 to 3, 68-8 to 10, 68-12, 69-13 to 17, 71-28, 72-32 to 34, 73-38, 74-40, 74-41, 74-43, 75-44, 75-46, 75-47, 75-49, 76-50, 77-54, 77-55, 77-59, 78-60 to 62, 79-64, 79-65, 81-1, 82-3, 82-5, 82-9, 83-13, 85-23, 85-26, 85-27, 86-34, 86-35, 87-36, 87-40, 88-47 to 49, 89-50 to 54, 90-56, 90-59, 90-61, 92-5, 93-10, 95-19, 96-21 to 23, 98-32, 98-33, 99-34, 102-1, 102-2, 103-3 to 106, 104-7 to 11, 105-12 to 14, 106-3, 106-4, 107-6 to 8, 108-9, 108-10, 108-13, 109-17, 109-18, 110-22, 111-24, 112-28 to 31, 113-33 to 35, 114-36 to 38, 114-40, 115-41, 115-43, 115-44, 116-45 to 48, 117-49, 117-51, 117-52, 118-53 to 57, 119-60, 120-64, 120-65, 121-67, 121-68, 122-3 to 5, 123-4, 124-6 to 8, 125-13, 126-17 to 19, 127-22, 127-23, 128-1 to 6, 129-7 to 11, 130-17, 130-18, 131-22, 131-23, 132-27 to 29, 133-30 to 32, 134-35, 134-37, 135-40 to 43, 137-52, 137-53, 137-55, 137-56, 137-58, 138-58, 138-59, 138-61 to 63, 139-66, 139-67, 140-71, 140-72, 142-82, 142-84, 143-87, 143-88, 143-90, 143-91, 144-92, 145-97 to 99, 146-106, 146-2, 147-4 to 6, 157-1 (top), 157-2, 157-3, 159-7, 175-13, 177-18 178-24, 178-25, 182-8, 182-10, 183-14, 184-16, 184-18, 185-20, 185-24, 186-25, 192-1, 194-10, 217-55, 218-59 to 62, 219-70, 224-1,224-2, 243-1, 243-3, 243-4, 244-8, 244-11, 245-12, 245-13, 245-15, 246-18, 247-1, 248-6 to 9, 249-12 to 15, 250-17, 250-1, 251-8, 253-25 to 27, 256-45, 256-46, 259-69, 261-81, 266-2 to 4, 272-30, 275-9, 276-12, 278-22, 278-23, 278-26, 278-27, 279-28, 279-30, 281-41, 283-47, 286-66, 288-1, 288-2, 289-7, 298-8, 292-4, 292-6, 302-50, 303-3, 304-4, 304-6, 305-8, 308-23, 308-24, 311-40, 312-41, 312-42, 313-47, 320-27, 321-28, 322-3, 323-6, 324-9, 325-2, 326-5, 331-10, 333-17, 335-21, 336-24, 338-29, 338-31, 338-32, 339-35, 341-39, 342-42, 343-47, 346-56, 346-57, 347-59, 350-71, 351-2, 351-3, 352-7, 353-8, 353-11, 354-14, 356-1 to 3, 356-6, 357-8, 357-10, 357-11, 358-12 to 15, 359-16 to 19, 363-8, 363-11, 364-12, 367-28, 367-30, 368-37, 368-28, 369-39, 369-44, 370-52, 372-59, 373-65, 374-72, 375-78, 376-85, 376-86, 377-88, 378-97, 380-113, 381-117 to 120, 383-9, 387-5, 389-22, 394-1, 394-2, 395-6 to 8, 395-12, 396-14, 396-15, 396-17, 396-19, 397-21, 397-22, 397-26, 398-28, 398-30 to 32, 399-35, 399-36, 399-38 to 43, 400-44 to 50, 401-51 to 54, 401-56, 402-57 to 63, 406-87 to 89, 407-99 to 102, 408-103 to 105, 408-111, 408-112, 409-6, 410-14 to 17, 411-18, 413-32 to 39, 414-41 to 50, 415-51, 415-52, 416-69, 417-72 to 75, 418-87 to 89, 419-90, 422-115, 422-116, 422-119, 422-120, 425-146 to 149, 427-165, 428-173 to 176, 429-178 to 182, 432-205 to 210, 433-211 to 217, 434-222 to 224, 437-240, 439-254, 440-262, 440-263, 442-284, 442-2, 443-3, 443-5, 444-10 to 13, 445-1, 445-2, 448-9, 451-10, 454-4, 463-54, 468-20, 470-4 to 7, 471-8, 475-35, 476-39, 481-47, 482-53, 483-59, 497-3 to 5, 498-7, 498-9, 498-10, 501-26, 501-27, 502-32, 502-33, 502-35, 507-24, 507-26, 508-27, 512-4, 513-5, 514-9, 516-11 to 13, 518-18, 519-20, 523-28, 523-29, 526-36, 526-37, 527-40, 528-41, 528-42, 531-47, 556-32, 562-1 to 5, 563-6 to 9, 564-10, 565-2, 567-14, 568-15, 568-17, 570-22, 571-27, 573-33, 574-35, 575-38, 575-39, 579-53.
Copyright Sotheby Parke Bernet, Inc., 1980 - 11-3, 11-5, 11-6, 12-8 to 10, 12-12, 16-39, 16-42, 16-43, 17-48 to 51, 18-54, 18-56, 18-58, 18-59, 19-61, 19-64, 19-66, 20-67, 20-69 to 71, 20-74, 21-78, 21-80, 21-81, 22-84, 22-85, 22-90, 22-91, 23-93, 23-96 to 98, 24-101, 24-102, 24-104 to 107, 25-109 to 111, 26-113 to 117, 29-1 (clasp), 32-6, 34-14, 35-23, 40-9, 41-13, 43-20, 43-21, 45-30, 46-33, 47-37, 47-38, 48-44 to 46, 49-47 to 52, 50-57, 51-61, 51-62, 52-63, 55-77, 58-88 to 90, 59-93, 59-94, 59-97, 68-11, 71-24 to 26, 71-29, 74-39, 75-45, 75-48, 76-51, 76-53, 77-56, 77-57, 78-63, 79-68, 82-8, 83-10, 83-11, 84-20, 84-21, 85-24, 86-31, 86-32, 87-37, 87-41, 88-43, 88-44, 88-46, 89-55, 90-58, 90-62 to 64, 91-67, 93-7 to 9, 97-25 to 27, 98-29 to 31, 106-1, 106-2, 109-15, 109-16, 110-19 to 21, 111-25, 111-27, 113-32, 114-39, 115-42, 119-59, 121-66, 121-1, 121-2, 122-6, 123-1 to 3, 124-5, 125-12, 125-14, 126-16, 129-9, 130-12 to 16, 131-19 to 21, 133-33, 134-36, 134-38, 135-44, 136-45, 136-46, 136-49, 137-54, 138-64, 139-68 to 70, 140-74, 140-76, 141-77 to 79, 142-83, 142-85, 142-86, 144-94 to 96, 146-3, 159-8, 167-4, 170-28, 173-4, 174-6, 177-17, 177-19, 181-1 to 3, 181-5, 182-6, 182-7, 182-9, 183-11, 183-13, 184-15, 184-17, 185-19, 185-21 to 23, 186-26, 186-28, 188-34, 188-35, 188-2, 209-3, 225-6 to 8, 233-19, 243-5, 244-6, 244-7, 244-10, 246-16, 246-17, 246-20 to 22, 247-3, 250-16, 251-7, 253-22, 257-50, 257-51, 257-53, 258-57, 259-60, 266-1, 270-17 to 19, 273-3, 275-8, 275-10, 277-18, 277-20, 280-35, 282-46, 283-50, 288-3 to 5, 289-9, 291-2, 292-3, 292-7, 293-9, 301-48, 302-52, 304-5, 304-7, 305-9, 305-11, 307-16, 309-26, 309-27, 310-29 to 36, 312-43, 313-46, 317-11, 320-24 to 26, 321-29, 321-1,322-2, 322-4, 323-5, 324-8, 324-11, 325-1, 325-3, 326-4, 329-2 to 4, 330-6, 330-7, 332-11, 334-19, 337-26, 340-37, 340-38, 342-45, 343-46, 345-52 to 54, 346-58, 348-63, 348-64, 349-66, 349-67, 351-1,352-4, 353-9, 353-10, 354-12, 356-4 to 5, 357-7, 357-9, 362-2, 362-3, 363-7, 364-15, 366-24, 367-31, 367-32, 369-43, 370-45 to 47, 371-53 to 55, 371-57, 371-58, 373-66, 373-67, 374-73, 375-75, 375-76, 376-80, 376-82 to 84, 377-90 to 92, 378-94, 378-98, 379-99, 380-112, 381-114, 381-118, 382-4, 382-5, 383-10, 383-11, 389-23, 389-1, 389-3, 390-4, 391-13, 391-14, 393-25, 394-4, 395-9, 395-11, 395-13, 396-16, 397-24, 398-29, 401-748, 407-97, 408-110, 410-13, 412-27, 412-28, 412-30, 412-31, 416-68, 417-70, 418-83 to 86, 419-94 to 96, 420-106, 422-118, 424-140, 425-142 to 144, 425-150, 432-204, 434-220, 434-221, 437-246, 438-247, 438-250 to 253, 440-264, 440-265, 441-274, 443-6, 444-15, 450-2, 450-5, 451-8, 452-17, 452-19, 453-23, 457-19, 458-25, 460-37 to 39, 467-13, 471-10, 473-23, 474-28, 475-33, 483-60, 484-63, 492-7, 493-12, 494-18, 498-6, 498-8, 499-11, 499-12, 499-14, 501-25, 502-34, 503-1, 507-23, 508-30, 511-1, 512-3, 515-10, 516-14, 517-15, 517-16, 519-19, 519-21, 520-23, 525-34, 525-35, 527-38, 527-39, 530-45, 531-46, 560-46, 564-1, 565-5, 566-7 to 11, 567-12, 569-18, 570-23, 571-24, 571-25, 572-30, 573-32, 573-34, 574-37, 575-40, 576-41, 576-43, 578-49, 580-55.
Courtesy Spinning Wheel Magazine, Antiques & Early Crafts, September, 1973 - 229-8, 230-11, 231-13, 233-20, 234-21, 234-22, 236-26, 237-27, 240-33, 240-34, 241-35, 242-39.
Courtesy of Kathleen Sullivan - 292-5.
Courtesy of Shirley Sue Swaab - 63-12, 148-2, 393-29.
Courtesy of Everna Marguerite Zabell - 160-1 to 3, 161-4, 161-5, 162-6, 162-7.

TABLE OF CONTENTS

COVER · DESCRIPTIONS

ABOUT THE AUTHOR

Arthur Guy Kaplan, a Maryland attorney, has been actively involved in the antique jewelry field for the past 12 years. In addition to participating in antique shows throughout the United States and lecturing on antique jewelry, items from Mr. Kaplan's collection have been exhibited nationally in several museum exhibitions, including *REMEMBER THE LADIES* co-sponsored by the National Endowment for the Arts, Philip Morris and Clairol, (1976); *A TIME TO MOURN* co-sponsored by the Museum of Stonybrook, N.Y. and the Brandywine Museum, Del. (1980-1981); and *MOURNING BECOMES AMERICA* sponsored by the Harrisburg Historical Society, PA (1976).

He has published numerous articles on various facets of antique jewelry both here and abroad and has recently acted as expert consultant for the article on antique jewelry in *THE ENCYCLOPEDIA OF COLLECTIBLES,* Time-Life Books, Inc., (1979).

The author requests that the reader forward any photographs and descriptions for inclusion in subsequent volumes. Information regarding any errors or other omissions would be welcomed. Send information to:

Arthur Guy Kaplan
P. O. Box 1942
Baltimore, Maryland 21203

INTRODUCTION

Antique jewelry, as in all fields of antiques, can be found almost anywhere. The major sources for the purchase of antique jewelry consist of organized indoor antique shows, retail stores, auction houses and outdoor flea markets, all of which are located throughout the United States and Europe. Each country has its own particular flavor in the kind of antique show or market available to the person interested in the purchase of antique jewelry. In Madrid, Spain, the Rastro is an area, open every Saturday and Sunday, consisting of block upon block of street vendors who lay down a sheet and set up a small wooden frame table to display and sell their wares. Jewelry and watches are often found among the items for sale. The following photograph illustrates one of the hundreds of booths at the Rastro selling pocket watches.

Rastro, Madrid Spain

Paris and Rome are both famous for their enormous flea markets. London is in a class by itself. It is possible to spend several weeks in London and visit antique shops or outdoor antique markets from morning to night without going to the same place twice. Every Saturday in London is an outdoor-combination-indoor market at Portobello Road. It has become as much a tourist attraction as a serious selling market. Camden Passage is open every Tuesday, Wednesday and Saturday, Bermondsey every Friday, and scores of indoor markets throughout the City are open the entire week. On almost any Sunday a one-day indoor fair of approximately 50 to 100 dealers can be found in the ballroom of one of the local hotels. The country outside of London is as active as the City of Dickens in its selling of antiques.

Both nationally known and local auction houses in the United States sell a tremendous volume of antique jewelry. As an example, one auction house in New York sold almost ten million dollars in jewelry during the fall of 1980. Indoor antique shows and outdoor flea markets have developed a large devoted following in the United States. Antique shows provide hours of entertainment and free education without the requirement of a single purchase. Most antique jewelry dealers are anxious to share their knowledge and allow the public to examine and handle their stock.

The purpose of this book is to present as many illustrations as possible of jewelry from 1750 to 1930 with the primary emphasis on the 19th century. This book is arranged in chapters according to the type of jewelry, i.e., rings, bracelets, pendants, chains, etc. Each chapter is then sub-divided. After each picture is a brief description and a price range, in order to enable you to compare the described item of jewelry to a similar piece that you own or might acquire. Unfortunately, some of the descriptions are not detailed due to the fact that photographs were supplied from many sources — private collections, museums, auction houses, and other antique dealers. When the jewelry photograph is from an auction catalogue, information from the description in the auction catalogue has been included in the written description in this book. Sometimes the description has been modified by the author. Descriptions were only supplied with some of the photographs, therefore it was impossible to give you specifics such as the length or weight of each item.

Bermondsey, London England

The data to calculate the retail prices listed in this book are from numerous sources, all of which were compiled and adjusted by the author. The photographs of jewelry from auction houses supplied the author both an estimated range that the items would sell for as well as the actual prices realized at the date of the auction. The photographs supplied from antique shops and dealers were also supplied with the current retail price of those items from the respective dealers locality. Individuals that supplied photograps from their private collections often presented the insurance appraisal as a guide. All of the above information was considered, with the ultimate responsibility for the price range falling upon the author. When an item is sold at auction the price can indicate one of many things - it can be a realistic indication of the retail price of that item on the current market or it can be either grossly lower or grossly higher than the actual retail price due to the lack of interest or a frenzy of activity on a particular day. Information has been supplied from several sources in London, England, as well as the United States and the Continent. One English pound has been valued at $2.35 and one Swiss franc has been valued at .62¢ in the price calculations.

The best and simplest advice that we can give to the individual interested in purchasing a piece of antique jewelry is that they should only purchase an expensive piece of jewelry from a dealer or auction house whom they have confidence in or who has a reliable reputation. A receipt should be given listing in detail the description of the item purchased along with the date and a statement that the item can be returned if found not to be accurately described.

ABBREVIATIONS AND EXPLANATIONS OF TERMS

c. . . . . Circa, approximate period of time when item was made.
ct. . . . . Carat, weight of gemstone, under one carat.
cts. . . . . Carat, weight of gemstone, over one carat.
Gold . . . . Yellow gold at least nine karat pure unless different color or karat stated.
Hair . . . . Human hair of brunette color unless noted otherwise.
HC . . . . Hunting case watch, cover on both sides of case.
MM . . . . Millimeter
OF . . . . Open face watch, cover on one side of case.
Sapphire . . . . Gemstone, blue in color unless noted otherwise.
9K . . . . Nine karat gold.
10K . . . . Ten karat gold.
14K . . . . Fourteen karat gold.
15K . . . . Fifteen karat gold.
18K . . . . Eighteen karat gold.
22K . . . . Twenty-two karat gold.

RECOMMENDED READING

Dozens of books have been written on antique jewelry, most of which include glossaries. Since the unique nature of this book is to present thousands of photographs of antique jewelry with accompanying descriptions, space limitations have not permitted a detailed glossary to be included in this edition. The following books offer excellent additional reading material on antique jewelry:

Armstrong, Nancy. *JEWELLERY AN HISTORICAL SURVEY OF BRITISH STYLES & JEWELS,* Luttenworth Press, 1977.

Armstrong, Nancy. *VICTORIAN JEWELRY,* Cassell & Collier Macmillan Publishers Ltd., 1976

Baillie, G. H. *WATCHMAKERS AND CLOCKMAKERS, OF THE WORLD,* N.A. G. Press Ltd., 1969.

Baillie, G. H., Clutton, C. and Ilbert, C. A. *OLD CLOCKS AND WATCHES AND THEIR MAKERS,* Bonanza Books, New York, 1956.

Bainbridge, Henry Charles, *PETER CARL FABERGÉ - GOLDSMITH AND JEWELER TO THE RUSSIAN IMPERIAL COURT,* Spring Books, 1971.

Bradford, Ernie. *ENGLISH VICTORIAN JEWELLERY, Spring Books, 1967.*

Bradford, Ernie. *FOUR CENTURIES OF EUROPEAN JEWELLERY,* Spring Books, 1967.

British Museum Publication. *JEWELLERY THROUGH 700 YEARS,* British Museum Publications Limited, 1976.

Burgess, Fred W. *ANTIQUE JEWELRY & TRINKETS,* Tudor Publishing Company.

Clifford, Anne. *CUT-STEEL & BERLIN IRON JEWELLERY,* Adams & Dart, 1971.

Cooper, Diana and Battershill, Norman. *VICTORIAN SENTIMENTAL JEWELLERY,* A. S. Barnes & Co., Inc., 1973.

Curran, Mona. *COLLECTING ANTIQUE JEWELLERY,* Emerson Books, Inc., 1970.

Delieb, Eric. *SILVER BOXES,* Ferndale Editions, London, 1979.

Evans, Joan. *A HISTORY OF JEWELLERY 1100-1870,* Boston Book and Art, Publisher, Boston, 1970.

Falkiner, Richard. *INVESTING IN ANTIQUE JEWELLERY,* Barrie & Rocklif, The Cressent Press, The Corgi Ed. 1976.

Flower, Margaret. *VICTORIAN JEWELLERY,* A. S. Barnes & Co., Inc., 1967.

Fregnac, Claude. *JEWELRY FROM RENAISSANCE TO ART NOUVEAU,* Octopus Books Limited, 1973.

Garside, Anne. *JEWELRY, ANCIENT TO MODERN,* Viking Press, 1980.

Gere, Charlotte. *AMERICAN & EUROPEAN JEWELRY 1830-1914,* Crown Publishers, Inc., 1975.

Goldenberg, Rose Leman. *ANTIQUE JEWELRY: A PRACTICAL & PASSIONATE GUIDE,* Crown Publishers, 1976.

Gregorietti, Guido. *JEWELRY THROUGH THE AGES,* American Heritage, New York, 1969.

Lewis, M. D. S. *ANTIQUE PASTE JEWELLERY,* Boston Book & Art, Publisher, 1973.

Mason, Anita and Packer, Diane. *AN ILLUSTRATED DICTIONARY OF JEWELLERY,* Harper & Pow, Publishers, 1974.

McNeil, Donald S., editor. *JEWELERS DICTIONARY 3RD EDITION,* Jewelers' Circular-Keystone, Radnor, Pennsylvania, 1979.

O'Day, Deirdre. *VICTORIAN JEWELLERY,* Charles Letts and Company, Limited, 1974.

Peter, Mary. *COLLECTING VICTORIAN JEWELLERY,* Emerson Books, Inc. 1971.

Poynder, Michael. *THE PRICE GUIDE TO JEWELLERY,* Baron Publishing, 1976.

Sataloff, Joseph and Richards, Alison. *THE PLEASURE OF JEWELRY AND GEMSTONES,* Octopus Books, 1975.

Tait, Hugh and Gere, Charlotte. *THE JEWELLER'S ART,* British Museum Publications Limited, 1978.

BASIC GLOSSARY

The definitions in this glossary are to acquaint the reader with some of the terms used in the descriptions of the pictured jewelry.

AMBER
Light weight fossilized sap, resin or gum from ancient trees which can be cut, etched, faceted or carved. Amber can be translucent or opaque and range in color from shades of yellow, brown, red and even grey or green.

BOG OAK
Natural oak wood which has been darkened and hardened as a result of being immersed in the bogs of Ireland.

CABOCHON
An unfaceted cut stone with a smoothly polished domed top.

CAMEO
A stone or shell cut in relief using the natural colors of the stone or shell to produce the different shadings of the carving. Opposite of an intaglio. See-intaglio.

CANNETILLE
Metal jewelry, usually made from fine wires, often in a pyramid or rosette motif.

CASTELLANI, FORTUNATO PIA
19th century Italian jeweler noted for his revival of Etruscan and Greek styles in jewelry which were sold as pieces as "Italian Archaological Jewelry."

CHAMPLEVÉ ENAMEL
The sections in which the different color enamel are placed are carved out of the surface of the base, rather than formed by soldering thin strips of metal to the base as in cloisonné enamel.

CHATELAINE
A decorative plaque with a hook attached to its rear to be worn from a belt or sash around the waist from which suspend a series of plaques or chains. Purses, watches, keys, sewing utensils, note pads, pencils, button hooks, etc. were the type of functional implements connected to the ends of the plaques or chains.

CLOISONNÉ ENAMEL
A type of enamel work in which thin strips of metal are soldered to the base to form the outlines of the design. Colored enamel is then placed in each section.

DISSOLVED HAIR
Human hair which has been chopped up and made into a paint or paste to be used for drawing pictures on ivory or porcelain plaques. The result of using dissolved hair is a fuzzy effect.

EDWARDIAN
Referring to that period of time encompassing the reign of England's King Edward VII, 1901-1910.

ENAMEL
Powdered colored glass is fused onto the surface of the piece of jewelry. The following types of enamel work are illustrated and defined in this book: Champleve, Cloisonne, Guilloche, Jaipur, plique a jour and polychrome.

ETRUSCAN
A 19th century antique revival style of jewelry resembling that which was produced in Tuscany, central Italy, during the 7th to 6th centuries B.C. by the ancient Etruscans. The work is characterized by minute beads of gold soldered onto a gold background forming a pattern. See granulation.

ÉTUIS
A case, hanging from a chatelaine, which contains useful implements, such as scissors, pencil, small spoon, pad, ear cup cleaner, toothpick, etc.

GEORGIAN
Referring to an era of English history encompassing the reigns of King George I 1714-1727; George II 1927-1760; George III 1760-1820; and George IV 1820-1830.

GRANULATION
Minute metal beads, usually gold, used to decorate jewelry. See Etruscan.

GUILLOCHE ENAMEL
A translucent polychrome enamel placed on top of a geometric engraved pattern on the jewelry or watchcase.

HAIR
Jewelry woven from human hair which was made either as a romantic token for a loved one or from the hair of a deceased friend or family member as a sentimental remembrance. Jewelry can also be found woven from horsehair and elephant hair.

INDIAN PITCH
A plaque made from pouring green glass onto gold foil, which has been cut-out in a mold in hunting scene motifs. After the glass is set, it is polished until the glass is level with the gold foil, forming a silhouette effect. Popular after Queen Victoria became Empress of India in 1876.

INTAGLIO
An engraved stone in which the design is carved into the surface of the stone so that the rim is the highest portion. The opposite of a cameo. See Cameo.

IRON
Berlin Iron jewelry is jewelry made from case iron primarily at the Berlin Iron Foundry, though some cast iron jewelry was made in France in the late 1820's. The Berlin Iron Foundry began producing the cast iron jewelry after 1804, with the height of popularity being 1813-1815, the time of the war of Liberation against Napoleon. During this period, faithful Germans donated their gold jewelry to the war effort and in return received cast iron jewelry. Relatively little cast iron jewelry has survived due to its lack of intrinsic value and its highly brittle and perishable nature.

JAIPUR ENAMEL
A region in India named Jaipur which is the center of the jewelry industry. Indian jewelry is characterized by brightly-colored enamels on both the front and back.

JET
Hard coal, mined at Whitby, England, was highly polished and carved and primarily sold as memorial jewelry.

LAVA
Lava found at Pompeii, Italy, was primarily carved as cameos, ranging in color from cream to dark brown and white to charcoal. It is very soft and therefore permits a skilled artisan to carve fine detail with high relief.

MACARONI
A style of chatelaine composed of a series of long chains with a watch on one end and on the other end a series of charms, such as watch keys and seals.

NUTMEG GRATER
A small box made from the 17th century to the middle of the 19th century with a removable grate under the lid for the grating of precious spices such as nutmeg.

PARURE
A matching set of jewelry usually including a necklace, pendant, brooch, earrings and bracelet.

PASTE
Colored or clean glass, often lead or flint glass, which are cut in the same fashion as gemstones. Antique paste jewelry was valued on its own merits and not as an imitation of another piece of jewelry.

PAVÉ
A style of setting stones where a number of small stones are set as close together as possible.

PINCHBECK
Christopher Pinchbeck, 1670-1732, was a London jeweler, watchmaker and alchemist who invented a substitute for gold made from an alloy of copper and zinc.

PIQUÉ
Tortoise shell or ivory which has been inlaid with gold, silver or mother-of-pearl.

PLIQUE Á JOUR ENAMEL
Transparent enamel which is placed between thin strips of metal which are soldered together to form the design, the end result of which is similar to stained glass. Plique a jour is distinguished from cloisonne in that there is no base to which the strips of metal and enamel rest.

POLYCHROME ENAMEL
Enamel in various colors.

SATSUMA
A Japanese ceramic overlaid with a glaze that forms hairline cracks. Over the glaze are figures, flowers and decorations painted in polychrome enamel.

SCARAB
A representation of the ancient Egyptian Scaraboeus bettle carved in either glazed pottery or in gemstones such as amethyst, corneilian, and lapis lazuli. Scarabs were customarily in swivel mountings so that the intaglio carved on the reverse side could be viewed.

SCARF RING
An oval ring to hold a scarf at the neck. The most common style available is one which opens on a hinge and has a pointed spike in the inside center to hold the scarf together. Hollow oval and pressure clip oval scarf rings can also be found in todays' marketplace.

TIGER CLAW
Tiger claws from India were imported to England, mounted in precious metals, and worn as jewelry. Popular in the 1870's, particularly after Queen Victoria became Empress of India in 1876.

TORTOISE SHELL
Jewelry carved, molded, inlaid, polished, welded and cut from the hard protective outer covering of the Hawksbill turtle and the Loggerhead turtle in a blond, translucent amber or dark opaque reddish amber color.

VICTORIAN
Referring to that period of time encompassing the reign of England's Queen Victoria 1837-1901. The Victorian ear is generally broken down into three phases, Early Victorian 1837-1850, Mid-Victorian 1850-1875 and Late Victorian 1875-1901.

VINAIGRETTE
A small box with a removable pierced grill under the lid in which a sponge or cotton was saturated with spirits of ammonia or Aromatic vinegar. Circa: late 18th century through 19th century.

WATCHCOCK
The escapement covers in watches made in the late 18th century were highly engraved and cutout in animal, flower and circular swirl motifs. During the 1870's these watches were junked and jewelry was made from combining the watchcocks.

HOW TO USE THIS BOOK

The reader has two avenues of approach for the retrieval of information. The detailed index is of value to pinpoint the page where a particular topic is located. For example, if you wish to see a photograph of an example of Etruscan granulation, simply look up Etruscan in the alphabetical index and it will refer you to those pages in the book where that style of workmanship is pictured.

A collector who desires to identify a personal piece of jewelry, should go immediately to the table of contents. The chapters are arranged according to the type of jewelry, i.e. bracelets, rings, watches, stickpins, etc. If a bracelet needs identification, locate the bracelet chapter, and either turn to the sub-division in that chapter, or if the collector is not sure as to which sub-division would be applicable, the collector can simply skim the entire chapter to identify his article of jewelry. The vast majority of books on antique jewelry are arranged in chapters according to either the period of the jewelry or the material out of which the jewelry is made, i.e. coral, hair, mosaic, diamond, etc. This book is divided simply as to the type of jewelry. As an example, if you have a bracelet made out of woven hair it will be located under the sub-division of hair bracelets in the bracelet chapter. Rings made out of hair will be in the ring chapter.

Antique jewelry cannot be sold or valued according to the weight of the gold in the individual piece, for this does not take into account the historical and artistic significance of the item. The uniqueness and rarity of a piece of antique jewelry can place a value on an item far in excess of the melt down value of the metal content of the piece of jewelry. Nevertheless, at the time of the calculation of the prices in this book, gold was selling for approximately $500.00 per ounce.

Photograph taken in Baltimore, Maryland in 1920. The young wife is wearing a pearl cluster bar pin and small gold ball earrings. The husband sports a gold link watch chain from his lapel and a stickpin of a skull and crossbones.

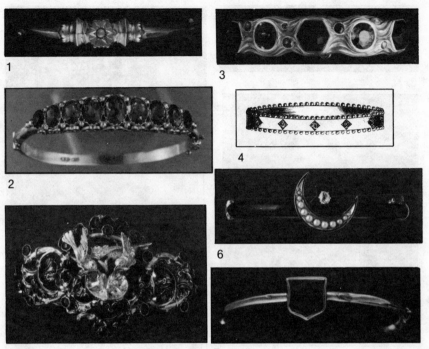

BRACELETS

BANGLE · GOLD

			PRICE RANGE	
☐	**1** Acid finish center motif, set with single turquoise, hollow triangular tube bangle, American, c. 1830-40		200.00	250.00
☐	**2** Amethyst bangle, eight faceted amethysts, ribbon motif, marked: "NBs," 9K gold, English		600.00	800.00
☐	**3** Art nouveau motif in a swirl design with faceted amethyst and colored stones, gold, maker: Tiffany & Co., American, c. 1915		5000.00	5500.00
☐	**4** Beaded edge flat bangle, five round diamonds in front, gold, English, c. 1903-04		425.00	475.00
☐	**5** Bird and flower motif, green enamel oak leaves, round red cabochon translucent red stones, gold, c. 1870		2500.00	2800.00
☐	**6** Black opaque enamel hollow tubular bangle, 11 pearls in crescent, one round diamond in star, gold, c. 1850		1200.00	1500.00
☐	**7** Bloodstone intaglio shield motif, hollow tubular bangle, 15K gold, marked: "R° 8228," English . . .		300.00	350.00

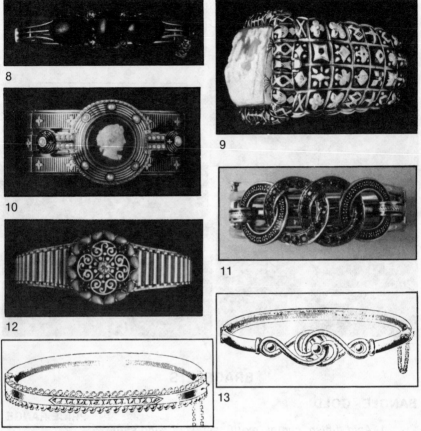

8

9

10

11

12

13

14

☐ **8** *Cabochon garnets, four rose diamonds, gold, c. late 19th* **1500.00 1800.00**

☐ **9** *Cameo center, shell cameo of an outdoor market, bangle with black and white enamel in a geometric motic, gold, c. 1880* **2000.00 2500.00**

☐ **10** *Chalcedony cameo, seed pearls, black enamel, gold, c. late 19th* **1800.00 2200.00**

☐ **11** *Circle motif bangle, rubies in one circle, sapphires in one circle, enamel design, gold* **2200.00 2600.00**

☐ **12** *Circular motif center, one round diamond, four round sapphires, 16 pear-shape turquoise, white enamel, gold, c. late 19th* **1100.00 1200.00**

☐ **13** *Cultured pearl bangle, modified loveknot motif, three pearls, gold, English, c. 1900* **240.00 280.00**

☐ **14** *Cultured pearl bangle, 17 pearls in straight row in center, gold, English, c. 1903-04* **260.00 300.00**

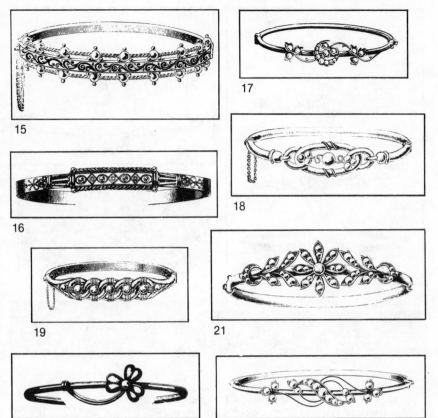

☐	**15**	*Cultured pearl flat bangle, 18 pearls, engraved scroll motif, gold, English, c. 1903-04*	**340.00** **380.00**
☐	**16**	*Cultured pearl flat bangle, seven pearls in center, rope motif, engraved, gold, English, c. late 19th* .	**260.00** **300.00**
☐	**17**	*Cultured pearl hollow tubular bangle, 18 pearls in crescent and flower motif, gold, English, c. 1903-04*	**300.00** **350.00**
☐	**18**	*Cultured pearl hollow tubular bangle, pearls in flower and circle motif, gold, English, c. 1903-04* .	**260.00** **300.00**
☐	**19**	*Cultured pearl hollow tubular bangle, nine pearls in circle motif, gold, English, c. 1903-04*	**260.00** **300.00**
☐	**20**	*Cultured pearl hollow tubular bangle, single pearl in clover, gold, English, c. 1903-04*	**150.00** **200.00**
☐	**21**	*Cultured pearl hollow tubular bangle, 45 pearls in flower and leaf motif, gold, English, c. 1903-04* . .	**350.00** **400.00**
☐	**22**	*Cultured pearl knife-edge bangle, seven turquoise in center swirl, ten pearls in leaf motif, gold, English, c. 1903-04*	**300.00** **350.00**

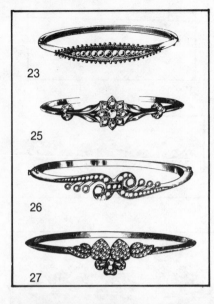

29

31   30

☐	23	*Cultured pearl knife-edge bangle, 14 pearls in straight row in center, gold, English, c. 1903-04* . .	260.00	300.00
☐	24	*Cultured pearl knife-edge bangle, 28 pearls, one cabachon garnet, gold, English, c. 1903-04*	280.00	320.00
☐	25	*Cultured pearl knife-edge bangle, 19 pearls in flower motif, gold, English, c. 1903-04*	300.00	350.00
☐	26	*Cultured pearl knife-edge bangle, 40 pearls in scroll motif, gold, English, c. 1903-04*	300.00	350.00
☐	27	*Cultured pearl knife-edge bangle, 73 pearls pavé set in two hearts, bow, and cluster motif, small round diamond in center of each heart, gold, English, c. 1903-04*	525.00	575.00
☐	28	*Cultured pearl knife-edge bangle, 42 pearls in horseshoe and flower motif, gold, English, c. 1903-04*	325.00	375.00
☐	29	*Devils head carved from labradorite, rose diamond eyes, plain bangle, 15K gold, English*	1200.00	1500.00
☐	30	*Diamonds, five old mine diamonds approx. 1.0 ct., engraved bangle, gold*	1200.00	1400.00
☐	31	*Diamonds, three round diamonds, engraved bangle, gold, inscribed: "A.C.," 1911*	650.00	850.00

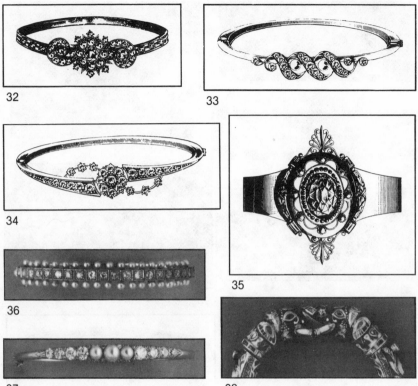

☐ **32** *Diamond flat bangle, 43 round diamonds in cluster and scrolls, gold, English, c. 1903-04* **2800.00   3200.00**

☐ **33** *Diamond knife-edge bangle, 19 round diamonds and two pearls in scroll motif, gold, English, c. 1903-04* **800.00   900.00**

☐ **34** *Diamond knife-edge bangle, 29 round diamonds in cluster and scroll motif, gold, English, c. 1903-04* **2200.00   2500.00**

☐ **35** *Diamond wide flat bangle, rose diamond approx. 2.5 cts. in elaborate gold on gold motif, designed by Prof. R. Reinhardt, Stuttgart, Germany, c. 1902* **3500.00   4000.00**

☐ **36** *Diamonds and pearls, 20 round diamonds approx. 1.50 cts., two rows of cultured pearls, 14K gold* **1600.00   2000.00**

☐ **37** *Diamonds and pearls, eight round diamonds approx. 1.50 cts., three cultured pearls, platinum prong setting, plain gold bangle* **2600.00   3000.00**

☐ **38** *Elephant heads, champlevé enamel round bangle in translucent blue, red, green and opaque white, rose diamonds, gold, Indian, c. 19th* **1700.00   2000.00**

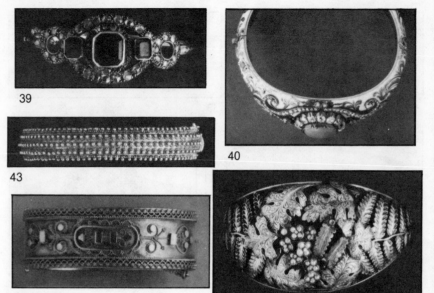

39

40

43

41

42

44

45

□ **39** *Emeralds and diamonds, three emerald-cut emeralds, rose diamonds in circle motif, silver topped gold, c. late 19th* **4000.00 5000.00**

□ **40** *Enamelled opaque white motif engraved bangle, round blue cabochon stone surrounded by old mine diamonds in center, rose diamond swirl design, gold, c. mid 19th* **3000.00 3500.00**

□ **41** *Etruscan granulation wide bangle, gold, c. 1840* . **550.00 650.00**

□ **42** *Fern and oak leaf motif, cut-out and engraved leaves, seed pearl flowers, gold, c. 1840* **1200.00 1500.00**

□ **43** *Flat bangle, Etruscan granulation, 18K gold, c. late 19th* **1000.00 1200.00**

□ **44** *Flat bangle, 13 round rubies in straight row in center, ten round diamonds along each edge, gold, English, c. 1903-04* **1200.00 1500.00**

□ **45** *Flat bangle, two round diamonds and one round ruby in center, Etruscan granulation, engraved, gold, English, c. late 19th* **225.00 300.00**

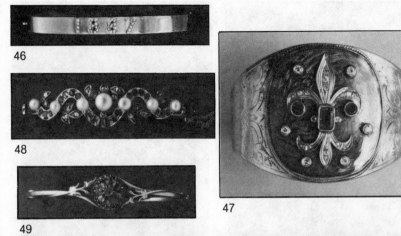

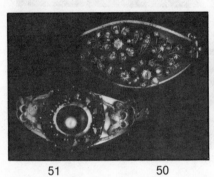

☐ **46** *Flat narrow bangle, the date "1887" is set with oriental seed pearls commemorating the Golden Jubilee (50 years) of the reign of Queen Victoria, gold, English, c. 1887* 300.00 350.00

☐ **47** *Fleur-de-lys motif on wide engraved bangle, blue enamel, 22 round diamonds, one emerald-cut and two round emeralds, gold, c. 1820* 1800.00 2300.00

☐ **48** *Floral openwork motif, 22 emerald-cut emeralds, one round emerald, seven pearls, rose diamonds, gold, c. early 20th* 1200.00 1400.00

☐ **49** *Flower motif, hollow flat band, rose diamond cluster in silver, gold, c. 1880* 550.00 700.00

☐ **50** *Flower motif, rose diamonds, translucent blue enamel, gold, c. 1860* 1800.00 2200.00

☐ **51** *Garnet cluster center, one round pearl, guilloche translucent red enamel, gold, c. 1870* 700.00 900.00

☐ **52** *Garnets pavé set in flat bangle with flower cluster in center, low karat gold, c. late 19th* 400.00 500.00

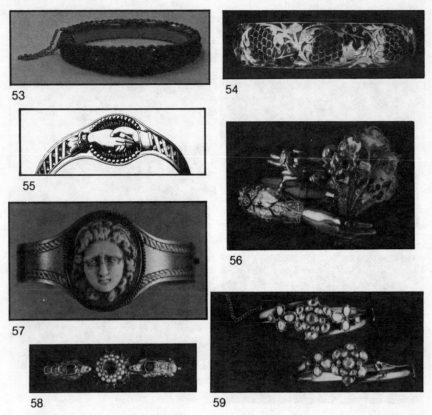

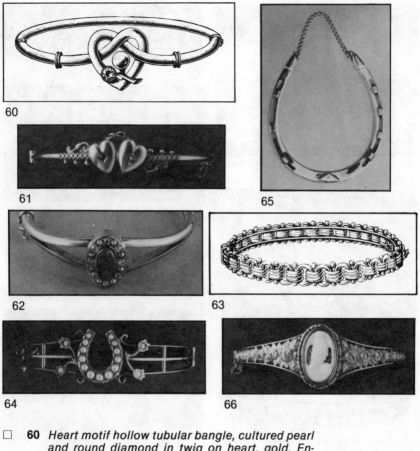

60

61

65

62

63

64

66

☐ **60** *Heart motif hollow tubular bangle, cultured pearl and round diamond in twig on heart, gold, English* 380.00 450.00

☐ **61** *Heart motif hollow tubular bangle, scroll and gold ball design, one pearl and one ruby in hearts, gold, c. 1900.* 200.00 250.00

☐ **62** *Hollow tubular bangle, opal doublet surrounded by round diamonds and pearls, 15K gold, inscribed: "In Memoriam, July 25, 1887, May 19, 1890, Pro Pat 254," English, c. 1880-90* 2000.00 2400.00

☐ **63** *Hollow oval and ball design links, gold, English, c. 1903-04* 300.00 350.00

☐ **64** *Horseshoe motif, knife-edge bangle, seed pearls, gold, c. 1900* 300.00 400.00

☐ **65** *Horseshoe motif bangle with a hinge, fitted leather box, inscribed: "M.L.M. 1905," maker: The Goldsmiths & Silversmiths Company Ltd., 112 Regent St., London, gold, c. 1905* 900.00 1200.00

☐ **66** *Ivory cameo and floral motif, carved, gold, c. late 19th* 1000.00 1200.00

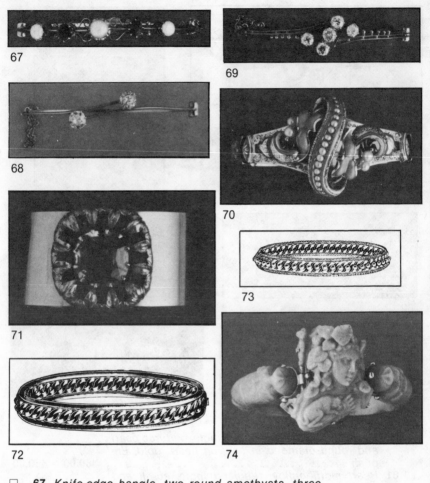

67

69

68

70

73

71

72

74

☐	**67**	*Knife-edge bangle, two round amethysts, three half pearls, gold, c. 1880*	**600.00** **800.00**
☐	**68**	*Knife-edge bangle, two old mine diamonds approx. 1.50 cts., gold, c. 1879*	**3400.00** **3800.00**
☐	**69**	*Knife-edge bangle, five old mine diamonds approx. 1.65 cts., gold, c. late 19th*	**900.00** **1100.00**
☐	**70**	*Leaf motif, pearls, turquoise enamel, gold, c. 1870* .	**900.00** **1200.00**
☐	**71**	*Leaf motif with cushion-cut chrysoberyl center, some enamel on leaves, wide bangle, maker: Cartier, 14K gold, c. early 20th*	**2000.00** **2400.00**
☐	**72**	*Link motif bangle, gold, English, c. 1903-04*	**300.00** **350.00**
☐	**73**	*Link and bead motif bangle, gold, English, c. 1903-04*	**300.00** **350.00**
☐	**74**	*Lion heads, carved lady and small dog in center, coral, gold, c. 1860*	**1600.00** **2000.00**

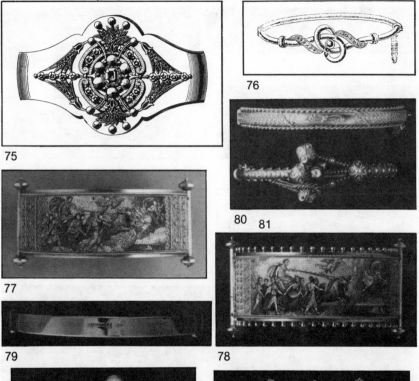

75

76

80 81

77

79

78

82

83

☐	**75**	*Lotus flower design wide flat bangle, blue and red stones, maker: O. Weber, gold, c. 1868-83* . . .	2600.00	3400.00
☐	**76**	*Loveknot hollow tubular motif, engraved scrolls, gold, English, c. 1903-04*	150.00	200.00
☐	**77**	*Mosaic of chariot, people and angels, Etruscan granulation borders, gold, Italian, c. 1860*	3800.00	4200.00
☐	**78**	*Mosaic of chariot, people and angels, Etruscan granulation borders, beaded rim, fitted leather box marked: "G. Roccheggiani, Rome," gold, Italian, c. 1860*	4000.00	4500.00
☐	**79**	*Narrow bangle, 9K gold, English*	125.00	150.00
☐	**80**	*Narrow flat bangle, Etruscan granulation, gold, c. 1870.*	500.00	550.00
☐	**81**	*Tubular asymmetric bangle, Etruscan granulation, one old mine diamond, gold, c. 1865*	650.00	850.00
☐	**82**	*Opal, hollow tubular bangle, gold*	280.00	325.00
☐	**83**	*Opal straight row surrounded by rope motif, 9K gold, English*	250.00	300.00

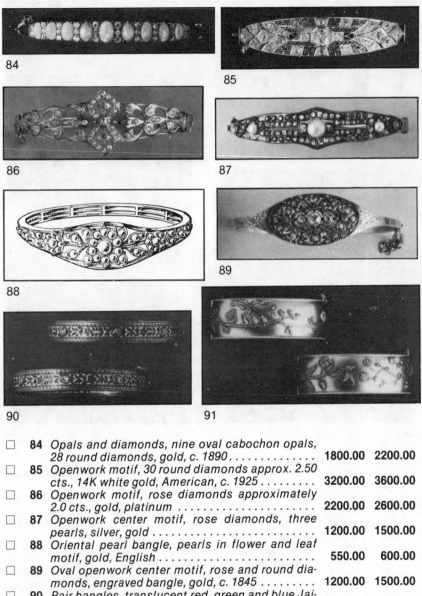

84

85

86

87

88

89

90

91

☐	**84**	Opals and diamonds, nine oval cabochon opals, 28 round diamonds, gold, c. 1890	1800.00	2200.00
☐	**85**	Openwork motif, 30 round diamonds approx. 2.50 cts., 14K white gold, American, c. 1925	3200.00	3600.00
☐	**86**	Openwork motif, rose diamonds approximately 2.0 cts., gold, platinum	2200.00	2600.00
☐	**87**	Openwork center motif, rose diamonds, three pearls, silver, gold	1200.00	1500.00
☐	**88**	Oriental pearl bangle, pearls in flower and leaf motif, gold, English	550.00	600.00
☐	**89**	Oval openwork center motif, rose and round diamonds, engraved bangle, gold, c. 1845	1200.00	1500.00
☐	**90**	Pair bangles, translucent red, green and blue Jaipur enamel, rose diamonds, gold, Indian, c. 19th .	2200.00	2600.00
☐	**91**	Pair bangles, platinum, rose and green gold applied flowers and leaves, yellow gold, fitted leather box, maker: Tiffany & Co., American, c. 1890	4000.00	5000.00

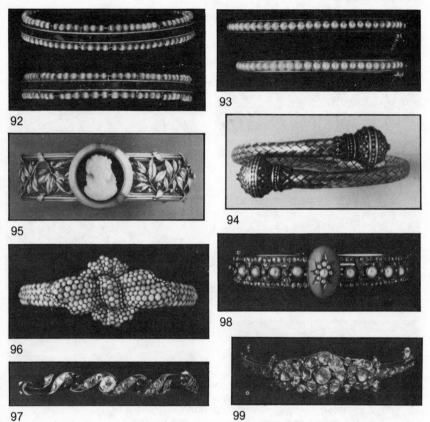

92

93

94

95

96

97

98

99

☐ **92** *Pair bangles, emerald-cut black onyx in center with a row of genuine oriental seed pearls on either side, c. late 19th* 2500.00 3000.00

☐ **93** *Pair narrow bangles, pavé oriental seed pearls in top half of each bracelet, gold, c. 1860* 900.00 1100.00

☐ **94** *Plaited bangle, Etruscan granulation ends, gold, c. 1870.* 1000.00 1200.00

☐ **95** *Renaissance revival motif, hardstone cameo, green gold foliage, yellow gold rims, French owl hallmarks* 3200.00 3400.00

☐ **96** *Ribbon motif, pavé turquoise, seed pearl borders, silver, c. 1820* 1500.00 2200.00

☐ **97** *Ribbon motif, one emerald-cut emerald, one oval sapphire, 15 old mine diamonds, tubular band, gold, c. 1880* 1600.00 1800.00

☐ **98** *Rose diamonds in silver, blue enamel oval center with seed pearls, seed pearls collet-set around center of bracelet, gold, c. 1850* 1600.00 2000.00

☐ **99** *Rosette motif, 45 rose diamonds, gold, c. 1860* .. 3500.00 4500.00

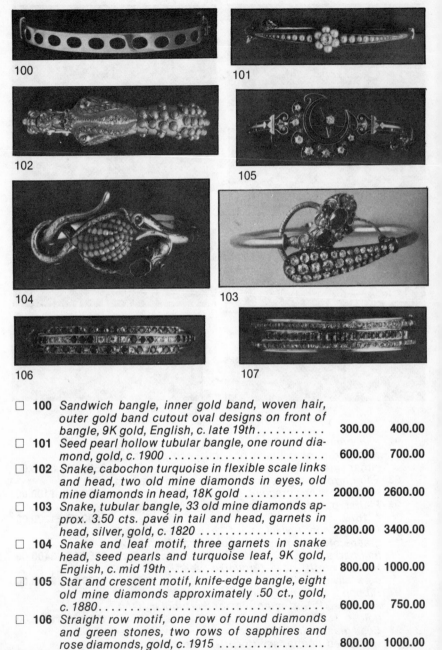

100

101

102

105

104

103

106

107

☐ **100** *Sandwich bangle, inner gold band, woven hair, outer gold band cutout oval designs on front of bangle, 9K gold, English, c. late 19th* 300.00   400.00

☐ **101** *Seed pearl hollow tubular bangle, one round diamond, gold, c. 1900* 600.00   700.00

☐ **102** *Snake, cabochon turquoise in flexible scale links and head, two old mine diamonds in eyes, old mine diamonds in head, 18K gold* 2000.00 2600.00

☐ **103** *Snake, tubular bangle, 33 old mine diamonds approx. 3.50 cts. pavé in tail and head, garnets in head, silver, gold, c. 1820* 2800.00 3400.00

☐ **104** *Snake and leaf motif, three garnets in snake head, seed pearls and turquoise leaf, 9K gold, English, c. mid 19th* 800.00 1000.00

☐ **105** *Star and crescent motif, knife-edge bangle, eight old mine diamonds approximately .50 ct., gold, c. 1880* 600.00   750.00

☐ **106** *Straight row motif, one row of round diamonds and green stones, two rows of sapphires and rose diamonds, gold, c. 1915* 800.00 1000.00

☐ **107** *Straight row motif, one row of round rubies, two rows of rose diamonds, gold, c. 1920* 1000.00 1200.00

108

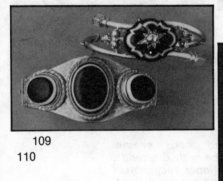

109
110

111

☐ **108** *Tiger heads, beast, flower and bird motifs, Jaipur champlevé enamel in translucent red, green, blue, yellow and opaque white, rose diamonds, gold, Indian, c. 19th* 4200.00 5000.00

☐ **109** *Tubular bangle, carved banded-onyx center medallion, rose diamonds in white gold, bangle in yellow gold, c. mid 19th* 1200.00 1500.00

☐ **110** *Wide bangle, three cabachon banded onyx, rope twist borders, engraved flat bangle, gold, c. 1870* 900.00 1200.00

☐ **111** *Watch, keywind and separates as pendant, champlevé opaque floral design on movable fan cover, garnets, seed pearls, gold, c. 1840* 2500.00 3000.00

112

113

114

115

116

117

☐ **112** Watch and leaf motif, seed pearls, enamel leaves, watch: visible balance with diamonds, enamel dial, steel hands, cylinder escapement with gold slide, maker: Pierre Gregson A Paris, French, c. 1790................................ **25000.00 30000.00**

☐ **113** Water lily motif, chased, blank initial medallions, gold, Art Nouveau, probable maker: Riker Bros., Newark, NJ, American, c. 1900................ **1500.00 1800.00**

☐ **114** Wide bangle set with seed pearls, rose diamonds, fitted leather box marked: "Mackay, Cunningham & Co., Edinburgh, Scotland," gold, c. 1875.................................... **2000.00 2500.00**

☐ **115** Wide bangle, champlevé black enamel geometric motic, center cluster of nine old mine diamonds approx. 2.50 cts., gold, c. 1880................ **2200.00 2600.00**

☐ **116** Wide bangle, floral motif, champlevé opaque black enamel, gold, c. 1860.................. **500.00 650.00**

☐ **117** Woven bangle with slide and end with cabochon opals, old mine diamonds, black enamel leaf motif, gold, c. 1850........................... **1800.00 2200.00**

BANGLE · SILVER

			PRICE RANGE	
☐	1	*Birds in rose and yellow gold applied to bangle, engraved bamboo motif, sterling silver, c. 1900* . .	175.00	200.00
☐	2	*Corset motif, gold wire as lace, applied gold flowers, engraved flower and leaf design, silver, English, c. 1890*	285.00	325.00
☐	3	*Flowers and leaves in green, yellow and rose gold applied to wide bangle, engraved leaves, sterling silver, American, c. 1890*	225.00	250.00
☐	4	*French paste: emerald-cut, gold bead edges, pair of late 18th shoe buckles attached together as bangle in mid 19th*	350.00	400.00
☐	5	*Hollow oval bangle, hand-engraved, sterling silver, American, c. 1902*	85.00	110.00

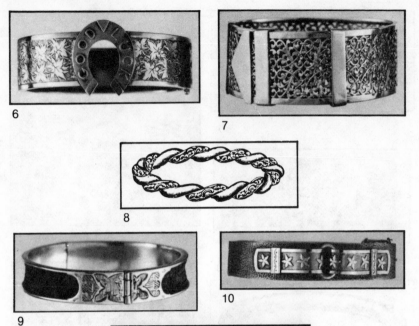

☐	**6**	*Horseshoe center with leaf engraved motif, maker: J.M.B., Birmingham, England, silver, c. 1882*	**100.00**	**125.00**
☐	**7**	*Renaissance motif, bangle slides through plain bars to enlarge, sterling silver, c. 1910*	**150.00**	**175.00**
☐	**8**	*Rope pattern, one plain band, one embossed band, sterling silver, American, c. 1902*	**85.00**	**110.00**
☐	**9**	*Sandwich bangle, ridges of inner band hold woven hair, engraved edge designs, sterling silver, gold-washed, c. late 19th*	**160.00**	**180.00**
☐	**10**	*Star design in gold plated silver ribbon attached to lizard engraved narrow bangle, 800 silver, c. 1915*	**80.00**	**110.00**
☐	**11**	*Tubular hinged bangle, cabochon tiger eye center, leaf motif, seed pearls, sterling silver, American, c. mid 20th*	**90.00**	**125.00**

1

2

CAST IRON

		PRICE RANGE	
☐	**1** *Cast iron, maker: M. Devarannes, Berlin, Germany, c. 1860*	**600.00**	**800.00**
☐	**2** *Cast iron, maker: M. Devarannes, Berlin, Germany, c. 1860*	**500.00**	**650.00**

1

2

CLASPS

		PRICE RANGE	
☐	**1** *Hummingbird and flower motif, rose, yellow and green gold, platinum, American, c. 1875*	**700.00**	**800.00**
☐	**2** *Ivory miniature portrait of officer by Ozias Humphrey, 1742-1810, 1½ in. high, gold, English*	**3500.00**	**4000.00**

☐ **3** *Ivory miniature portrait of Mrs. Hoskins by James Nixon, 1741-1812, 1½ in. high, gold, English* 2000.00 2200.00

☐ **4** *Ivory miniature portrait of Lieutenant Henry Hoskins by James Nixon, 1741-1812, 1½ in. high, gold, English* 1200.00 1500.00

☐ **5** *Ivory miniature portrait of a gentleman by J. Jennings, 1763-1793, 1½ in. high, gold, English, dated 1769* 900.00 1100.00

☐ **6** *Ivory miniature portrait of a gentleman by Daniel Dodd, 1752-1780, 1½ in. high, gold, English* 900.00 1000.00

☐ **7** *Ivory miniature portrait of Wilson Gail Broadqill by Richard Crosse, 1742-1810, 1½ in. high, gold, English* 500.00 600.00

☐ **8** *Ivory miniature portrait of a gentleman by John Bogle, 1746-1803, Scottish, worked in Scotland and England, 1⅜ in. high, gold* 2200.00 2400.00

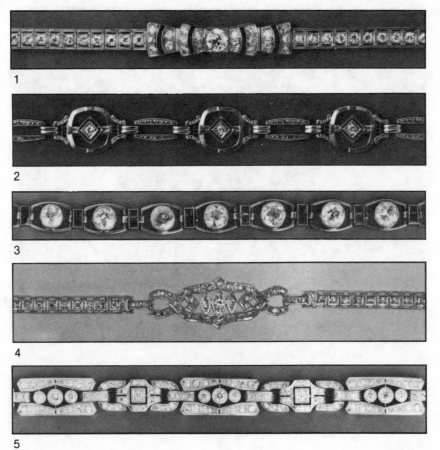

DIAMOND LINK

PRICE RANGE

☐ **1** *Bow center straight line, French-cut onyx, round diamond approx. .90 ct. in center, 56 round diamonds approx. 5 cts., platinum, c. 1910* **8500.00 10000.00**

☐ **2** *Box oval link, round diamonds in alternating links, white gold, American, c. 1915* **600.00 800.00**

☐ **3** *Box oval link, 13 old mine diamonds approx. 9 cts., two square-cut sapphires between each link, platinum, American, c. 1930* **12000.00 15000.00**

☐ **4** *Openwork center straight row, one marquise-shape diamond approx. .15 ct. in center, 70 round diamonds approx. 2.85 cts., platinum, c. 1930* . . . **3000.00 4000.00**

☐ **5** *Openwork links, round diamonds approx. 5.0 cts., platinum, American, c. 1920* **7000.00 9000.00**

6

7

8

9

☐ **6** *Openwork oblong links, 295 round diamonds approx. 22.50 cts., white gold, American, c. 1930 . . .* **1200.00 1500.00**

☐ **7** *Openwork panels, 67 round diamonds approx. 2.0 cts., rectangular rubies in center panel, gold topped silver, American, c. 1890 . . . .* **2500.00 3200.00**

☐ **8** *Openwork square links, six emerald-cut emeralds, triangular-cut diamonds approx. 2.0 cts., 428 round diamonds approx. 20 cts., platinum, American, c. 1920 . . . .* **18000.00 22000.00**

☐ **9** *Oval links, 120 round diamonds approx. 3.75 cts., 32 French-cut sapphires approx. 3.20 cts., platinum, c. 1925 . . . .* **8000.00 10000.00**

10

11

12

13

☐ **10** *Pierced center section, one round diamond approx. 1.35 cts., calibre sapphire and 40 round diamonds approx. 1.50 cts. in center panel, 22 round diamonds approx. 5.25 cts. in remaining panels, platinum, American, c. 1920* **10000.00 12000.00**

☐ **11** *Pierced panels, one round diamond approx. 1.0 cts. surrounded by calibre sapphires in center panel, round diamonds alternate with diamond-shape sapphires in remaining panels, platinum, American, c. 1920* **3200.00 3800.00**

☐ **12** *Pierced panels, two round diamonds in center panel approx. 1.20 cts., calibre black onyx and 78 round diamonds approx. 8.50 cts. in remaining panels, platinum, American, c. 1910* **8000.00 10000.00**

☐ **13** *Scroll links, rose diamonds, gold topped platinum, French, c. 1890* **650.00   850.00**

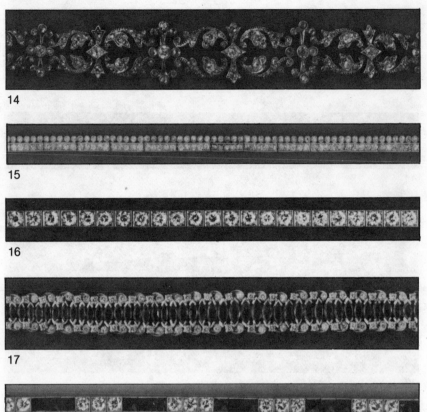

14

15

16

17

18

☐ **14** *Scroll motif links, old mine and rose diamonds, silver, French, c. early 19th* **2200.00 2400.00**

☐ **15** *Straight line, round diamonds approx. 3.0 cts. in square panels with collet-set diamonds on top, platinum, American, c. 1900* **4600.00 5000.00**

☐ **16** *Straight line, 37 round diamonds approx. 7.50 cts., platinum, American, c. 1925* **8000.00 10000.00**

☐ **17** *Straight line, graduated marquise-shape emeralds in center, 124 round diamonds approx. 3.75 cts., gold, silver, c. 1940* **6000.00 8000.00**

☐ **18** *Straight line, 21 round diamonds approx. 4.20 cts., 21 French-cut emeralds approx. 4.50 cts., platinum, c. 1930* **14000.00 16000.00**

19

20 21

22

23

☐ **19** Straight line modified, three old mine diamonds approx. 2.60 cts., 54 round diamonds approx. 2.0 cts., platinum, American, c. 1900 . . . . **2800.00 3500.00**

☐ **20** Straight line modified, one marquise-shape and 88 round diamonds approx. 5.50 cts., platinum, American, c. 1930 . . . . **4200.00 4600.00**

☐ **21** Straight line modified, one marquise-shape and 77 round diamonds approx. 3.30 cts., platinum, American, c. 1930 . . . . **2800.00 3200.00**

☐ **22** Straight line modified, round diamond approx. .60 ct. in center, 78 round diamonds approx. 4.70 cts., nine French-cut emeralds in center panels, platinum, c. 1920 . . . . **5500.00 6500.00**

☐ **23** Straight line modified, one marquise-shape diamond in center and 82 round diamonds approx. 3.50 cts., platinum, American, c. 1930 . . . . **4000.00 5500.00**

24

25

- ☐ **24** *Straight line modified, one round diamond approx. .85 ct. in center, two round diamonds approx. .25 ct., 30 round diamonds approx. 1.50 cts., eight French-cut sapphires approx. .24 ct., 14K white gold, c. 1920* **3000.00 3600.00**
- ☐ **25** *Square cluster center, four genuine oriental seed pearls, 11 diamonds, oblong openwork links, platinum topped gold, French, c. 1890-1900* **800.00 1200.00**

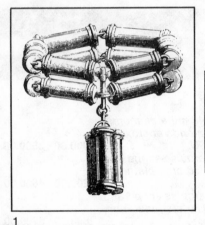

1

2

FLEXIBLE

		PRICE RANGE	
☐	**1** *Column motif, granite, silver, maker: Rettie & Sons, Aberdeen, Scotland, c. 1869*	**265.00**	**320.00**
☐	**2** *Curb engraved link, heart motif lock clasp, sterling, American, c. 1894-95*	**125.00**	**140.00**
☐	*Same as above but gold filled*	**25.00**	**45.00**
☐	*Same as above but 14K gold*	**265.00**	**285.00**

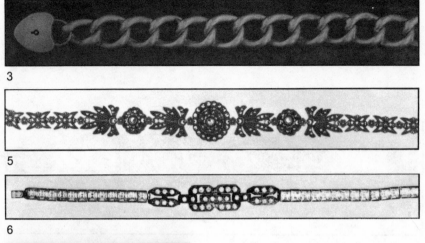

3

5

6

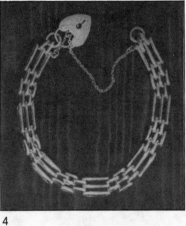

4   7

☐	**3**	*Curb link, heart motif lock clasp, sterling, American, c. late 19th*	**85.00**	**100.00**
☐	**4**	*Fancy link, heart motif lock clasp, silver, English, c. early 20th*	**65.00**	**85.00**
☐	**5**	*Flower motif, marcasites, sterling, American, c. 1920*	**85.00**	**125.00**
☐	**6**	*Geometric motif, rhinestones, sterling, Art Deco, American, c. 1935*	**45.00**	**60.00**
☐	**7**	*Heart motif, cabochon turquoise and opals, engraved, sterling, American, c. 1902*	**225.00**	**250.00**

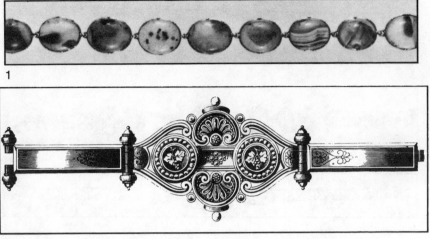

1

2

3

4

FLEXIBLE - GEM, GOLD OR PLATINUM

		PRICE RANGE	
☐	**1** *Agate, gold, English, c. 1800*	**450.00**	**500.00**
☐	**2** *Ancient Architectual motif center panel bordered by two flat plain panels, gold, maker: von Demfelben of Germany, c. 1868-83*	**1600.00**	**2000.00**
☐	**3** *Angel and cloud motif center, flat engraved links, gold, American, c. 1868*	**2000.00**	**2400.00**
☐	**4** *Animal gold silhouettes on green glass - Indian Pitch, engraved floral reverse, 22K gold, Indian, c. 19th*	**1000.00**	**1200.00**

5

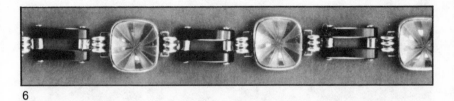

6

7

8

□ **5** Art Deco motif, two opaline glass squares with a leaf motif, center rectangle is lapis lazuli carved and pierced with a bird motif, links are blue and white enamel, gold, 7½ in. long, c. 1925 . . . . **900.00 1200.00**

□ **6** Art Deco motif, four rock crystal carved squares, onyx and gold links, 7 in. long. c. 1925. . . . . **2000.00 2200.00**

□ **7** Black opals, sapphires and demantoid garnets on either side of seven black opals alternating with oval enamelled links, bead chains, gold, Arts and Crafts style, signed: Tiffany & Co., c. late 19th **2200.00 2600.00**

□ **8** Bloodstone panels, 15K gold bezels, English, c. late 19th **600.00 800.00**

9

10

11

☐ **9** *Button motif, repoussé links, three round diamonds, gold, c. 1920* **600.00** **800.00**

☐ **10** *Cameos, seven different hued oval lava cameos
of classical portraits in gold bezels alternating
with gold half-beads, Italian, c. mid 19th* **1200.00** **1400.00**

☐ **11** *Charm bracelet, nine charms with gemstones,
pearls and some enamelled, two rope and three
open curb chain link strands, gold, American,
charms, c. late 19th to early 20th, contemporary
assembly* **1500.00** **1800.00**

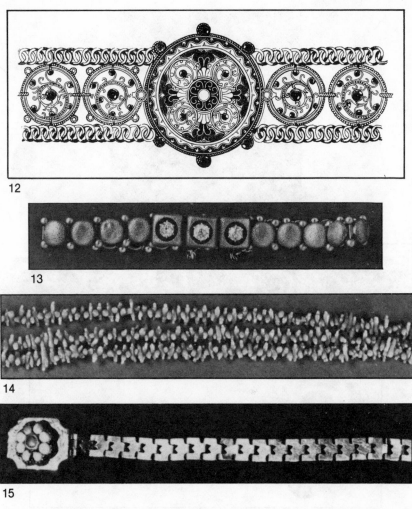

12

13

14

15

☐ **12** *Circle medallion motif, bordered by oval link chains, polychrome enamell, gold, German, c. 1871* **2600.00 2800.00**

☐ **13** *Circular motif links, three old mine diamonds approx. 1.0 ct., 14K gold, c. late 19th* **600.00 800.00**

☐ **14** *Coral, three branch coral chains, seed pearls surrounding glass locket with woven hair clasp, gold, c. 1870* **200.00 350.00**

☐ **15** *Doll bracelets, hollow book link chains, turquoise, engraved clasps, gold, pair, c. 1840* **300.00 350.00**

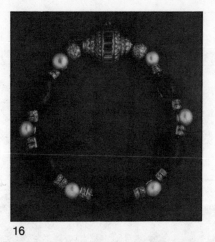

16

17

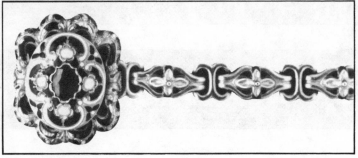

18

☐ **16** *Emerald beads alternating with round diamonds pave set in white gold, button pearls, 11 baguette diamonds, 186 round diamonds approximately 2.75 cts., c. 1925* **9000.00 11000.00**

☐ **17** *Enamel leaf motif, ribbon hollow links, gold, maker: Martin, Baskett & Martin of Cheltanham, England, c. 1869* **1200.00 1500.00**

☐ **18** *Enamelled center oval, garnet, four pearls, gold, c. 1840* **1800.00 2000.00**

19

20

21

☐	**19**	*Escapement covers known as watchcocks from verge watches, c. late 18th, assembled as bracelet c. late 19th, hand-engraved and pierced with animals and designs, cabochon garnets, basemetal, English*	350.00 400.00
☐	**20**	*Fancy scroll hollow stamped link motif, oval foilbacked amethyst in clasp, French, gold, c. 1840* .	2000.00 2500.00
☐	**21**	*Flower motif, robin's egg blue and white champlevé enamel, gold, c. 1830*	550.00 650.00

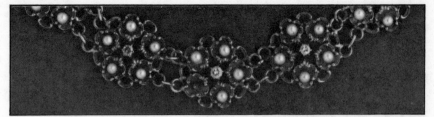

22

23

24

25

☐	**22**	*Flower motif links, five pearls and one round diamond in each link, gold*	**1500.00**	**1800.00**
☐	**23**	*Flower motif links, garnets, gold, c. 1870*	**800.00**	**900.00**
☐	**24**	*Flower cluster motif links, opaque white and black enamel, cabochon turquoise, garnets, silver gilt, c. 1840*	**300.00**	**375.00**
☐	**25**	*Flower motif heart and fancy links, turquoise, gold, English, c. 1903-04*	**650.00**	**850.00**

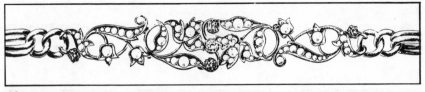

26

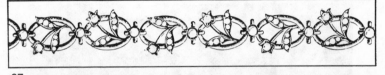

27

28

29

30

☐	**26** Flower and leaf motif, seed pearls, five diamonds, twisted trace link chain, gold, English, c. 1903-04	900.00	1200.00
☐	**27** Flower and leaf motif on oval links, seed pearls, gold, English, c. 1903-04	600.00	800.00
☐	**28** Garnet bead chains in gold caps, gold engraved clasp, c. 1850	450.00	650.00
☐	**29** Geometric motif flat links, one round emerald, one round ruby, one round sapphire, two round diamonds, 14K gold, c. 1930	950.00	1200.00
☐	**30** Hand motif, cannetille link bracelet, turquoise, rubies, gold, c. 1820	2200.00	2600.00

31

33

32

34

35

☐	**31**	*Heart and bow motif, cabochon turquoise, locket on reverse of heart, snake link chain, c. 1860-80* .	**700.00**	**800.00**
☐	**32**	*Heart lock motif, curb links, 9K gold, English, c. 20th*	**85.00**	**135.00**
☐	**33**	*Heart locket with one table-cut diamond attached to fancy round link bracelet, gold, c 1860* .	**600.00**	**800.00**
☐	**34**	*Hollow leaf motif links, gold, c. 1840*	**400.00**	**600.00**
☐	**35**	*Ivory carved flower center motif, ivory squares held together with elastic cord, c. early 20th*	**200.00**	**400.00**

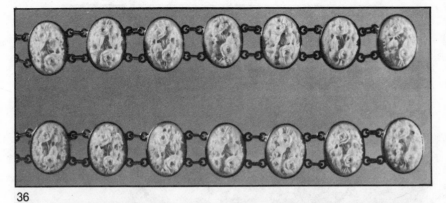

36

37

38

39

☐	**36** *Ivory carved oval flower plaques, silver bezel, pair of bracelets, c. mid 19th*	650.00	850.00
☐	**37** *Jade carved circular motif, seed pearls, gold, c. 20th*	500.00	600.00
☐	**38** *Jade plaques, carved carnelian plaques, gold fittings*	450.00	600.00
☐	**39** *Lady head bracelet, two Georgian chains with eight miniatures of ladies heads, heads in Art Nouveau style, c. 1890-1920*	2000.00	2400.00

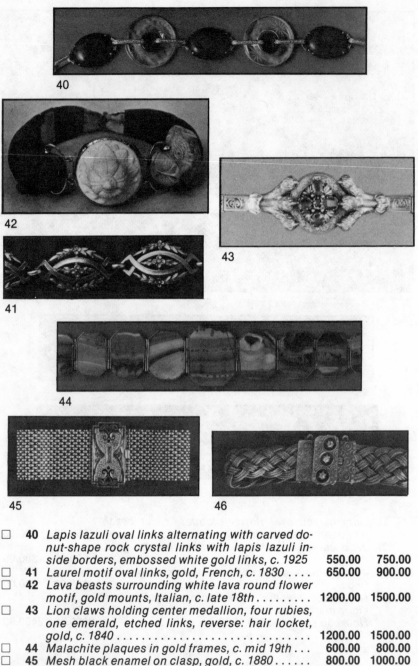

40

42

43

41

44

45

46

☐	**40**	*Lapis lazuli oval links alternating with carved do-nut-shape rock crystal links with lapis lazuli inside borders, embossed white gold links, c. 1925*	550.00	750.00
☐	**41**	*Laurel motif oval links, gold, French, c. 1830 . . . .*	650.00	900.00
☐	**42**	*Lava beasts surrounding white lava round flower motif, gold mounts, Italian, c. late 18th . . . .*	1200.00	1500.00
☐	**43**	*Lion claws holding center medallion, four rubies, one emerald, etched links, reverse: hair locket, gold, c. 1840 . . . .*	1200.00	1500.00
☐	**44**	*Malachite plaques in gold frames, c. mid 19th . . .*	600.00	800.00
☐	**45**	*Mesh black enamel on clasp, gold, c. 1880 . . . . . .*	800.00	1000.00
☐	**46**	*Mesh woven, Etruscan granulation on catch, three round diamonds, gold, c. 1860 . . . .*	1000.00	1200.00

47

48

49

50

51

53

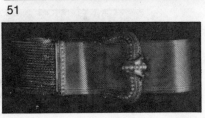

52

☐ **47** *Mesh woven, one round amethyst and six seed pearls in detachable brooch, gold, c. 1860* **1400.00 1600.00**

☐ **48** *Mesh woven, link fringe, black enamel design on two slides and end plaque, catch, gold, c. 1880* .. **1200.00 1500.00**

☐ **49** *Mesh woven, Etruscan granulation on catch, one round diamond, gold, c. 1860* **900.00 1200.00**

☐ **50** *Mesh woven, buckle motif, gold, c. 1880* **600.00 700.00**

☐ **51** *Mesh woven, Greek key motif on oval slide, black enamel, gold, c. 1860* **700.00 800.00**

☐ **52** *Mesh woven with link fringe, pearls in buckle motif, gold, c. 1835* **1600.00 2200.00**

☐ **53** *Mesh woven with rose, yellow, green and white gold flowers, oval locket with miniature of a lady, gold, c. 1860-70* **4500.00 5000.00**

54 55

56

57

☐ **54** *Mosaic flower motif in center, filigree flower motif link chain, silver, Italian, c. mid 19th* **400.00   500.00**

☐ **55** *Tiger claws, seven, engraved fittings and clasp in shape of tiger claw, gold, English, c. 1870* **1200.00 1500.00**

☐ **56** *Mosaic motif, hexagonal plaques, silver cloisonné wire on black mosaic plaques, Byzantine Christian motifs, framed in gold, signed: Castellani, Italian, c. mid 19th* **8000.00 10000.00**

☐ **57** *Mosaic motifs of the Pantheon, Hadrion's Villa, the Forum and Trajan's column, blue glass plaques, gold, c. 1850* **1600.00 1800.00**

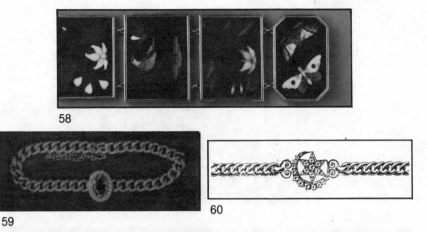

58

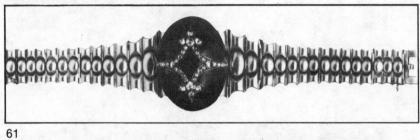

59

60

61

62

□ **58** *Mosaic plaques of flowers, birds and butterflies, gold, Italian* **1200.00 1500.00**

□ **59** *Open curb link bracelet, seed pearls surrounding oval citrine clasp, 9K gold, English, c. early 20th* . **600.00 800.00**

□ **60** *Open curb link bracelet, 20 round diamonds in star and crescent center panel, gold, English, c. late 19th* **1600.00 2000.00**

□ **61** *Oval motif center, graduated fancy scallop edged links, oval foil-backed amethyst in center with rose diamonds, gold, c. 1860* **4000.00 5000.00**

□ **62** *Oval link motif, three round peridots and two cushion-cut peridots alternating with chain links, gold, American, c. 1900* **450.00 550.00**

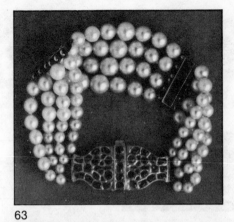

63

64

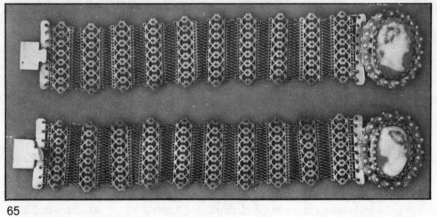

65

☐ **63** *Pearls, four strands, cushion-cut rubies in rectangular plaques, cushion-cut foil-back rubies in
clasp, gold, Indian, c. 19th* **800.00 1200.00**

☐ **64** *Pearls bordered by rose diamonds, gold, platinum, French, c. 1890* **600.00 800.00**

☐ **65** *Pinchbeck fancy link bracelets, sulfide cameo
clasps, pair, English, c. 19th* **700.00 1000.00**

66

67

68

☐ **66** *Portrait miniatures in center plaque of Queen Victoria and the Prince of Wales, hollow half-circle links, diamonds, gold, maker: S.H. & D. Gass of London, England, c. 1851* **10000.00 12000.00**

☐ **67** *Renaissance motif, polychrome enamel, gold, c. 1868-1883* **2300.00 2600.00**

☐ **68** *Renaissance revival motif, enamelled cabochon garnet in center surrounded by four pair of looped circles set with rose diamonds, gold, maker: C. Rowlands & Son of London, England, c. 1869* **4000.00 5000.00**

69

70

71

73

72

☐	**69**	*Ribbon and flower motif center panel on wide band, 17 rose diamonds in flowers, gold, maker: G. Ehni, c. 1871*	**2800.00** **3200.00**
☐	**70**	*Ribbon and musical note motif links, alternating with blue and white opaque enamel, gold, maker: Phillips Bros. of London, England, c. 1869*	**1200.00** **1500.00**
☐	**71**	*Rock crystal panels set with one round diamond, etched, alternating with silver and black enamel baton links, platinum, Art deco, c. 1930*	**1800.00** **2200.00**
☐	**72**	*Rope chains, 20 round amethysts and four pearls in center panel and clasp, silver gold-washed, Italian, c. mid 19th*	**350.00** **450.00**
☐	**73**	*Rope chains, woven gold, black enamel and gold clasp, c. mid 19th*	**650.00** **850.00**

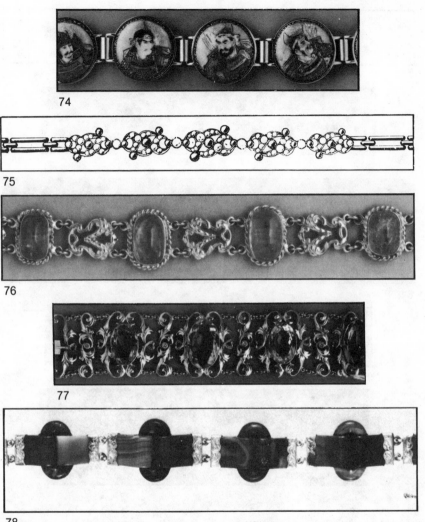

74

75

76

77

78

☐ **74** *Satsuma buttons of Samurai, five buttons, gold,*
signed: Cartier **1200.00** **1500.00**
☐ **75** *Scroll motif links, seed pearls, rectangular link*
chain, gold, English, c. late 19th **600.00** **800.00**
☐ **76** *Scroll motif links alternating with light green ca-*
bochon emeralds, gold **2000.00** **2400.00**
☐ **77** *Scroll motif links and frames, four oval faceted*
citrines, 14K gold, c. 1860 .... **1200.00** **1400.00**
☐ **78** *Scottish agates, 15K gold mounts, 9K gold heart*
lock clasp, English, c. 1860 .... **1000.00** **1200.00**

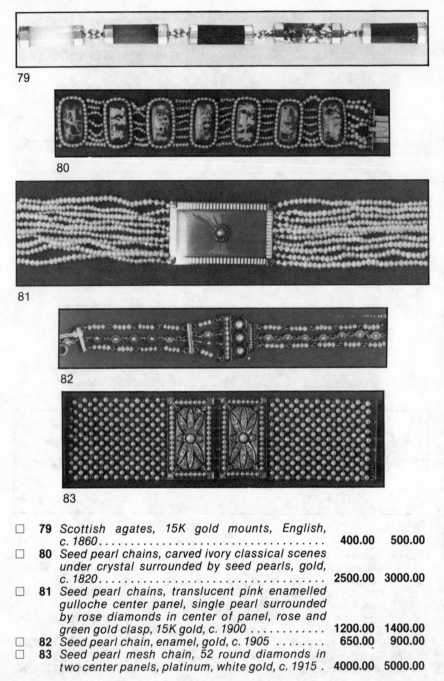

79

80

81

82

83

84

85

86

☐ **84** *Seed pearls strung on white horsehair on mother-of-pearl templates, fitted velvet-lined leather box marked: J. W. Carr, Goldsmith, 29 Commercial St., Leeds, English, c. 1860* **1500.00 1800.00**

☐ **85** *Shell cameo of four heads — one lady, two men, and a ram, flat sandwich link chain, gold, c. 1830* **600.00 900.00**

☐ **86** *Shield motif, three emeralds in center, diamonds, trace links alternating with small enamelled shields, gold, maker: Phillips Bros. of London, England, c. 1869* **6000.00 9000.00**

87

91

88

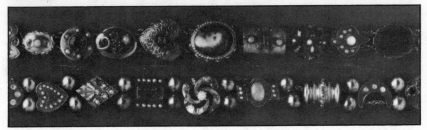

89 90

☐	**87**	*Slide bracelet, ten yellow, green, white and rose gold slides strung on gold wires with gold beads, slides c. late 19th, contemporary assembly*	1800.00	2000.00
☐	**88**	*Slide bracelet of 11 slides of ladies heads, each set with one round diamond, gold, Art Nouveau, c. 1910*	4500.00	5000.00
☐	**89**	*Slide bracelet of 13 slides with various gemstones, gold, c. 1860*	1600.00	1800.00
☐	**90**	*Slide bracelet of slides with various gemstones alternating with gold beads, gold, c. 1860*	1400.00	1800.00
☐	**91**	*Snake, woven flexible band, engraved head, gemstone eyes, gold, c. 1840*	1000.00	1200.00

92

93

94

95

96

97

☐ **92** *Snake center, scale motif links, turquoise in snake head, gold, English, c. 1840* 800.00 1000.00

☐ **93** *Star motif, openwork panels, 21 rose diamonds in center oval, plique á jour blue enamel background, each link with round sapphires and rose diamonds, silver topped gold, c. 1870* 4500.00 5500.00

☐ **94** *Straight row motif, opal doublets, gold, c. early 20th.* 600.00 800.00

☐ **95** *Straight row motif, 41 calibre French-cut sapphires, platinum* 4000.00 5000.00

☐ **96** *Straight row motif, 23 round multi-colored gemstones, gold, c. early 20th* 800.00 1000.00

☐ **97** *Turquoise pave set in three clusters, old mine diamond centers, snake link bracelet, gold, c. 1840* .. 3000.00 3500.00

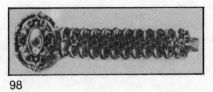

98

☐ **98** *Watch motif, watch cover: blue enamel with ru-*
bies and diamonds, watch: oval enamel dial, cylin-
der escapement, gold links, Paris, French, c. 1800 **15000.00 18000.00**

1

2

3

HAIR
All items made from hair referred to throughout this section are of brunette
human hair unless stated otherwise.

			PRICE RANGE	
☐	**1**	*Braided white hair, clasp with braided white hair under glass, gold, c. 1880*	**125.00**	**140.00**
☐	**2**	*Clasp, engraved, lock of hair under glass under oval lid, gold, c. 1890*	**125.00**	**150.00**
☐	**3**	*Expandable woven hair, heart and bow motif connector, gold, c. 1860-80*	**70.00**	**80.00**

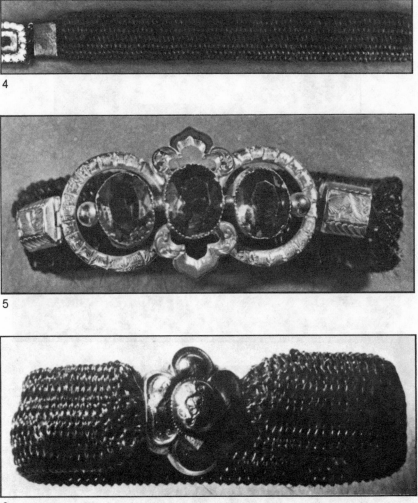

4

5

6

- [ ] **4** Expandable woven hair motif, clasps with seed pearl border, woven hair and gold foil under glass, gold, c. 1860-80 . . . . **100.00 125.00**
- [ ] **5** Expandable woven hair motif, scroll motif clasp with three faceted amethyst, gold, c. 1860-80 . . . . **80.00 90.00**
- [ ] **6** Expandable woven hair motif, engraved flower connector, gold, c. 1860-80 . . . . **50.00 70.00**

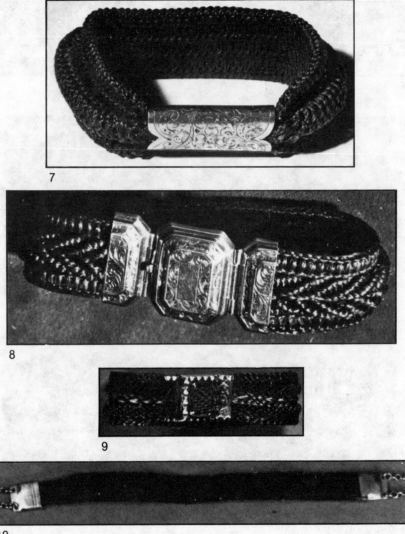

7

8

9

10

☐ **7** *Expandable woven hair motif, engraved connec-*
tor, gold, c. 1860-80 . . . . **45.00** **65.00**

☐ **8** *Fancy woven hair motif, engraved clasp, gold,*
c. 1860-80 . . . . **65.00** **75.00**

☐ **9** *Fancy woven hair motif, clasp with woven hair*
under glass, gold, c. 1860-80 . . . . **50.00** **70.00**

☐ **10** *Flat woven hair moif, engraved clasp, gold,*
c. 1820-40 . . . . **65.00** **85.00**

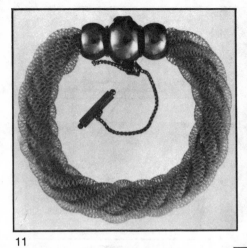

11

13

12

14

☐ **11** *Hollow tube motif of open weave woven white hair, engraved clasp with buckle inlaid with woven brunette hair, c. 1800-30* 350.00   375.00

☐ **12** *Hollow tube motif of closed woven hair, gold, c. 1860-80* 145.00   160.00

☐ **13** *Hollow tube motif of tightly woven white and brunette hair, engraved clasp, c. 1800-40* 160.00   180.00

☐ **14** *Hollow tube motif of woven hair with two dangles, three wooden beads covered with hair, c. 1840-65* 40.00   65.00

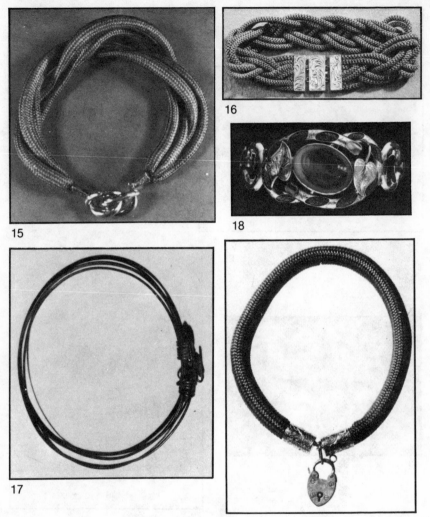

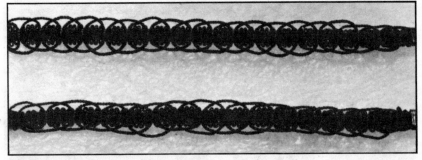

20

21

22

23

☐	**20**	Ribbon woven hair motif, gold clasps, c. 1840-60, pair	250.00	300.00
☐	**21**	Sandwich bangle of inner band, woven hair and outer engraved and cutout band, gold, English, c. early 20th	145.00	165.00
☐	**22**	Sandwich bangle of inner band, woven hair and outer engraved and cutout band, colored gold flowers applied to outside of reverse of band, silver, English, c. early 20th	285.00	325.00
☐	**23**	Snake motif, tightly woven hair over solid core, cabochon garnets in head and eyes, gold, c. 1800	650.00	750.00

Photograph of a husband and wife with the wife wearing a hunting case watch attached to a watch pin and a heavy link gold chain.

BROOCHES

ANIMAL and BUG

			PRICE RANGE	
☐	1	*Bee, rose diamond and silver body, pearl and ruby wings, gold backed, c. 1870*	1000.00	1200.00
☐	2	*Bee, emerald and rose diamond body, coral set terminal to bar, c. 1860*	1500.00	1800.00
☐	3	*Bee, large Baroque pearl and full Holland rose diamond body, bead set diamond and sapphire wings, gold, c. 1880*	2200.00	2600.00
☐	4	*Bee, rubies, sapphires, pearls, gold, c. 1900*	250.00	275.00
☐	5	*Beetle, amethyst beetle and leaves perched on approximately 40 cts. oval amethyst, 15K gold, English, c. 1840-60*	2000.00	2500.00
☐	6	*Beetle, rose diamonds, fancy-shape cabochon garnets, gold, c. 1870*	800.00	1000.00

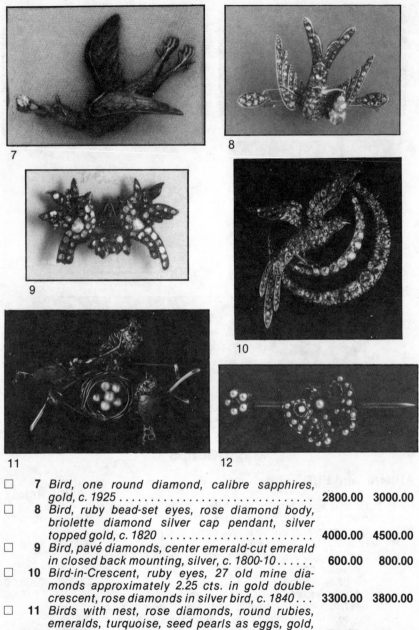

7

8

9

10

11

12

☐ **7** *Bird, one round diamond, calibre sapphires, gold, c. 1925* **2800.00 3000.00**

☐ **8** *Bird, ruby bead-set eyes, rose diamond body, briolette diamond silver cap pendant, silver topped gold, c. 1820* **4000.00 4500.00**

☐ **9** *Bird, pavé diamonds, center emerald-cut emerald in closed back mounting, silver, c. 1800-10* **600.00 800.00**

☐ **10** *Bird-in-Crescent, ruby eyes, 27 old mine diamonds approximately 2.25 cts. in gold double-crescent, rose diamonds in silver bird, c. 1840* ... **3300.00 3800.00**

☐ **11** *Birds with nest, rose diamonds, round rubies, emeralds, turquoise, seed pearls as eggs, gold, c. 1880* **1200.00 1400.00**

☐ **12** *Butterfly, pearl, sapphire, ruby and diamond body, ruby and pearl terminal to bar, gold, c. 1870* **950.00 1150.00**

13

14

15

16

17

18

☐ **13** *Butterfly, ruby, diamond, sapphire, silver, gold, c. 1850* 500.00 600.00

☐ **14** *Butterfly, old mine diamond approximately .45 ct., pavé rose diamond body and wings, gold, c. 1860* 1600.00 2000.00

☐ **15** *Butterfly, opaque enamel wings on spring hinges, jeweled eyes, gold, c. 1900* 750.00 900.00

☐ **16** *Butterfly, blue and green opaque enamel wings, 62 round diamonds approximately 1.10 cts., platinum, c. 1900* 2300.00 2600.00

☐ **17** *Butterfly, emerald and ruby wings, old mine diamond in body, ruby eyes, gold, c. 1860* 2600.00 3000.00

☐ **18** *Butterfly, enamel, four old mine diamonds, gold, c. 1900* 850.00 1000.00

19

20

21

22

23

☐	**19**	*Butterfly, rose diamonds, rubies, gold, c. 1860...*	**550.00**	**650.00**
☐	**20**	*Butterfly, cabochon turquoise, rose diamonds, cabochon ruby eye, gold, c. 1880 . . . .*	**1200.00**	**1500.00**
☐	**21**	*Butterfly, rose diamonds, three rubies, fancy-shape cabochon chrysoprase, silver, gold, c. 1860. . . . . . .*	**1800.00**	**2000.00**
☐	**22**	*Butterfly, mother-of-pearl wings, 13 round rubies, gold, c. 1915 . . . .*	**300.00**	**400.00**
☐	**23**	*Butterfly, gem set, Etruscan granulation and cannetille, gold, c. 1800 . . . .*	**350.00**	**450.00**

25

24

27

28

26

29

☐	**24**	*Butterfly, two old mine diamonds, rose diamonds, oval rubies, pavé, gold, silver, c. 1830* ...	**3500.00** **4000.00**
☐	**25**	*Butterfly, one seed pearl, rose diamonds, silver, French, c. late 18th*	**1400.00** **1600.00**
☐	**26**	*Butterfly, foil-back faceted stones, Etruscan granulation, gold, c. 1820*	**700.00** **800.00**
☐	**27**	*Butterflies, mosaic, gold, c. 1880*	**250.00** **300.00**
☐	**28**	*Cat, pavé rose diamond body, ruby eyes, pearl ball, white gold, French, c. 1935*	**800.00** **1000.00**
☐	**29**	*Chicks in shoe, ruby eyes, diamond bodies, gold, c. 1870*	**1500.00** **2000.00**

30

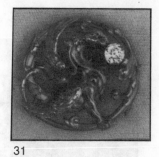

31

33

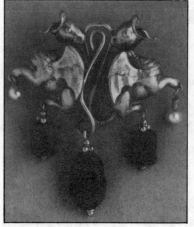

32

34

☐	**30**	*Deer, carved from single piece of boxwood, English, c. 1870*	**200.00**	**250.00**
☐	**31**	*Dragon, one round diamond, gold, Art Nouveau, c. 1880*	**4000.00**	**4200.00**
☐	**32**	*Dragons, two pearls, two faceted greed stones, one carnelian scarab, gold, c. 19th*	**3200.00**	**3500.00**
☐	**33**	*Dragonfly, colored stones, silver, c. mid 19th*	**150.00**	**180.00**
☐	**34**	*Dragonfly, three cabochon emeralds in gold body, nine emerald-cut emeralds in tail, rose diamonds in silver topped gold wings, detachable brooch fitting, c. 1870-80*	**2400.00**	**2800.00**

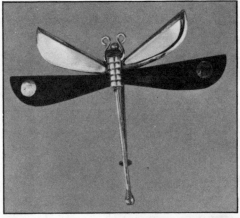

35

37

36

38

- [ ] **35** *Dragonfly, tortoise shell, sterling, maker: Carl Schon, Baltimore, Maryland, American, c. 1930-50* **35.00** **65.00**
- [ ] **36** *Dragonfly, one pearl, two emeralds, four rubies, rose diamonds, gold, c. 1870-80* **3800.00** **4200.00**
- [ ] **37** *Eagle and snake, carved, gold, c. mid to late 19th* **3300.00** **3500.00**
- [ ] **38** *Eagle, turquoise, 20K gold, c. late 19th* **600.00** **800.00**

39

40

41

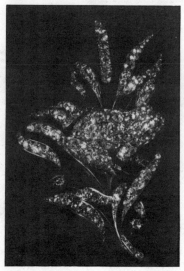

42

43

 39 *Elephant, rose diamonds, translucent green, red and blue enamel, Indian, gold, c. 19th* **1200.00 1500.00**

☐ **40** *Fly, cabochon ruby eyes and body, old mine diamond body and wings, pearl, gold, c. 1860* **1600.00 1900.00**

☐ **41** *Fox head, round emerald eyes, pavé set diamond head and bar brooch, calibre-cut emeralds in bar brooch ends, platinum, gold, c. 1900-20* **3800.00 4200.00**

☐ **42** *Frog, pavé diamond frog and plants, removable tremblant frog, silver, 18K gold, c. 1840* **35000.00 38000.00**

☐ **43** *Frog, carved jasper, rope twist borders, Etruscan granuation, white enamel circlets, maker: Castellani, Italian, c. 1860* **6500.00 7500.00**

44

45

47

46

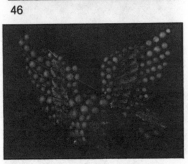

48

49

□ **44** *Heron, rose diamond branches, demantoid gar-*
net ferns, gold, c. 1890 .... 3400.00 3600.00
□ **45** *Heron, bird and flower relief on three bronze*
fans, gold, silver, Japanese (Shakudo) metal
work, c. late 19th 1000.00 1200.00
□ **46** *Insect, garnet, rose diamonds, silver, gold, c. 1850* . 800.00 1100.00
□ **47** *Insect, cabochon emerald and ruby body, dia-*
mond wings and eyes, gold, c. 1860. .... 2200.00 2600.00
□ **48** *Parrot, pave cabochon turquoise wings, pavé ca-*
bochon garnet beak, vermeil, c. 1840 .... 600.00 750.00
□ **49** *Pelican, translucent pink and yellow enamel*
body, baroque pearl, green translucent plique á
jour wings with rose diamonds in edges, Art Nou-
veau, c. 1890-1910 .... 4300.00 4800.00

50

51

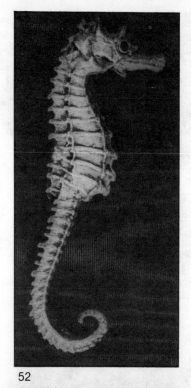

52

53

☐ **50** *Ram's Head, Etruscan rope motif, gold, maker: Castellani, Italian, c. 1860* **2500.00 3000.00**

☐ **51** *Ram's head, Etruscan granulation, rope motif, gold, c. 1860* **1000.00 1200.00**

☐ **52** *Seahorse, cabochon garnet eye, cast silver, maker: Carl Schon, Baltimore, Maryland, American, c. 1930-50* **60.00 80.00**

☐ **53** *Shrimp, ruby eye, rose diamond body, gold, silver, c. 1860* **1200.00 1400.00**

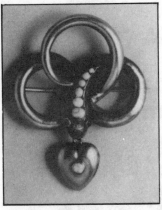

54

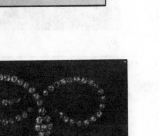

55

56

58

57

59

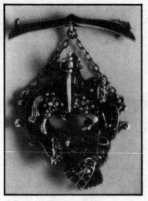

60

61

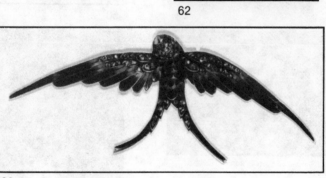

62

63

☐ **60** *St. George-and-the-Dragon, enamelled St. George, pearl horse, emerald and green enamel dragon, ruby cartouche, simple link chain to pin, silver, Hungarian, c. 1850* **500.00   550.00**

☐ **61** *Swallow, pavé rose diamond wings and body, old mine diamond in crestail, ruby eyes, c. 1810* **2400.00   2800.00**

☐ **62** *Swallow, 70 old mine diamonds, ruby in head, silver, c. 1850* **1200.00   1500.00**

☐ **63** *Swallow, rose diamonds in feathers, rubies in eyes, blue, black and white enamel, gold, silver, c. 1860* **2000.00   2500.00**

64

65

66

68

67

☐ **64** *Swallows, rose diamond body and wings in silver topped gold, gold safety pin, c. 1830* 650.00   800.00

☐ **65** *Turtle, emerald eyes, cabochon opal body surrounded with diamonds, gold, c. 1935* 1500.00   1800.00

☐ **66** *Turtle, six rose diamonds, 36 demantoid garnets, gold, c. early 20th* 350.00   450.00

☐ **67** *Turtle, engraved, demantoid garnets, gold, c. late 19th* 400.00   500.00

☐ **68** *Winged lion, Etruscan granulation, Gothic revival, gold, c. 1860-80* 1000.00   1200.00

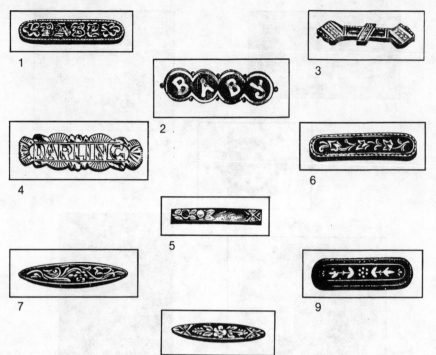

BABY PIN

			PRICE RANGE	
☐	**1**	*"BABY" raised letter motif, gold front, American, c. 1894-95*	**20.00**	**30.00**
☐	**2**	*"BABY" raised letter motif, gold front, American, c. 1894-95*	**25.00**	**35.00**
☐	**3**	*Cutout motif, engraved, gold front, American, c. 1894-95*	**25.00**	**30.00**
☐		*Same as above but gold filled*	**10.00**	**15.00**
☐	**4**	*"DARLING" cutout letter motif, gold front, American, c. 1894-95*..........................	**25.00**	**35.00**
☐	**5**	*Flower motif, engraved, one round garnet, one seed pearl, gold front, American, c. 1894-95*	**35.00**	**40.00**
☐	**6**	*Flower motif, blue enamel, 14K gold, American, c. 1894-95*	**40.00**	**55.00**
☐	**7**	*Flower motif, enamel, 14K gold, American, c. 1894-95*	**40.00**	**55.00**
☐	**8**	*Flower motif, engraved, 14K gold, American, c. 1894-95*	**35.00**	**45.00**
☐		*Same as above but gold filled*	**10.00**	**15.00**
☐	**9**	*Flower motif, enamel, sterling silver, American, c. 1896*.......................................	**25.00**	**35.00**

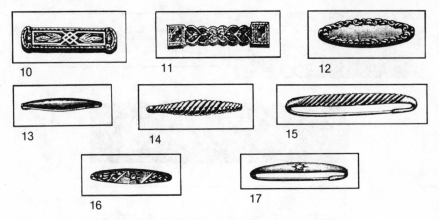

10   11   12

13   14   15

16   17

☐	**10**	*Geometric engraved motif, gold plate on sterling silver, American, c. 1894-95*	25.00	35.00
☐	**11**	*Heart and square cutout motif, engraved, gold plate on sterling silver, American, c. 1894-95*	25.00	35.00
☐		*Same as above but gold filled*	10.00	15.00
☐	**12**	*Oval chased edge motif, 14K gold, American, c. 1894-95*	35.00	45.00
☐		*Same as above but gold filled*	10.00	15.00
☐	**13**	*Polished motif, 14K gold, American, c. 1894-95* ..	25.00	35.00
☐	**14**	*Ribbed motif, 14K gold, American, c. 1894-95*	35.00	45.00
☐	**15**	*Ribbed motif, sterling silver, American, c. 1896* ..	25.00	35.00
☐	**16**	*Star motif, chased, one seed pearl, 14K gold, American, c. 1894-95*	45.00	50.00
☐	**17**	*Star motif, one cabochon turquoise, sterling silver, American, 1896*	20.00	30.00

1

2

BAR

			PRICE RANGE	
☐	**1**	*Amethysts: six round, diamonds, platinum, c. 1915, pair*	250.00	300.00
☐	**2**	*Amethyst, two seed pearls, 15K gold, American, c. 1894-95*	200.00	225.00

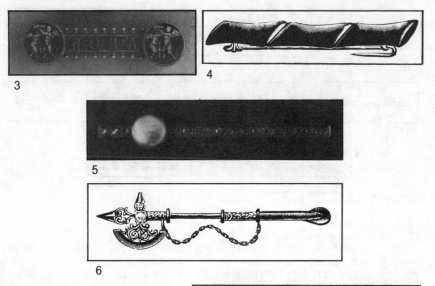

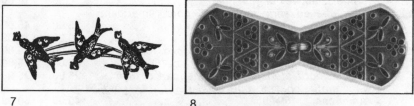

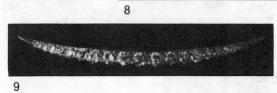

10

11

12

13

14

☐ **10** *Clover flower motif, guilloche translucent green enamel, two seed pearls, round diamonds, gold, fitted leather box, c. 1880* **1000.00   1200.00**

☐ **11** *Crown motif, round diamonds, square sapphires, platinum topped gold, c. early 20th* **400.00   450.00**

☐ **12** *Crescent and star motif, 14K gold, American, c. 1894-95* **150.00   175.00**

☐ **13** *Diamonds, onyx, platinum, c. 1925* **300.00   350.00**

☐ **14** *Elephant hair, gold, c. early 20th* **125.00   150.00**

15

16

17

18

19

20

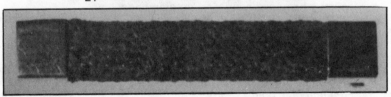

21

22

☐	15	*Flower motif, two seed pearls, 14K gold, American, c. 1894-95*	125.00	140.00
☐	16	*Flower motif, black onyx, 14K gold, American, c. 1896*	65.00	85.00
☐	17	*Flower motif, three seed pearls, 14K gold, American, c. 1894-95*	135.00	150.00
☐	18	*Flower motif, 14K gold, American, c. 1894-95*	125.00	150.00
☐	19	*Flower motif, sterling, American, c. 1896*	40.00	45.00
☐	20	*Gold, Etruscan granulation, classical Revival motif, c. 1870*	325.00	375.00
☐	21	*Gold miner motif, 14K gold, American, c. 1865*	1000.00	1200.00
☐	22	*Hair woven with gold square tips, c. mid 19th*	55.00	85.00

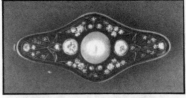

23

26

24

25

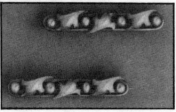

27

28

29

☐	**23** *Half pearl, round and rose diamonds, gold, silver, c. mid 19th*	700.00	800.00
☐	**24** *Half pearls, rose diamonds, platinum, c. 1900* . . .	1200.00	1300.00
☐	**25** *Heart motif, hair under glass, gold, c. late 19th* . .	85.00	125.00
☐	**26** *Ladies heads motif, carved, Art Nouveau, gold, c. 1900*	85.00	100.00
☐	**27** *Leaf motif, translucent enamel, seed pearls, gold, Art Nouveau, c. 1900, pair*	300.00	400.00
☐	**28** *Leaf motif, one round diamond, 14K gold, American, c. 1894-95*	175.00	225.00
☐	**29** *Leaf motif, three round diamonds, 14K gold, American, c. 1894-95*	275.00	325.00

30

31

32

33

34

35

☐ **30** *Lily-of-the-valley flower motif, 11 seed pearls, 14K gold, American, c. 1894-95* **130.00**   **145.00**

☐ **31** *Lily-of-the-valley flower motif, seed pearls, translucent green enamel, gold, Art Nouveau, c. 1915, pair* **350.00**   **400.00**

☐ **32** *Miniature of a lady, translucent pink and red enamel, emeralds in tiara, six cabochon opals in bar, engraved, gold, Art Nouveau, c. 1900* **1200.00** **1400.00**

☐ **33** *Moonstone, knife-edge bar, 14K gold, American, c. 1894-95* **65.00**   **85.00**

☐ **34** *One oblong hexagonal diamond approx. .50 ct., 129 round diamonds approx. 3.0 cts. pavé, platinum, French, c. 1925* **3500.00** **3800.00**

☐ **35** *Onyx center, two pearls, one round diamond, rose diamonds, gold, platinum, c. 1920* **825.00**   **875.00**

36

37

38

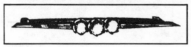

39

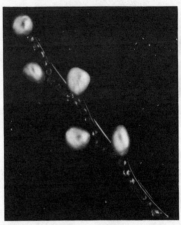

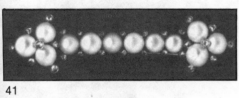

41

42

40

☐	**36**	*Onyx: French-cut, one round diamond approx. 1.80 cts., round diamonds approx. 3.25 cts., platinum, c. 1910*	**4200.00**	**4500.00**
☐	**37**	*Opals: ten cabochon, rose diamonds, silver, gold, c. 1860, pair*	**900.00**	**1000.00**
☐	**38**	*Pearl, 14K gold, American, c. 1894-95*	**65.00**	**85.00**
☐	**39**	*Pearls, knife-edge bar, 14K, American, c. 1894-95*	**70.00**	**90.00**
☐	**40**	*Pearls: natural baroque, rose diamonds, gold, silver, c. 1840*	**800.00**	**900.00**
☐	**41**	*Pearls, rose diamonds, gold, c. 1840*	**850.00**	**950.00**
☐	**42**	*Peridot, seed pearls, 14K gold, Art Nouveau, c. 1890*	**150.00**	**200.00**

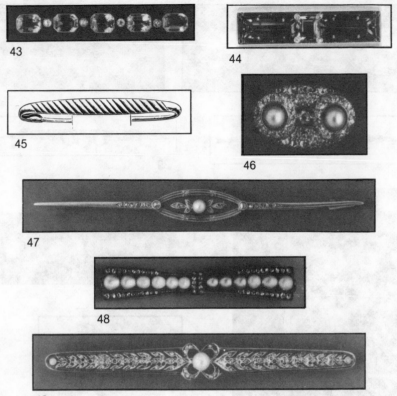

43

44

45

46

47

48

49

☐	**43**	*Peridots: five emerald-cut, four round diamonds, platinum, c. 1910*	**300.00**	**350.00**
☐	**44**	*Pink tourmaline: emerald-cut in center, two rectangular emerald-cut watermelon tourmalines, four round diamonds, gold, platinum, c. 1910....*	**800.00**	**900.00**
☐	**45**	*Ribbed motif, sterling, American, c. 1896*	**40.00**	**45.00**
☐	**46**	*Rose diamonds, pavé, two pearls, platinum topped gold, c. 1880*	**1200.00**	**1400.00**
☐	**47**	*Rose diamonds, one pearl, blue enamel, gold, c. 1910*.....................................	**225.00**	**275.00**
☐	**48**	*Rose diamonds, 12 pearls, silver topped gold, c. 1840*....................................	**450.00**	**550.00**
☐	**49**	*Rose diamonds, one natural pearl, silver, c. late 19th*	**600.00**	**650.00**

50

51

52

53

54

55

☐ **50** *Round diamonds: five approx. .50 ct., rose diamonds, four button pearls, white gold, c. 1905* **600.00 700.00**

☐ **51** *Round diamonds: 59 approx. 4.0 cts., gold, platinum, c. 1870* **1800.00 2000.00**

☐ **52** *Round diamond approx. 1.50 cts., 100 round diamonds approx. 2.0 cts., platinum, c. 1815* **2400.00 2800.00**

☐ **53** *Round ruby, rose diamonds, silver topped gold, c. 19th* **650.00 700.00**

☐ **54** *Round diamonds approx. .75 ct., 14K gold, platinum, c. 1915* **800.00 850.00**

☐ **55** *Round diamonds, five seed pearls, platinum, c. 1905* **1200.00 1500.00**

☐	**56**	*Rubies: three cabochon, rose diamonds, silver topped gold, c. 1880*	1100.00	1300.00
☐	**57**	*Ruby doublets, knife-edge bar, 14K gold, American, c. 1894-95*	85.00	135.00
☐	**58**	*Sapphire: one round, eight rose diamonds, Etruscan granulation, gold, c. 1860*	200.00	250.00
☐	**59**	*Sapphires: French-cut, 80 round diamonds approx. 6.50 cts., platinum, c. 1915*	8000.00	9000.00
☐	**60**	*Scimitar motif, 14K gold, American, c. 1894-95* . .	85.00	135.00
☐	**61**	*Seed pearls, 12 round diamonds, platinum, c. 1915*	550.00	600.00
☐	**62**	*Seed pearls, one round diamond, rose diamonds, platinum, c. 1915*	500.00	650.00
☐	**63**	*Seed pearls, one round diamond, rose diamonds, platinum, gold, c. 1910*	700.00	800.00

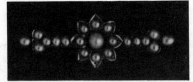

64

65

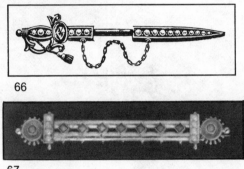

66

67

1

2

CAMEO

☐	**3**	*Crystalline quartz cameo of a lady, gold, c. 18th* .	**2250.00** **2600.00**
☐	**4**	*Green onyx cameo of a Greek Muse, pearls, gold, c. early 20th*	**1200.00** **1400.00**
☐	**5**	*Hardstone cameo of a lady, half pearls, gold, c. 19th*	**800.00** **1000.00**
☐	**6**	*Hardstone brown, beige and white cameo of a mythological scene, Queen Anne motif frame, diamonds, gold, c. late 17th*	**7500.00** **8000.00**

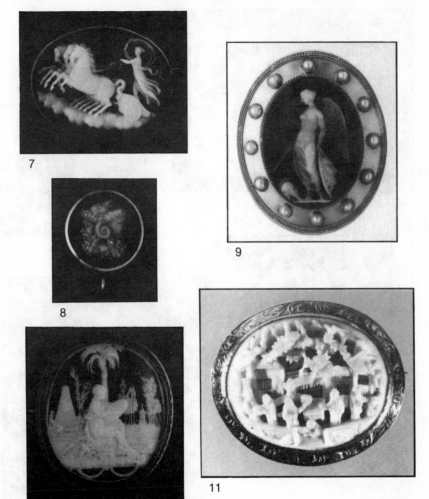

12

13

14

15

☐	**12**	*Ivory scenic cameo with Oriental figures, gold, c. 19th*	500.00	600.00
☐	**13**	*Lapis lazuli cameo of a lady, silver, c. late 19th* ..	300.00	350.00
☐	**14**	*Lava cameo of a warrior with a dragon on his helmet, gold, c. 1860*	200.00	250.00
☐	**15**	*Lava cameo of an angel riding a lion, gold, c. 18th*	650.00	750.00

16   17

19

18   20

☐	**16**	*Lava cameo of a lady with roses in her hair, gold, c. 1860*	**250.00**	**300.00**
☐	**17**	*Lava cameo of a lady with grape vines in her hair, gold, c. 1860*	**275.00**	**325.00**
☐	**18**	*Lava cameo of a mythological figure, three amethyst teardrops, gold, c. late 18th*	**450.00**	**550.00**
☐	**19**	*Moonstone cameo of a lady, round diamonds, platinum topped gold, c. 1900*	**2600.00**	**3200.00**
☐	**20**	*Mother-of-pearl scenic cameo with oriental figures, gold, c. 19th*	**400.00**	**450.00**

25

26

27

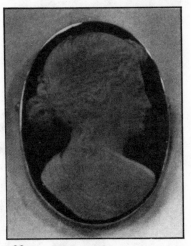

28

☐ **25** *Onyx cameo of a lady, Etruscan granulation frame, gold, c. 1870* **1000.00 1200.00**

☐ **26** *Onyx cameo of a lady, half pearls, black enamel, gold, c. 1870* **700.00 800.00**

☐ **27** *Onyx cameo of a gentleman, gold, c. 1850-75* **300.00 400.00**

☐ **28** *Onyx cameo of a lady, gold, c. 19th* **400.00 450.00**

29

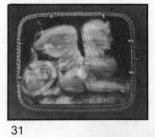

31

33

30

32

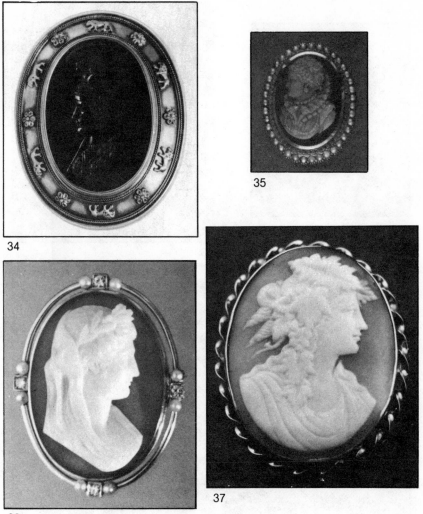

34

35

36

37

38

39

40

41

42

43

44

☐ **41** Shell scenic cameo of Rebecca-at-the-Well with
two ducks, gold, c. 19th **175.00 200.00**

☐ **42** Shell scenic cameo with an Oriental lady, carved
flower frame, gold, c. 19th **250.00 300.00**

☐ **43** Shell scenic cameo of Rebecca-at-the-Well, rose
twist frame, gold, c. 19th.................... **250.00 300.00**

☐ **44** Shell scenic cameos of Rebecca-at-the-Well,
three attached, gold, c. 19th **150.00 200.00**

3

4

5

6

☐	**3**	*Flower en tremblant with drops, rose diamonds, two natural pearls, gold, silver, c. 1840*	**1500.00**	**1800.00**
☐	**4**	*Flower motif, eight diamonds approx. 3.50 cts. and one diamond approx. 1.30 cts. in flower, 22 diamonds approx. 2.0 cts. in leaves, silver, gold, c. 1850*	**4000.00**	**4500.00**
☐	**5**	*Flower motif, rose diamonds, gold, silver, c. 1840*	**1500.00**	**2000.00**
☐	**6**	*Flower motif, one round emerald in center, eight pear emeralds, rose diamonds, silver topped, gold, c. 1850*	**4000.00**	**5000.00**

45

46

☐ **45** *Shell scenic cameo of Rebecca-at-the-Well, gold, c. 19th* **175.00** **200.00**

☐ **46** *Wedgewood cameo of a Muse c. 1840, blue enamelled 10K gold frame c. 1900* **400.00** **500.00**

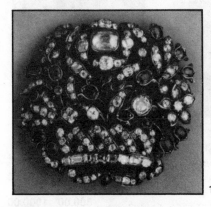

1

2

DIAMOND — PRE 1860

PRICE RANGE

☐ **1** *Basket and flower motif, one old mine diamond approx. .75 ct., 112 old mine diamonds approx. 4.0 cts., four demantoid garnets, emeralds, rubies, sapphires, gold, silver, c. 1860* **8000.00 10000.00**

☐ **2** *Flowers en tremblant, rose diamonds, silver topped gold, c. 1840* **2000.00 2500.00**

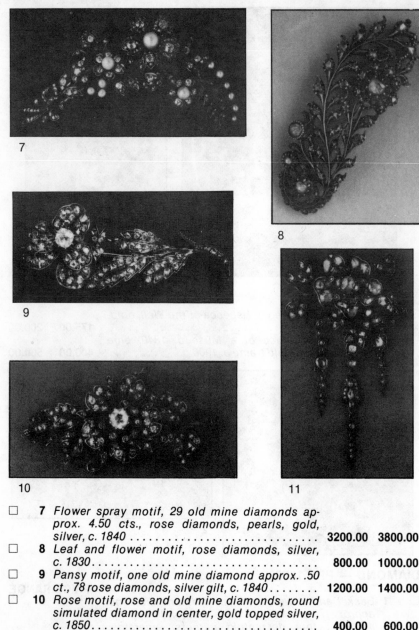

☐ **7** Flower spray motif, 29 old mine diamonds approx. 4.50 cts., rose diamonds, pearls, gold, silver, c. 1840 .... 3200.00 3800.00

☐ **8** Leaf and flower motif, rose diamonds, silver, c. 1830 .... 800.00 1000.00

☐ **9** Pansy motif, one old mine diamond approx. .50 ct., 78 rose diamonds, silver gilt, c. 1840 .... 1200.00 1400.00

☐ **10** Rose motif, rose and old mine diamonds, round simulated diamond in center, gold topped silver, c. 1850 .... 400.00 600.00

☐ **11** Rose with tassels motif, Holland-cut diamonds, table-cut heart-shape diamonds, fancy-cut and rose diamonds, silver, c. 1840 .... 800.00 1200.00

12

13

14

☐ **12** *Shield and drop motif, 106 old mine diamonds approx. 3.50 cts., rose diamonds, natural baroque pearls: one 8.5MM, two 9MM by 14MM, one 10MM by 16MM, brooch or pendant, gold, silver, c. 1860* **4000.00 5000.00**

☐ **13** *Shield motif, rose diamonds, round and cabochon emeralds, emerald teardrop, silver topped gold, c. 1850* **1000.00 1500.00**

☐ **14** *Wagon wheel motif, eight old mine diamonds approx. 1.0 ct., rose diamonds, one button natural pearl, eight cultured pearls, gold, silver, c. 1860* . **1500.00 2000.00**

1

2

4

3

DIAMOND

PRICE RANGE

☐ **1** *Anchor, crown and leaf motif, rose diamonds, gold, silver, c. 1880* **900.00 1200.00**

☐ **2** *Art Nouveau motif, 11 round diamonds approx. .90 ct., one pearl, lapel watch holder, gold, c. 1890* **1500.00 1600.00**

☐ **3** *Bow motif, round diamonds, platinum topped gold* **2000.00 2500.00**

☐ **4** *Bow with hinged tassels, 208 round diamonds approx. 5.0 cts., two gold European diamonds approx. 2.15 cts., platinum, c. 1900* **10000.00 12000.00**

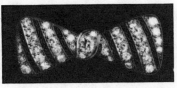

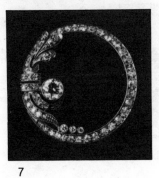

☐	**5**	*Bow with hinged tassels, round diamond in center approx. 1.0 cts., ten round diamonds, brooch or pendant, c. 1900*	**2200.00**	**2800.00**
☐	**6**	*Bow openwork motif, round diamonds, platinum, c. 1920*..................................	**2200.00**	**2500.00**
☐	**7**	*Circle motif, one round diamond approx. .80 ct., 55 round diamonds approx. 1.25 cts., 14K white gold clasp, platinum, c. 1910*	**2200.00**	**2500.00**
☐	**8**	*Circle bow motif, round diamonds, calibre sapphires, platinum, c. 1920*.....................	**1400.00**	**1600.00**

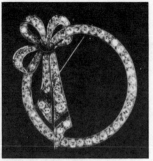
9

10

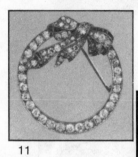
11

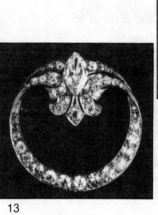
13

12

☐ **9** *Circle bow motif, 81 round diamonds approx.*
3.25 cts., calibre emeralds, platinum, c. 1910 . . . . **1800.00 2200.00**
☐ **10** *Circle bow motif, 81 round diamonds approx. 3.75*
cts., platinum, signed: J.E.C. & Co., c. late 19th . . . **2200.00 2400.00**
☐ **11** *Circle bow motif, emeralds, 64 round diamonds*
approx. 2.50 cts., platinum, c. 1910 . . . . **1400.00 1600.00**
☐ **12** *Circle wreath motif, old mine diamond approx.*
2.30 cts., rose diamonds, 14K gold, c. 1890 . . . . . . **3000.00 4000.00**
☐ **13** *Circle wreath motif, one marquise-shape dia-*
mond approx. 1.25 cts., 32 old mine diamonds ap-
prox. 2.75 cts., eight rose diamonds, platinum,
c. 1910 . . . . **3000.00 4000.00**

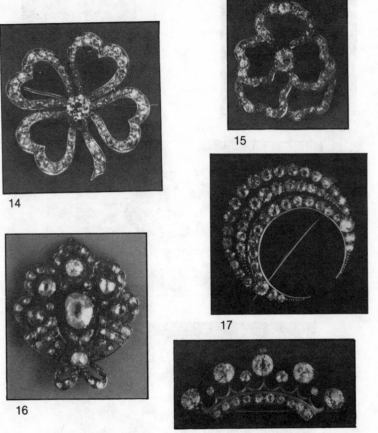

19

21

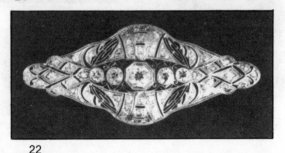

22

□ **19** Crown, star and septre motif, round diamonds, gold, c. 1900 .... **600.00 700.00**

□ **20** Crown motif, one emerald-cut emerald, one round emerald, old mine and rose diamonds, silver, gold, c. 1830 .... **2000.00 2400.00**

□ **21** Crown and flower motif, rose diamonds, red stones, silver, gold, c. 1840 .... **800.00 1000.00**

□ **22** Cutout motif, five round diamonds approx. 1.75 cts., 50 round diamonds approx. 1.0 cts., platinum, c. 1910 .... **1400.00 1600.00**

23

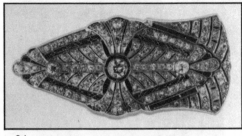

24

25

26

27

☐ **23** *Cutout motif, one pearl approx. 6.2MM, two round diamonds approx. .66 ct., platinum, c. 1925* **800.00 1000.00**

☐ **24** *Cutout modified triangular motif, 110 round diamonds approx. 4.0 cts., emeralds, brooch or pendant, platinum, c. 1900* **3000.00 3500.00**

☐ **25** *Flower motif, translucent pink and yellow enamel flowers with seed pearls, rose diamonds in silver leaves, gold, Art Nouveau, c. 1905* **2000.00 2500.00**

☐ **26** *Flower motif, enamel petals, one old mine diamond approx. .68 ct., gold, c. 1870* . . . .-. . **1500.00 1800.00**

☐ **27** *Flower basket motif, rose diamonds, round rubies, table-cut emeralds, silver, c. 1820* **800.00 900.00**

28

29

30

31

☐ **28** *Flower bouquet motif, 12 old mine diamonds approx. 2.50 cts., 141 round diamonds approx. 2.0 cts., rose diamonds, signed: K. Mikimoto, platinum* **5000.00 6000.00**

☐ **29** *Flower bow motif, rose diamonds, platinum topped gold, c. late 19th* **800.00 1000.00**

☐ **30** *Flower freeform motif, one round diamond approx. 1.20 cts., 25 round diamonds approx. 1.60 cts., platinum topped gold, c. 1920* **1800.00 2000.00**

☐ **31** *Flower and leaf motif, one old mine diamond approx. .70 ct., 73 old mine diamonds and rose diamonds approx. 5.75 cts., silver topped gold, c. 1850* **5000.00 6000.00**

32

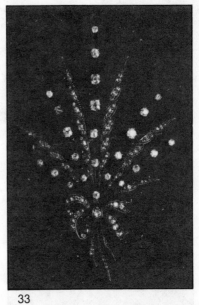

33

34

35

☐ **32** *Flower spray motif, two round diamonds approx.*
2.0 cts., four round diamonds approx. 2.5 cts.,
160 round diamonds approx. 7.0 cts., 128 dia-
monds approx. 2.0 cts., c. late 19th **20000.00 25000.00**

☐ **33** *Flower spray motif, 24 old mine diamonds ap-*
prox. 2.50 cts., rose diamonds, gold topped
silver, c. 1840 . . . . **2500.00 3000.00**

☐ **34** *Flowing scroll motif, 11 round diamonds approx.*
3.75 cts., gold and platinum, Art Nouveau, c. 1900 **3000.00 3500.00**

☐ **35** *Freeform motif, six old mine diamonds, rose dia-*
monds, platinum topped gold, French, c. late 19th **1200.00 1500.00**

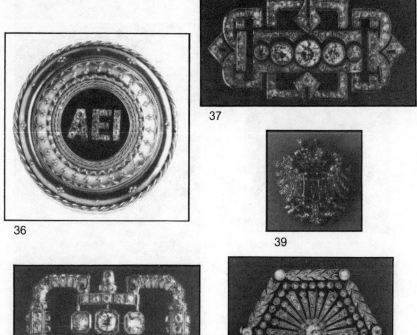

37

39

38

36

40

☐ **36** *Greek revival Etruscan motif, old mine diamond letters AEI on enamel center, fitted box, maker: Waterson and Brogden, c. mid 19th* 1000.00   1200.00

☐ **37** *Geometric motif, 75 round diamonds approx. 3.0 cts., platinum, c. 1920* 2200.00   2600.00

☐ **38** *Geometric motif, one round diamond approx. 1.10 cts., two round diamonds approx.1.50 cts., 114 round diamonds approx.4.50 cts., platinum, c. 1920* 6000.00   7000.00

☐ **39** *Hapsburg double-headed eagle motif, rose diamonds, square sapphires, silver, gold, c. 1880* . . . 800.00   1000.00

☐ **40** *Hexagonal shape openwork, round diamonds, platinum, c. 1900* 2500.00   3000.00

41

42

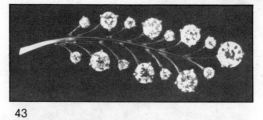

43

44

☐ **41** *Jubilee motif, translucent green enamel, opaque enamel, one old mine diamond, gold, souvenir of Queen Victoria's Diamond Jubilee, English, c. 1897* **600.00**   **800.00**

☐ **42** *Leaf and hollow tube motif, blue enamel on leaves, one rose diamond in silver, gold, c. 1840* . **700.00**   **800.00**

☐ **43** *Leaf motif, one round diamond approx. 1.20 cts., 14 round diamonds approx. 5.0 cts., platinum, gold, c. 1910* **6000.00**   **6500.00**

☐ **44** *Oblong motif, round diamonds approx. 3.0 cts., platinum, c. 1910* **5000.00**   **6000.00**

45

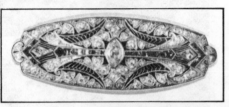

46

47

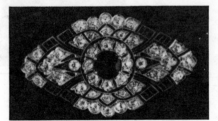

48

☐ **45** *Oblong cutout geometric motif, one marquise-shape diamond approx. .75 ct., two fancy triangular diamonds and 175 round diamonds approx. 1.25 cts., platinum, signed: Dreicer & Co., c. 1930* **4500.00 5500.00**

☐ **46** *Openwork motif, 12 calibre sapphires, one oval diamond approx. 1.35 cts., 65 round diamonds approx. 4.50 cts., platinum, c. 1900* **5000.00 5500.00**

☐ **47** *Openwork motif, one marquise-shape diamond, round diamonds, calibre diamonds, platinum, c. 1910*................................... **2000.00 2500.00**

☐ **48** *Openwork motif, 42 round diamonds approx. 2.50 cts., one cushion-shape sapphire in center, platinum, c. 1910* **1500.00 2000.00**

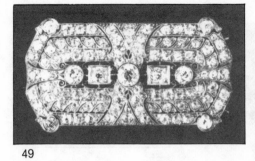

49

51

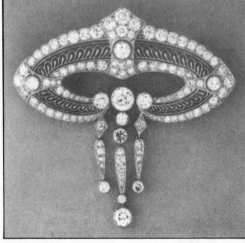

50

52

☐ **49** *Openwork modified rectangular motif, 101 old mine diamonds approx. 10.0 cts., platinum, c. 1910* **8000.00 9000.00**

☐ **50** *Openwork and tassel motif, 110 round diamonds approx. 5.50 cts., one round diamond approx. .50 ct., platinum, c. 1910* **5500.00 6500.00**

☐ **51** *Oval leaf openwork motif, 79 old mine diamonds approx. 4.75 cts., c. late 19th* **5000.00 6000.00**

☐ **52** *Rectangular cutout motif, five old mine diamonds approx. 1.25 cts., 44 old mine diamonds approx. 1.50 cts., marquise and calibre sapphires, brooch or pendant, white gold, c. 1920* ... **1200.00 1400.00**

53

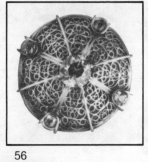

56

54

55

57

☐ **53** Rectangular geometric motif, three round diamonds, rose diamonds, gold topped platinum, c. 1900 . . . . **1500.00 2000.00**

☐ **54** Ribbon motif, one old European diamond approx. .60 ct., round diamonds approx. 1.50 cts., French-cut sapphires, platinum, c. 1900 . . . . **2000.00 2500.00**

☐ **55** Rock crystal center, carved and frosted, surrounded by calibre sapphires, 76 round diamonds approx. 3.50 cts., brooch or pendant, c. 1920 . . . . . . **3500.00 4000.00**

☐ **56** Round openwork motif, natural fancy color round diamond in center approx. 2.50 cts., four old mine diamonds, gold, signed: Tiffany & Co., c. 1900. . . . . **6000.00 6500.00**

☐ **57** Scroll motif, 11 round diamonds approx. .90 ct., gold, c. 1905 . . . . **1200.00 1500.00**

58

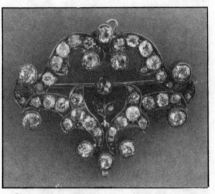

59

60

61

☐ **58** *Scroll freeform motif, 14 old mine diamonds, round and rose diamonds, 18K gold, Art Nouveau, c. 1890-1900* **2200.00 2600.00**

☐ **59** *Sheaf-of-wheat motif, flower en tremblant, rose diamonds, silver, c. 1820.* **450.00   650.00**

☐ **60** *Shield motif, two round diamonds approx. 2.10 cts., 41 round diamonds approx. 4.0 cts., platinum, c. 1910* **6000.00 7000.00**

☐ **61** *Shield motif, 61 old mine diamonds, .01 ct. to .25 ct. approx. 6.0 cts., gold topped silver, c. 1840* ... **4000.00 5000.00**

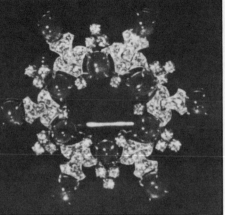

63

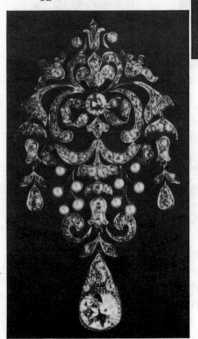

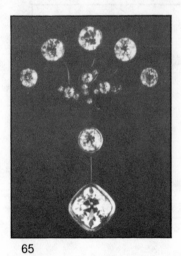

65

64

- [ ] **62** *Snake motif, rose diamonds, one natural ba-roque pearl, platinum, English, c. 1860* **600.00** **800.00**
- [ ] **63** *Snowflake motif, round diamonds approx. 3.0 cts., 12 cabochon star sapphires, gold, c. 1910* **6000.00** **6500.00**
- [ ] **64** *Scroll freeform motif, 160 round diamonds ap-prox. 8.50 cts., one round diamond approx. 4.40 cts., ten pearls, gold, platinum, c. 1925* **14000.00** **16000.00**
- [ ] **65** *Spray and dangle motif, one old mine diamond approx. 5.0 cts., 18 round diamonds approx. 6.60 cts., silver topped gold, c. mid 19th* **20000.00** **25000.00**

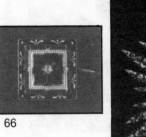

66

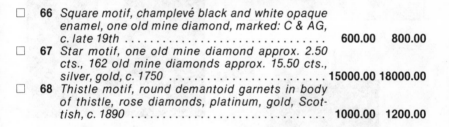

67

68

☐ **66** *Square motif, champlevé black and white opaque enamel, one old mine diamond, marked: C & AG, c. late 19th* **600.00   800.00**

☐ **67** *Star motif, one old mine diamond approx. 2.50 cts., 162 old mine diamonds approx. 15.50 cts., silver, gold, c. 1750* **15000.00 18000.00**

☐ **68** *Thistle motif, round demantoid garnets in body of thistle, rose diamonds, platinum, gold, Scottish, c. 1890* **1000.00   1200.00**

1

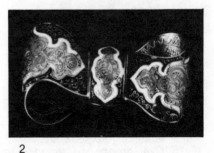

2

ENAMEL · GOLD

PRICE RANGE

☐ **1** *Belt and circle motif, champlevé opaque white and black enamel, rose diamonds and rubies in buckle, gold, c. 1880* **600.00   700.00**

☐ **2** *Bow motif, champlevé opaque white, blue and turquoise enamel, gold, c. 1820* **450.00   650.00**

4

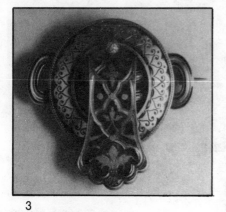

3

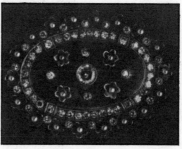

5

6

☐	3	*Enamel motif, blue and black, gold, c. 1860*	**400.00**	**500.00**
☐	4	*Flower motif rose diamonds on translucent blue enamel, gold, c. 1800*	**600.00**	**800.00**
☐	5	*Oval brooch, 54 round diamonds approx. 2.25 cts., guilloche translucent blue enamel, green enamel flowers, c. mid 19th*	**1500.00**	**2000.00**
☐	6	*Pansy motif, purple, black and white opaque enamel, one round diamond, gold, c. 1890*	**450.00**	**650.00**

1

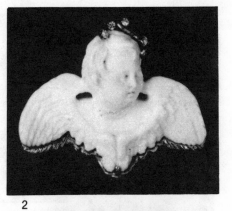

2

3

4

FACE and FIGURE

			PRICE RANGE	
☐	**1**	*Ancient coins with faces, gold frame, c. 1860* ...	1800.00	2000.00
☐	**2**	*Angel, carved coral, five round diamonds, contemporary gold mount, c. 1860*	1000.00	1200.00
☐	**3**	*Angel, enamelled on plaque, rose diamond wings, gold, c. 1870*	900.00	1100.00
☐	**4**	*Angel, one heart-shape peridot, green enamel leaves, silver gilt, c. 19th*	600.00	800.00

5

6

7

8

9

☐ **5** *Angel, carved, gold, maker: Wiese, c. late 19th* .. **1600.00 1700.00**
☐ **6** *Blackamoor, round rubies, one round blue stone,*
    gold, c. 19th **500.00 600.00**
☐ **7** *Egyptian motif, rose diamonds, emerald-cut em-*
    eralds, round rubies, gold, silver, c. 1925 .... **4400.00 4800.00**
☐ **8** *Egyptian motif of God Maáet, emerald-cut emer-*
    alds in legs, carnelian torso, mother-of-pearl
    base, diamonds, Art Deco, c. 1925 .... **4000.00 4200.00**
☐ **9** *Egyptian motif of goddess, translucent pink,*
    blue, yellow and red enamel, 44 rose diamonds in
    border, gold, c. 1925 .... **1200.00 1500.00**

10

11

12

13

14

☐ **10** *Enamel portrait of a lady with a Blackamoor, pink, blue, yellow, green, white and black opaque and translucent enamel, four rose diamonds, gold, brooch or pendant, c. 19th* **1400.00 1600.00**

☐ **11** *Enamel portrait of an Indian child, gold, c. mid-late 19th* **350.00 450.00**

☐ **12** *Grisaille enamel scene of three classical ladies with three angels, red background, rose diamond border, gold, French, c. 1810* **1800.00 2000.00**

☐ **13** *Medallion portrait of a lady, rose diamonds in flowers, gold, French, c. late 19th* **800.00 900.00**

☐ **14** *Medallion portrait of a young lady, rose diamond neck collar, gold, Art Nouveau, maker: Rasumny, French, c. 1880* **800.00 900.00**

☐ **15** *Medallion portrait of a winged warrior with helmet, gold, 1 in. diameter, Art Nouveau, inscribed: V. Prouve, French, c. 1900-10* **1200.00   1500.00**
☐ **16** *Medieval motif, enamel, gold frame, c. 1840-60* . .   **600.00   800.00**
☐ **17** *Mosaic portrait of the Madonna, Etruscan motif frame, gold, c. 1870* **550.00   650.00**
☐ **18** *Mosaic portrait of the Madonna, Etruscan motif frame, gold, c. 1860* **2400.00   2800.00**
☐ **19** *Mosaic portrait of St. Joseph, gold, c. mid 19th* . . **1200.00   1400.00**

20

22

23

21

24

☐	**20**	*Porcelain miniature portrait of a lady, base metal frame, c. 1920*	30.00	40.00
☐	**21**	*Sculptured lady and heart motif, blue and green enamel wings, gold, 1¾ in. high, inscribed: Lalique, Art Nouveau, French, c. 1890*	7000.00	9000.00
☐	**22**	*Sculptured lady with bat wings, translucent blue enamel, gold, maker: Lalique, French, c. 1900* . . .	5000.00	6000.00
☐	**23**	*Translucent enamel portrait of a lady, diamonds in headband, two pearls, gold, Art Nouveau, c. 1890-1910*	1200.00	1500.00
☐	**24**	*Vogue magazine promotional, brass, c. 1926*	50.00	80.00

1

3

2

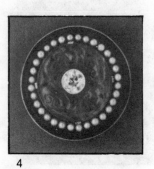

4

5

6

GEMSTONE

		PRICE RANGE	
☐	**1** *Amethysts: three faceted, two clear faceted stones, gold, c. 1850*	**200.00**	**250.00**
☐	**2** *Amethysts: three faceted, rose diamonds, platinum topped gold, c. late 19th*	**1500.00**	**1800.00**
☐	**3** *Art Deco motif, carved jade, rose diamonds, gold, c. 1930*	**300.00**	**400.00**
☐	**4** *Art Deco motif, carved jade, one diamond approx. .90 ct., black onyx, platinum, c. 1930*	**1200.00**	**1500.00**
☐	**5** *Art Deco clip, two cabochon sapphires, old mine diamonds, white gold, platinum, c. 1930*	**1800.00**	**2000.00**
☐	**6** *Art Nouveau motif, one amethyst, four seed pearls, 14K gold, c. 1900*	**375.00**	**475.00**

7

8

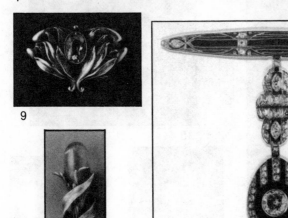

9

10   11

☐ **7** *Art Nouveau motif, rose diamonds, one round*
pearl, emerald bead, platinum, gold, c. 1890-1900 **2200.00   2500.00**

☐ **8** *Art Nouveau motif, one round ruby, rose dia-*
monds, six pearls, platinum, gold, c. 1890 ...... **1500.00   1700.00**

☐ **9** *Art Nouveau flower motif, one oval peridot, 14K*
gold, pendant for lapel watch on reverse, Ameri-
can, c. 1890-1900 .... **500.00   550.00**

☐ **10** *Art Nouveau flower motif, translucent green*
enamel, rose quartz bead, gold, c. 1890 .... **450.00   550.00**

☐ **11** *Bar and pendant motif, onyx, round diamonds,*
one round diamond approx. 1.0 ct., platinum,
c. 1925 .... **4500.00   4800.00**

12

13

14

15

16

17   18

☐ **12** *Bow motif, table-cut emeralds, gold, Spanish, c. 1750....................................* **350.00**   **450.00**

☐ **13** *Bow motif, seed pearls alternating with pink coral beads, gold, c. 1840 ....* **300.00**   **400.00**

☐ **14** *Bow motif, one round diamond, seed pearls, four turquoise, gold, c. 1860....................* **400.00**   **475.00**

☐ **15** *Bow and tassel motif, engraved, fancy link chains, turquoise, gold, c. 1830 ....* **900.00**   **1000.00**

☐ **16** *Cartouche motif, five faceted citrines, gold, c. 1840....................................* **400.00**   **500.00**

☐ **17** *Circle motif, 19 pearls, 22 round diamonds, gold, c. 1910..................................* **600.00**   **800.00**

☐ **18** *Circle motif, eight round demantoid garnets, eight round diamonds, gold, c. 1910 ....* **2200.00**   **2500.00**

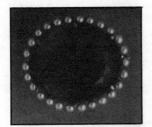

19

20

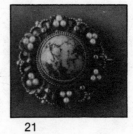

21

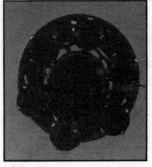

22

23

24

☐	**19**	*Circle motif, amethyst, seed pearls, gold, c. 1910*	**800.00**	**900.00**
☐	**20**	*Circle motif, amethyst, seed pearls, gold, c. 1860*	**350.00**	**400.00**
☐	**21**	*Circle motif, cabochon turquoise, seed pearls, gold, c. 1900*	**200.00**	**300.00**
☐	**22**	*Circle motif, six round sapphires, 37 rose dia- monds, silver topped gold, c. mid to late 19th* . . .	**1000.00**	**1200.00**
☐	**23**	*Circular motif, Etruscan granulation, seven pearls, gold, c. mid 19th*	**600.00**	**675.00**
☐	**24**	*Citrine: seven round faceted, gold, English, c. 1860*	**350.00**	**450.00**

25

26

27

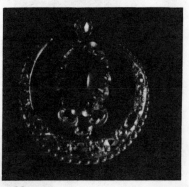

28

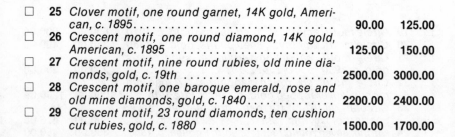

29

☐	**25**	*Clover motif, one round garnet, 14K gold, American, c. 1895*	90.00	125.00
☐	**26**	*Crescent motif, one round diamond, 14K gold, American, c. 1895*	125.00	150.00
☐	**27**	*Crescent motif, nine round rubies, old mine diamonds, gold, c. 19th*	2500.00	3000.00
☐	**28**	*Crescent motif, one baroque emerald, rose and old mine diamonds, gold, c. 1840*	2200.00	2400.00
☐	**29**	*Crescent motif, 23 round diamonds, ten cushion cut rubies, gold, c. 1880*	1500.00	1700.00

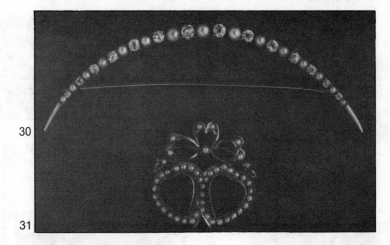

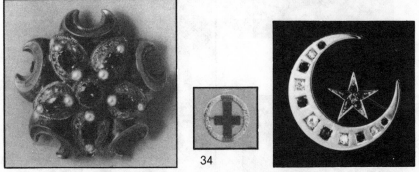

32   34   33

☐ **30** *Crescent motif, 14 round diamonds approx. 1.20*
   cts., pearls, gold, c. 19th **800.00   1000.00**
☐ **31** *Heart and bow motif, two heart-shape citrines,*
   half pearls, 9K gold, English, c. 1822 . . . .   **1400.00   1500.00**
☐ **32** *Crescent and flower motif, six garnets, ten*
   pearls, gold, c. 1830 . . . .   **600.00   650.00**
☐ **33** *Crescent and star motif, six old mine diamonds,*
   11 oval rubies, gold, c. 19th **600.00   700.00**
☐ **34** *Cross: carved wood, engraved circle frame, gold,*
   c. early 20th **80.00   100.00**

35

36

37

38

39

☐	**35** Cross motif, hardstone scarab, letters spell "ROMA," gold, c. 1840-60	**600.00**	**650.00**
☐	**36** Crown motif, pearls, gold, brooch or pendant, c. mid 19th	**300.00**	**350.00**
☐	**37** Crown motif, seven natural pearls, round diamonds, gold, c. 1880	**800.00**	**900.00**
☐	**38** Crown motif, six baroque pearls, six diamonds, gold, c. 20th	**800.00**	**900.00**
☐	**39** Crown and dangle motif, pavé pyrope garnets, gold, c. 1850	**800.00**	**1000.00**

40

41

42

43

44

☐ **40** *Emerald: emerald-cut approx. 3.75 cts., two old mine diamonds approx. 3.75 cts., ten old mine diamonds approx. 1.75 cts., gold topped platinum, c. 1900* **15000.00 18000.00**

☐ **41** *Emeralds: 11 foil-backed emerald-cut, gold, c. late 18th* **1600.00 2000.00**

☐ **42** *Fire opal, old mine diamonds, gold, Art Nouveau, c. 1890* **1000.00 1200.00**

☐ **43** *Fire opal, 32 old European cut diamonds, gold, c. 19th* **2200.00 2500.00**

☐ **44** *Floral openwork motif, one button pearl, three seed pearls, rose diamonds, three round sapphires, gold, c. 1850* **2000.00 2200.00**

45
46
47
48
49
50
51

☐	**45**	*Flower motif, one baroque pearl, rubies in petals, emeralds and rose diamonds in leaves, silver gilt, c. 18th*	**350.00**	**400.00**
☐	**46**	*Flower motif, translucent green enamel petals, seven rose diamonds, gold, c. 1860*	**300.00**	**400.00**
☐	**47**	*Flower motif, carved black onyx, 14K gold, American, c. 1895*	**100.00**	**125.00**
☐		*Same as above but gold filled mounting*	**34.00**	**45.00**
☐	**48**	*Flower motif, carved black onyx, 14K gold, American, c. 1895*	**100.00**	**125.00**
☐		*Same as above but gold filled mounting*	**30.00**	**40.00**
☐	**49**	*Flower motif, five calibre cabochon white opals, rose diamonds, silver, gold, c. late 19th*	**2000.00**	**2200.00**
☐	**50**	*Flower motif, green enamel, seed pearls, 14K gold, c. 1915*	**85.00**	**125.00**
☐	**51**	*Flower motif, one oval sapphire, gold, c. 1890* . . .	**1200.00**	**1500.00**

52

53

55

54

56

57

☐ **52** *Flower motif, 67 round diamonds approx. 1.25 cts., three pearls, gold, platinum, signed: Tiffany & Co., France, c. 1880* **2000.00 2500.00**

☐ **53** *Flower motif, five old mine diamonds approx. 1.25 cts., six cushion-cut rubies, yellow and green gold, c. mid 19th* **1200.00 1400.00**

☐ **54** *Flower motif, three faceted citrines, gold, c. 1840* **250.00 350.00**

☐ **55** *Flower motif, 13 pink topaz, gold, signed: Walton & Co., c. late 19th* **1000.00 1200.00**

☐ **56** *Flower motif, carved black onyx, one seed pearl, gold, c. 1860-80* **125.00 150.00**

☐ **57** *Flower basket motif, diamonds, emeralds, sapphires, rubies, gold, c. 1940* **400.00 600.00**

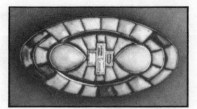

59

60

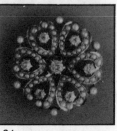

61

58

62

63

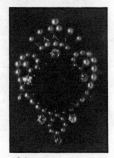

64

☐	**58** Flower spray motif, turquoise, diamonds, gold, silver, c. 1830	1400.00	1600.00
☐	**59** Geometric oval motif, calibre cabochon turquoise, four baguette diamonds, gold, c. 1850...	500.00	600.00
☐	**60** Grape cluster motif, seed pearls, translucent green enamel, gold, c. 1900	150.00	200.00
☐	**61** Heart motif, seven round diamonds, 1.0 ct., seed pearls, gold, American, c. 1870	1200.00	1400.00
☐	**62** Heart motif, cabochon turquoise frames, gold, c. 1840	500.00	600.00
☐	**63** Heart and bow motif, turquoise, rose diamonds, c. 1830	900.00	1200.00
☐	**64** Heart and crown motif, one round amethyst, five round diamonds, seed pearls, gold, c. 1880	1200.00	1500.00

65

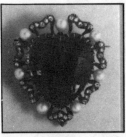

66

67

68

70

69

71

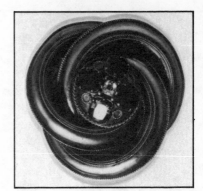

72

73

74

75   76

☐	**71**	*Lily motif, pink and green translucent enamel, four diamonds, 14K gold, c. 1900*	550.00	650.00
☐	**72**	*Loveknot motif, four cushion-cut garnets, one cushion-cut diamond, gold, c. 1830*	350.00	425.00
☐	**73**	*Loveknot motif, engraved, one round diamond, 14K gold, American, c. 1895*	125.00	150.00
☐	**74**	*Melon motif, four carved chalcedony beads, gold stems, rose diamonds set in silver, c. 1840*	1200.00	1500.00
☐	**75**	*Mosaic motif, gold, c. 1870*	100.00	150.00
☐	**76**	*Mosaic conch shell motif, flower motif frame, gold, c. 1870*	2200.00	2400.00

77

78

80

79

81

☐	**77**	Mosaic flower motif, Etruscan granulation frame, gold, c. 1860	500.00	650.00
☐	**78**	Mosaic religious motif in white, blue and red, gold, c. 1865	300.00	350.00
☐	**79**	Mosaic of St. Peter's Basilica of Rome, malachite background, gold, c. 1870	1000.00	1200.00
☐	**80**	Openwork motif, one round white sapphire, 14K gold, American, c. 1895	125.00	150.00
☐	**81**	Openwork motif, one emerald-cut garnet, 14K gold, American, c. 1895	125.00	150.00

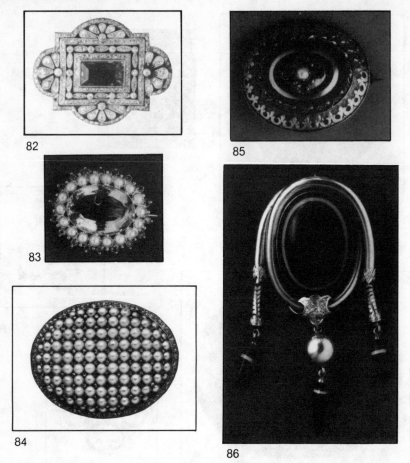

87

88

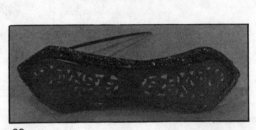

89

90

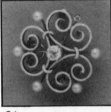

91

☐ **87** *Peacock feather motif, square cut sapphires,*
round diamonds, platinum, gold, c. 1920 . . . .   **1800.00 2000.00**

☐ **88** *Pineapple motif clip, rubies, seed pearls, rose*
diamonds, gold, silver, c. late 19th **700.00   800.00**

☐ **89** *Plaque motif, carved and pierced jade, gold*
frame, c. early 20th **600.00   800.00**

☐ **90** *Ribbon motif, one cushion-cut citrine, rose dia-*
monds, gold, silver, c. 1820 . . . .   **800.00   900.00**

☐ **91** *Scroll motif, one round diamond, pearls, white*
enamel, gold, c. early 20th **600.00   700.00**

92

93

94

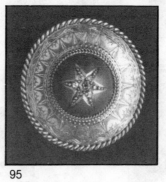

95

96

☐ **92** *Shell motif, oval faceted citrine, engraved, gold,*
c. mid 19th **800.00 1000.00**

☐ **93** *Snowflake cluster motif, pave pyrope garnets,*
low karat gold, c. 1860-80 . . . . **150.00 200.00**

☐ **94** *Star motif, one old mine diamond, one pear-*
shape cabochon garnet, 14K gold, c. 1860 . . . . . . **800.00 900.00**

☐ **95** *Star motif, diamonds set in a turquoise enamel*
circle, engraved, gold, c. 1870 . . . . **600.00 650.00**

☐ **96** *Star motif, rose diamonds set in cabochon gar-*
net, Etruscan granulation, gold, c. 1860 . . . . **500.00 600.00**

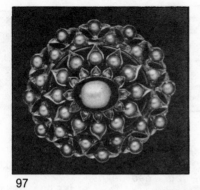

97

98

99

100

101

103

102

☐	**97**	Sunburst motif, 12 diamonds, one baroque pearl, 36 seed pearls, gold, c. 1870	**800.00**	**900.00**
☐	**98**	White opal approx. 11 cts. surrounded by 19 rubies, gold, c. late 19th	**900.00**	**1200.00**
☐	**99**	Wing motif, rose diamonds, green onyx, white gold, c. 1910	**800.00**	**900.00**
☐	**100**	Wreath motif, carved black onyx, 14K gold, American, c. 1895	**100.00**	**125.00**
☐	**101**	Wreath motif, six turquoise, 14K gold, American, c. 1895	**100.00**	**125.00**
☐	**102**	Wreath motif, one turquoise, 14K gold, American, c. 1895	**80.00**	**100.00**
☐	**103**	Wreath motif, ten seed pearls, 14K gold, American, c. 1895	**125.00**	**150.00**

104   105   106

☐ **104** *Wreath motif, one opal, 14K gold, American, c. 1895* **80.00   100.00**
☐ **105** *Wreath motif, green enamel, four seed pearls, 14K gold, American, c. 1895* **165.00   185.00**
☐ **106** *Wreath motif, six diamonds, oval faceted amethyst, gold, c. mid 19th* **900.00   1000.00**

1

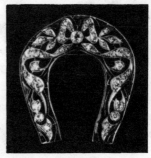

2

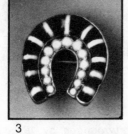

3

HORSESHOE

                                                    PRICE RANGE

☐ **1** *Horseshoe circle motif, 43 round diamonds approx. .50 ct., platinum, c. 1925* **500.00   600.00**
☐ **2** *Horseshoe motif, openwork, 41 round diamonds approx. 1.75 cts., platinum, c. 1920* **1000.00   1200.00**
☐ **3** *Horseshoe motif, banded onyx, half pearls, gold, c. 1840* **300.00   350.00**

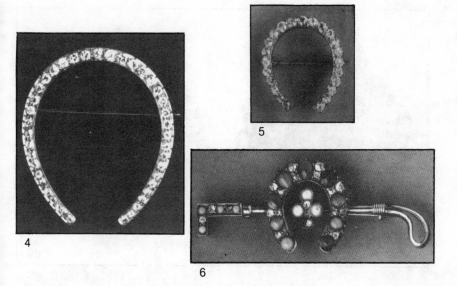

4

5

6

☐ **4** *Horseshoe motif, 41 round diamonds, platinum*
topped gold, c. 1910 .... **1600.00 2000.00**
☐ **5** *Horseshoe motif, 23 old European-cut diamonds*
approx. 1.25 cts., platinum topped gold,
c. 1900 .... **900.00 1200.00**
☐ **6** *Riding crop, horseshoe and clover motif, rose*
diamonds, turquoise, pearls, gold, c. 1880 ...... **600.00 800.00**

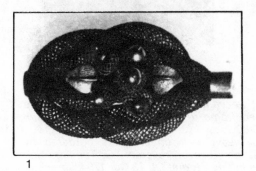

1

HAIR
All items made from hair referred to throughout this section are of brunette
human hair unless stated otherwise.

PRICE RANGE

☐ **1** *Acorn and loveknot motif of woven hair, gold,*
c. 1840-80 .... **125.00 150.00**

2

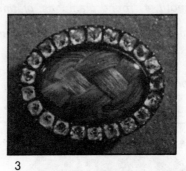

3

☐ **2** *Basket weave hair under glass, hollow machine stamped frame, reverse: picture of lady, gold, c. 1860-80* **125.00**   **150.00**

☐ **3** *Basket weave hair under glass bordered by pastes, inscribed on reverse: "G. Tomkins She blooms in Life Eternal Ob 23 Oct 1794," bracelet clasp converted to brooch, gold, English, c. 1794*   **285.00**   **325.00**

6

4

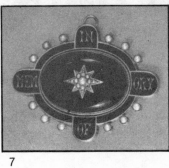

7

5

☐ **4** Basket weave hair with cutout urn and name plaque motif under glass, inscribed on reverse: "Thos. Cooking OB 5 July 1787 at 51," gold, English, c. 1787 .... **500.00 550.00**

☐ **5** Black enamel flower motif on hollow tube frame for woven hair under oval glass, gold, c. 1880.... **175.00 200.00**

☐ **6** Black enamel border around braided white and brunette hair under glass, chased bezel, outer woven hair border with gold spacers, initial shield, gold, English, c. 1860-80 .... **140.00 160.00**

☐ **7** Black enamel motif, "In Memory Of," seed pearls, gold, English, c. mid 19th **400.00 450.00**

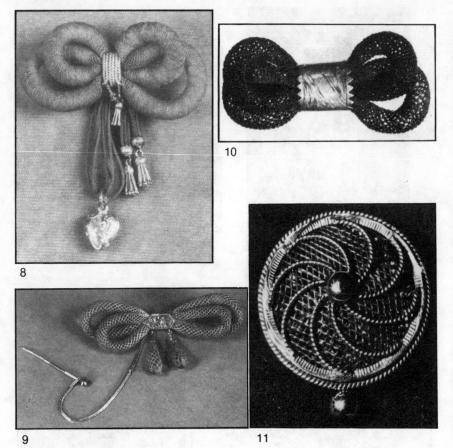

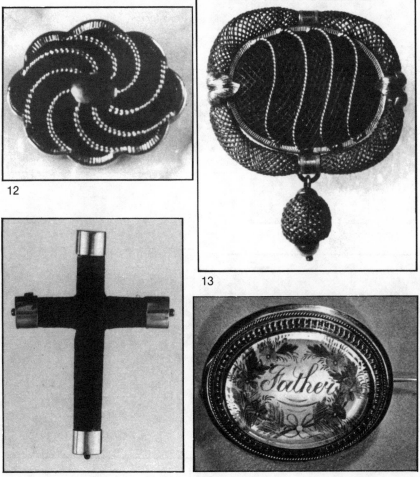

12

13

14

15

□ **12** *Cage motif with woven hair, scalloped edges, gold, c. 1870-90* **60.00** **80.00**

□ **13** *Cage motif with woven hair and woven hair tube border and dangle, gold, English, c. 1840-80*..... **80.00** **110.00**

□ **14** *Cross motif of tightly woven hair over solid core, gold fittings, c. 1860-80* **85.00** **125.00**

□ **15** *"Father" and flower wreath motif of cut and paste hair on an opalescent porcelain plaque, Etruscan granulation frame, gold, c. 1860* **200.00** **250.00**

16

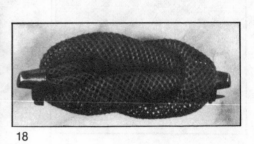

18

17

19

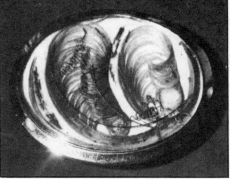

21

20

22

☐ **20** *Miniature of tree and building beside river painted with dissolved hair on ivory plaque, bordered by pastes, inscribed on reverse: "Mary Chetham Obt 10 October 1818 At 67.H," silver, gold, c. 1818* 350.00 400.00

☐ **21** *Prince of Wales feathers of hair with gold wires on porcelain plaque, gold frame, c. 1860* 225.00 250.00

☐ **22** *Prince of Wales feathers of hair with white and blue enamel plaque bordered by seed pearls inscribed: "Not Lost But Gone Before" on porcelain plaque, gold, English, c. 1860-80* 300.00 350.00

23

25

24

26

☐	**23**	*Prince of Wales feathers of hair with seed pearl, gold wire and sepia print on porcelain plaque under glass, gold filled, English, c. 1860-80*	**45.00**	**60.00**
☐	**24**	*Prince of Wales feather of hair with seed pearls and gold wire under glass, fancy cutout frame, gold, English, c. 1860-80*	**100.00**	**125.00**
☐	**25**	*Prince of Wales feathers of grey hair with gold wire on porcelain plaque under glass, braided grey hair border, engraved shields, gold, c. 1860-80*	**160.00**	**180.00**
☐	**26**	*Seed pearl border, lock of hair and gold inital under glass, gold, c. 1790*	**200.00**	**250.00**

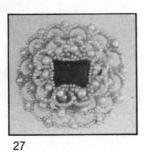

27

28

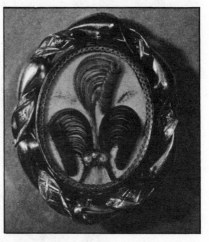

29

- **27** *Seed pearls strung on white horse hair on mother-of-pearl templets, lock of hair under glass in center, gold, c. 1860* **300.00   350.00**
- **28** *Swivel motif, black enamel frame "In Memory Of," reverse: picture of deceased, obverse: tree of hair with inscription: "Francis S. Crichton Born 18th May 1840 Died 7 March 1861," gold, English, c. 1861* **800.00   850.00**
- **29** *Swivel motif, engraved twisted frame, picture of a gentleman on one side, Prince of Wales feathers of hair with seed pearls and gold wire on other side, gold, c. 1890* **250.00   300.00**

30

☐ **30** *Swivel motif, engraved ribbon frame, lock of hair
on one side, Prince of Wales feathers of hair with
gold wire on other side, gold, c. 1880* **325.00 375.00**

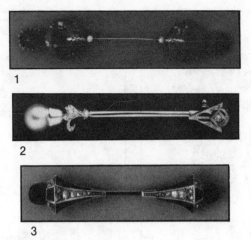

1

2

3

JABOT

			PRICE	RANGE
☐	**1**	*Jabot, lapis lazuli, two seed pearls, gold, c. 1900.*	**300.00**	**350.00**
☐	**2**	*Jabot, pearl, round diamonds, platinum topped gold, c. 1910 . . . . ,*	**500.00**	**600.00**
☐	**3**	*Jabot, diamonds, calibre-cut onyx and half-moon onyx beads, gold, platinum, c. 1925 . . . .*	**2200.00**	**2500.00**

1

MISCELLANEOUS · GOLD

			PRICE	RANGE
☐	**1**	*Astrological motif, gold, c. 19th . . . .*	**400.00**	**500.00**

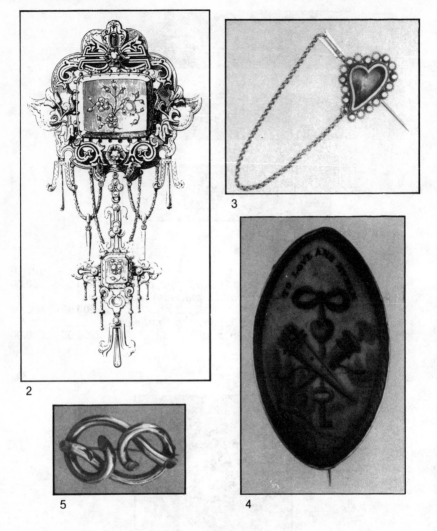

2

3

5

4

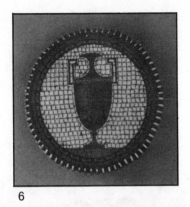

6

8

7

10

9

☐	**6**	*Micro mosaic urn motif, 15K gold, c. 1860*	**350.00**	**450.00**
☐	**7**	*Painted porcelain scene, carved frame, reverse: locket with hair, gold, c. mid to late 19th*	**600.00**	**700.00**
☐	**8**	*Scallop and tassel motif, three seed pearls, 14K gold, c. 1860*	**250.00**	**300.00**
☐	**9**	*Sheath-of-wheat motif, carved ivory, English, c. 19th*	**150.00**	**200.00**
☐	**10**	*World and life symbol motif, gold, c. 19th*	**400.00**	**500.00**

1

2

3

NAME

			PRICE RANGE	
☐	**1**	*Flower wreath motif, enamel, gilt metal, New Zealand, c. 20th*	**55.00**	**65.00**
☐	**2**	*Oval ivory cutout name brooch, English, c. late 19th*	**65.00**	**75.00**
☐	**3**	*"Queen Lizzie" commemorative wire brooch, mother-of-pearl, anchor denotes security, heart denotes love and cross denotes blessings, gold filled, c. early 20th*	**40.00**	**50.00**

4

5

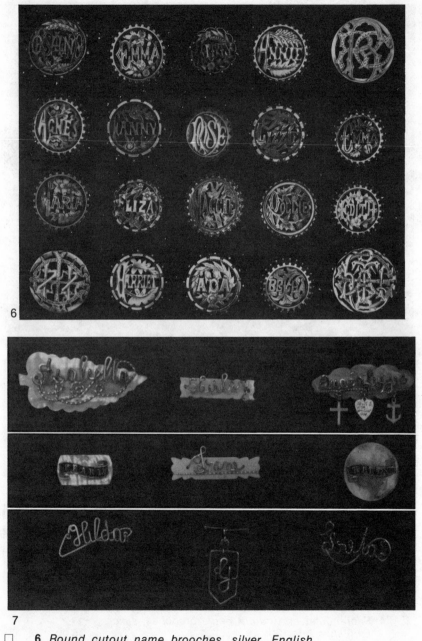

SCOTTISH AGATE

			PRICE RANGE	
☐	**1**	*Anchor motif, engraved, agate, silver, maker: Hilliard and Thomason, Birmingham, England, c. 1848*	**150.00**	**200.00**
☐	**2**	*Anchor motif, colored agate, silver, English, c. 1850*	**225.00**	**275.00**
☐	**3**	*Arrow motif, engraved, agate, silver, English, c. 1850*	**150.00**	**200.00**

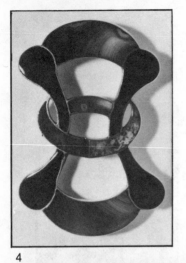

4

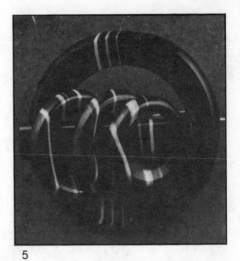

5

6

7

☐ **4** *Bow motif, colored agate, silver, c. 1850* **175.00** **225.00**

☐ **5** *Circle motif, black banded agate, silver, c. mid to late 19th* **85.00** **100.00**

☐ **6** *Cross and circle motif, engraved, colored agate, 15K gold, 1 in. diameter, English, c. 1870* **325.00** **375.00**

☐ **7** *Octagonal motif, engraved, bloodstone, carnelian, silver, English, c. 1850* **125.00** **150.00**

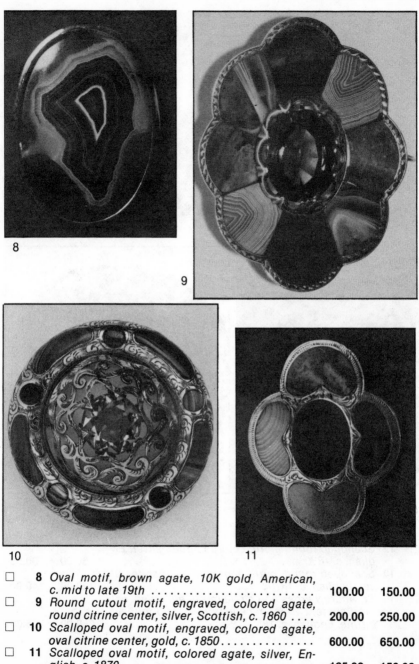

8

9

10

11

☐ **8** *Oval motif, brown agate, 10K gold, American, c. mid to late 19th* **100.00** **150.00**

☐ **9** *Round cutout motif, engraved, colored agate, round citrine center, silver, Scottish, c. 1860 ....* **200.00** **250.00**

☐ **10** *Scalloped oval motif, engraved, colored agate, oval citrine center, gold, c. 1850* **600.00** **650.00**

☐ **11** *Scalloped oval motif, colored agate, silver, English, c. 1870* **125.00** **150.00**

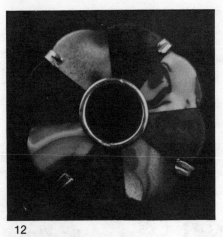

12

13

14

☐ **12** *Scalloped round motif, colored agate, silver, English, c. 1880* **65.00** **90.00**

☐ **13** *Scalloped round motif, engraved, malachite, silver, English, c. 1870*........................ **120.00** **140.00**

☐ **14** *St. Andrew cross and circle motif, engraved, colored agate, two foilback amethyst, two foilback citrine, English, c. 1850*..................... **250.00** **285.00**

1

2

3

4

5

6

SILVER

			PRICE RANGE	
☐	1	*Angel motif, sterling, American, c. 1896*	**125.00**	**140.00**
☐	2	*Berry motif, three simulated pearls, sterling, American, c. 1894-95*	**40.00**	**60.00**
☐	3	*Berry and flower motif, genuine sea shell, three pearls, one rhinestone, sterling, American, c. 1894-95*	**85.00**	**110.00**
☐	4	*Bow motif, one emerald-cut and one round emerald, rose and old mine diamonds, silver, c. late 19th*	**1200.00**	**1500.00**
☐	5	*Butterfly motif, chased, sterling, American, c. 1896*	**45.00**	**50.00**
☐	6	*Flower and leaf motif, one seed pearl, sterling, American, c. 1896*	**50.00**	**60.00**

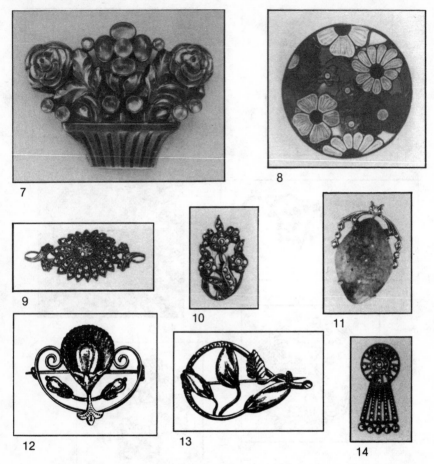

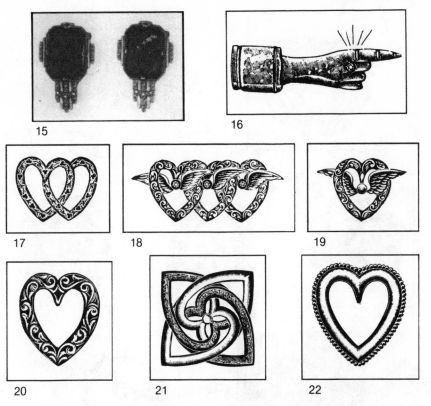

15

16

17

18

19

20

21

22

☐	**15**	Geometric motif, black onyx, marcasites, sterling silver, clip reverse, c. 1930. Pair	**65.00**	**80.00**
☐	**16**	Hand motif, carved mother-of-pearl, rhinestone in ring, sterling, American, c. 1894-95	**45.00**	**55.00**
☐	**17**	Heart motif, enamel, sterling, American, c. 1896 .	**35.00**	**45.00**
☐	**18**	Heart motif, three round red stones, sterling, American, c. 1896	**80.00**	**90.00**
☐	**19**	Heart motif, one cabochon turquoise, sterling, American, c. 1896	**40.00**	**50.00**
☐	**20**	Heart motif, chased, sterling, American, c. 1896 .	**30.00**	**40.00**
☐	**21**	Heart motif, one opal, sterling, American, c. 1896	**60.00**	**70.00**
☐	**22**	Heart motif, sterling, American, c. 1896	**35.00**	**45.00**

23

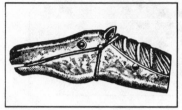

24

25

26

27

28

29

☐	**23** Heart motif, chased, sterling, American, c. 1896 .	**65.00**	**80.00**
☐	**24** Horsehead motif, carved mother-of-pearl, sterling, American, c. 1894-95	**90.00**	**120.00**
☐	**25** Loveknot motif, chased, sterling, American, c. 1896	**50.00**	**60.00**
☐	**26** Loveknot motif, enamel, sterling, American, c. 1896	**65.00**	**85.00**
☐	**27** Loveknot motif, chased, one opal, sterling, American, c. 1896	**60.00**	**70.00**
☐	**28** Madonna and child motif, bas-relief panel, blue enamel, four half-pearls, silver, c. 1905	**165.00**	**185.00**
☐	**29** Miniature painted on porcelain, sterling, American, c. 1896.	**90.00**	**115.00**

30

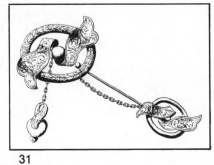

31

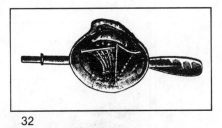

32

33

☐ **30** *Miniature painted on porcelain, six seed pearls, sterling, American, c. 1896* **125.00** **140.00**

☐ **31** *Ribbon, circle and dangle motif, engraved, maker: Ellis & Son, Exeter, England, silver, c. 1869* **125.00** **150.00**

☐ **32** *Ship and oar motif, genuine sea shell, ship is 14K gold, oar is sterling, American, c. 1894-95* **125.00** **140.00**

☐ **33** *Star of David motif, green marble, silver, English, c. 19th* **150.00** **200.00**

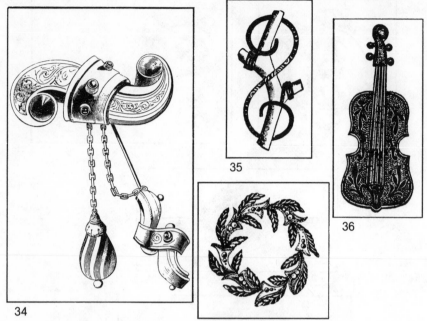

34

35

37

36

38

39

40

□ **34** *Swirl and dangle motif, engraved, maker: Ellis & Son, Exeter, England, silver, c. 1869* **100.00** **125.00**

□ **35** *Twig motif, carved mother-of-pearl, sterling, American, c. 1894-95* **30.00** **40.00**

□ **36** *Violin motif, enamel, chased, sterling, American, c. 1894-95* **85.00** **100.00**

□ **37** *Wreath motif, enamel, sterling, American, c. 1896* **55.00** **65.00**

□ **38** *Wreath motif, five seed pearls, sterling, American, c. 1896.* **50.00** **60.00**

□ **39** *Wreath motif, seven cabochon turquoise, sterling, American, c. 1896* **60.00** **70.00**

□ **40** *Wreath motif, sterling, American, c. 1896* **40.00** **60.00**

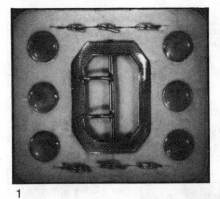
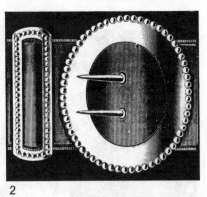

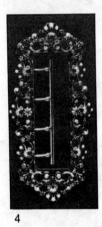
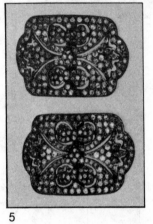

1

2

3

4

5

BUCKLES

			PRICE RANGE	
☐	1	*Buckle and button set, translucent apple green enamel, silver, English, c. 1920-30*	150.00	175.00
☐	2	*Circular motif buckle with beaded edge and slide with beaded edge, sterling silver, American, c. 1896*	110.00	125.00
☐	3	*Cluster motif pair of buckles, rhinestone, white metal, c. 1930-40*	4.00	8.00
☐	4	*Fan and scroll motif buckle, champlevé opaque black and white enamel, gold, c. 1870*	900.00	1100.00
☐	5	*Fancy shape motif pair of buckles, rhinestone, white metal, c. 1930-40*	5.00	10.00

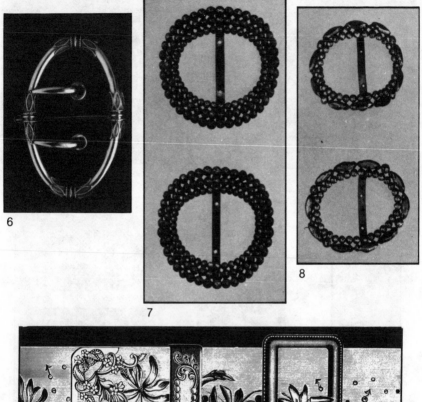

6

7

8

9

☐	**6**	Oval Etruscan granulation motif, buckle pin, gold, c. 1870	**180.00**	**200.00**
☐	**7**	Oval motif pair of buckles, cut steel, c. late 19th .	**20.00**	**24.00**
☐	**8**	Oval wreath motif pair of buckles, cut steel, c. late 19th	**12.00**	**15.00**
☐	**9**	Rectangular buckle and floral motif slide, floral motif belt, sterling silver, American, c. 1896	**50.00**	**65.00**

10

11

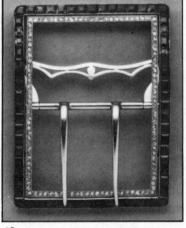

13

12

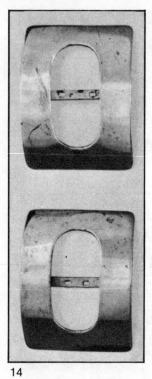

14

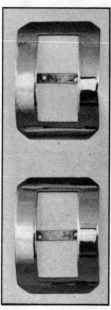

15

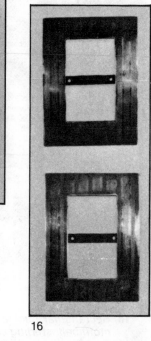

16

☐ **14** *Rectangular motif pair of buckles, silver plated,*
c. mid 20th **5.00** **10.00**

☐ **15** *Rectangular motif pair of buckles, silver plated,*
c. mid 20th **4.00** **8.00**

☐ **16** *Rectangular pair of buckles, engraved, sterling*
silver, c. 1920 .... **35.00** **45.00**

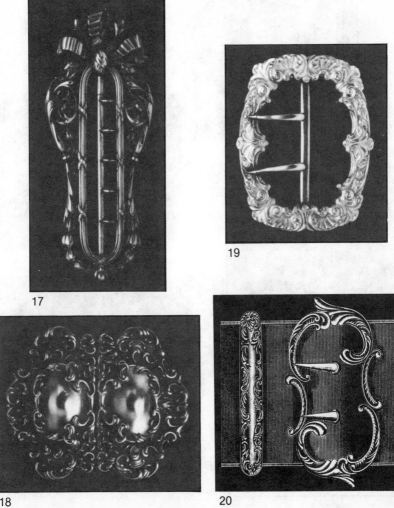

17

19

18

20

☐ **17** *Ribbon and leaf motif, gold, French, c. 1870* 800.00 900.00
☐ **18** *Scroll motif buckles, gold, c. 1900* 550.00 650.00
☐ **19** *Scroll motif buckle, gold, c. 1890* 350.00 450.00
☐ **20** *Scroll motif buckle and slide, sterling silver,*
American, c. 1896 . . . . 100.00 115.00

21

22

23

24

25

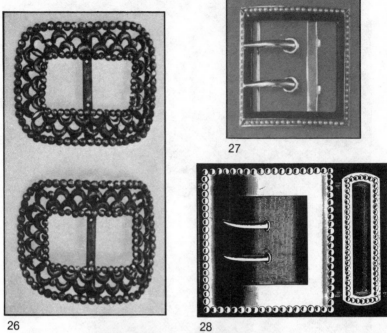

26

27

28

29

☐	**26** Square crescent motif pair of buckles, cut steel, c. 19th	**22.00**	**26.00**
☐	**27** Square motif buckle, seed pearl border, cobalt blue enamel, 14K gold, c. 1920	**225.00**	**300.00**
☐	**28** Square motif buckle with beaded edge and slide with beaded edge, sterling silver, American, c. 1896	**110.00**	**125.00**
☐	**29** Wide rectangular motif buckle and slide, sterling silver, American, c. 1896	**65.00**	**90.00**

Turn-of-the-century photograph of a man and wife with the wife wearing a slide chain and hunting case pendant watch with a watch pin. The wife is also wearing small pierced round gold earrings with a single cabochon turquoise gemstone in each earring. The photograph was taken in Baltimore, Maryland, in 1900.

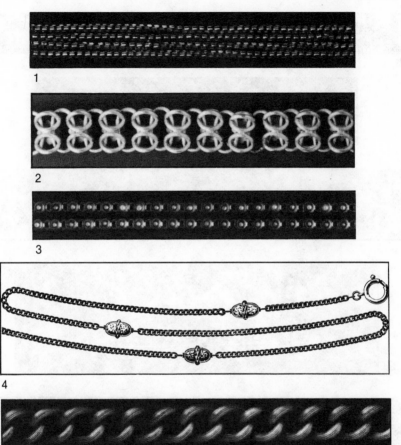

CHAINS

NECK

			PRICE	RANGE
☐	1	Box links, gold, 55 in. long, c. 20th	600.00	800.00
☐	2	Circular and oblong links, gold, c. 1860.........	1200.00	1400.00
☐	3	Circular links, seed pearls, gold, c. 1860	900.00	1000.00
☐	4	Curb links spaced with a crystal rondelle between two cabochon opal beads, gold, English, c. 1900...................................	600.00	800.00
☐	5	Curb ribbed links, gold, c. 1880	1500.00	1700.00

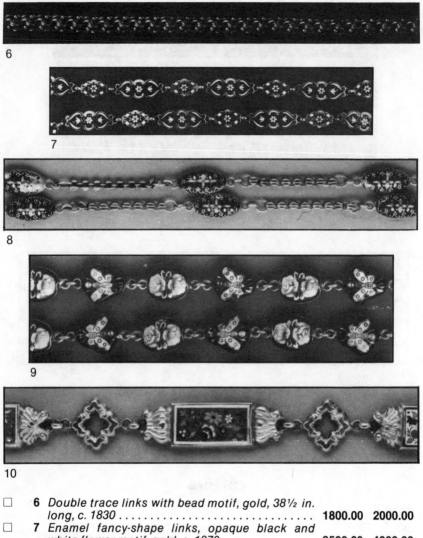

11

12

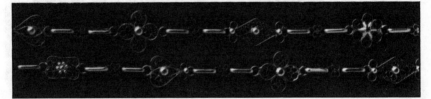

13

14

☐	**11**	*Fancy barrel and circular links, gold, c. 1830*	**500.00**	**600.00**
☐	**12**	*Fetter and five links with 11 contemporary and antique charms, gold, 65 in. long, c. 20th*	**1200.00**	**1500.00**
☐	**13**	*Filigree and oblong links, gold, 19 in. long, c. mid 19th*	**800.00**	**900.00**
☐	**14**	*Flat circular links, embossed, leaf motif clasp, gold, 41 in. long, c. 1830*	**1800.00**	**2000.00**

15

16

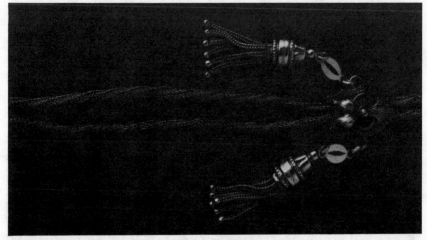

17

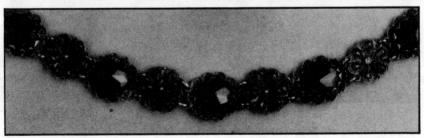

18

 15 *Flat oblong star motif links, gold, 52 in. long,*
c. 1850 . . . . **1900.00 2100.00**

☐ **16** *Fluted twisted links, swivel loop, gold, 60 in.*
long, c. 1860 . . . . **600.00   700.00**

☐ **17** *Foxtail woven chain, slide with one seed pearl*
and two tassels, gold, 60 in. long, c. 1860 . . . . **1200.00 1500.00**

☐ **18** *Garnets: large rose cut and pear-shape clusters,*
gold, c. mid 19th **800.00   900.00**

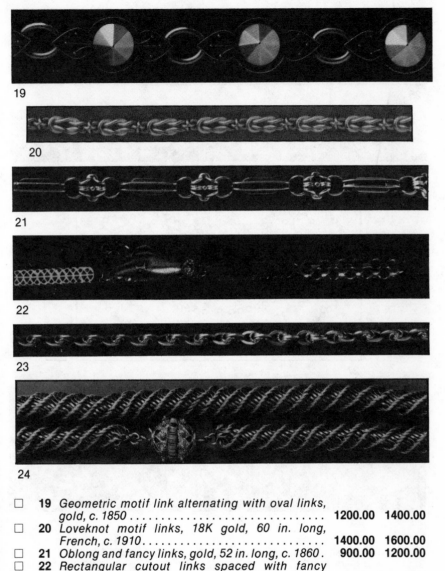

☐	**19**	Geometric motif link alternating with oval links, gold, c. 1850	1200.00	1400.00
☐	**20**	Loveknot motif links, 18K gold, 60 in. long, French, c. 1910.............................	1400.00	1600.00
☐	**21**	Oblong and fancy links, gold, 52 in. long, c. 1860 .	900.00	1200.00
☐	**22**	Rectangular cutout links spaced with fancy round links, hand motif clasp with blue stone in ring, gold, 45 in. long, c. 1820	3800.00	4000.00
☐	**23**	S-curb links, gold, 60 in. long, c. 1880	1800.00	2000.00
☐	**24**	Spiral woven links, cannetille motif clasp, gold, 38 in. long, c. 1830	2200.00	2400.00

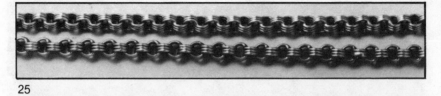

25

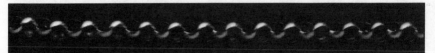

26

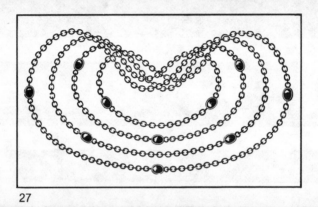

27

28

☐	**25**	*Three-banded circle links, gold, 52 in. long, c. late 19th*	**1000.00**	**1200.00**
☐	**26**	*Trace links, polished, gold, 59 in. long, c. 1830...*	**1500.00**	**1600.00**
☐	**27**	*Trace links spaced with cabochon turquoise, gold, English, c. 1900*	**550.00**	**750.00**
☐	**28**	*Trace links spaced with oval faceted amethysts, gold, c. 1860*	**1200.00**	**1500.00**

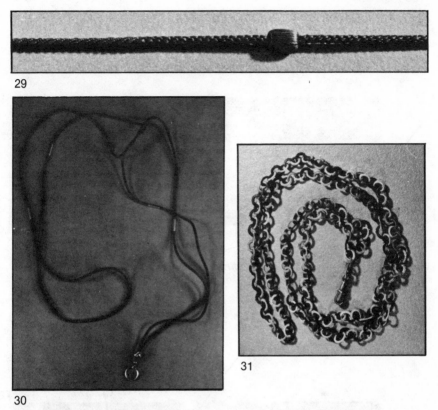

☐	**29**	Woven hair chain, hair covered wood bead connectors, 65 in. long, c. 1860.................	**85.00**	**100.00**
☐	**30**	Woven hair chain, tube connectors, repoussé clasp, gold, 68 in. long, c. 1860...............	**85.00**	**125.00**
☐	**31**	Woven interlocking circular horsehair links, swivel loop, c. 1880...........................	**45.00**	**65.00**
☐	**32**	Woven interlocking hair chains, 24 in. long, gold clasp, c. 1860.............................	**90.00**	**110.00**

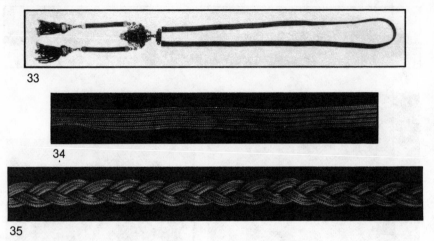

33

34

35

☐	**33**	Woven mesh chain, shield motif clasp with double tassel, seed pearls, 18K gold, 65 in. long, c. 1860......................................	1800.00	2000.00
☐	**34**	Woven mesh chain, gold, c. 1860..............	800.00	1000.00
☐	**35**	Woven mesh braided chain, gold, c. 1860.......	1200.00	1400.00

1

2

SLIDES and SLIDE CHAINS

PRICE RANGE

☐	**1**	Slide, engraved floral motif, gold, c. 1890.......	100.00	125.00
☐	**2**	Slide, oval crystal, woven basket weave hair mat over strands of hair, "MBL" in gold wire, black and white enameled skull and crossbones, insribed: "OB 15 OCT 1684," gold, c. 1684........	1000.00	1200.00

3

4

5

6

☐	**3** *Slide chain, small trace links, engraved slide, 14K gold, American, c. 1896*	**325.00**	**365.00**
☐	*Same as above but chain and slide gold filled .*	**110.00**	**140.00**
☐	*Same as above but slide only, 14K gold*	**35.00**	**55.00**
☐	**4** *Slide chain, short and long curb links, 14K, American, c. 1896*	**225.00**	**250.00**
☐	*Same as above but gold filled*	**80.00**	**100.00**
☐	*Same as above but sterling silver*	**100.00**	**125.00**
☐	**5** *Slide chain, curb links, 14K gold, American, c. 1896*	**225.00**	**250.00**
☐	*Same as above but gold filled*	**80.00**	**100.00**
☐	**6** *Slide chain, trace links, 14K gold, American, c. 1896*	**325.00**	**365.00**
☐	*Same as above but chain and slide gold filled .*	**110.00**	**140.00**
☐	*Same as above but slide only, 14K gold*	**35.00**	**55.00**

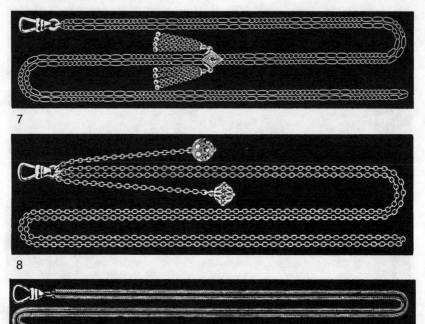

7

8

9

10

☐ **7** *Slide chain, short and long curb links, engraved slide with two trace link chain and ball tassels, 14K gold, American, c. 1896* **350.00** **375.00**
☐   *Same as above but chain and slide gold filled .* **110.00** **140.00**
☐   *Same as above but slide only, 14K gold* **50.00** **75.00**
☐ **8** *Slide chain, trace links, two trace link extensions with engraved balls, 14K gold, American, c. 1896* **350.00** **375.00**
☐   *Same as above but gold filled* **100.00** **140.00**
☐ **9** *Slide chain, foxtail links, 14K gold, American, c. 1896.* **225.00** **250.00**
☐   *Same as above but gold filled* **60.00** **70.00**
☐   *Same as above but sterling silver* **115.00** **125.00**
☐ **10** *Slide chain, short and long curb links, 14K gold, American, c. 1896* **225.00** **250.00**

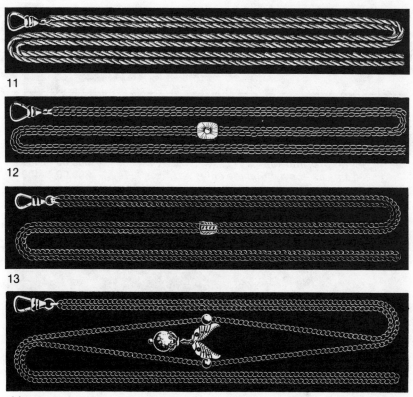

☐ **11** *Slide chain, rope links, 14K gold, American,*
    c. 1896 . . . . **250.00**   **300.00**
☐   *Same as above but gold filled* **60.00**   **80.00**
☐   *Same as above but sterling silver* **125.00**   **145.00**
☐ **12** *Slide chain, curb links, engraved slide with pearl*
    center, 14K gold, American, c. 1896 . . . . **325.00**   **375.00**
☐   *Same as above but chain and slide gold filled* . **100.00**   **125.00**
☐   *Same as above but slide only, 14K gold* **40.00**   **60.00**
☐ **13** *Slide chain, curb links, engraved slide with four*
    pearls, 14K gold, American, c. 1896 . . . . **350.00**   **375.00**
☐   *Same as above but chain and slide gold filled* . **100.00**   **125.00**
☐   *Same as above but slide only, 14K gold* **50.00**   **70.00**
☐ **14** *Slide chain, curb links, fancy shape engraved*
    slide, 14K gold, American, c. 1896 . . . . **400.00**   **450.00**
☐   *Same as above but chain and slide gold filled* . **110.00**   **140.00**
☐   *Same as above but slide only, 14K gold* **110.00**   **125.00**

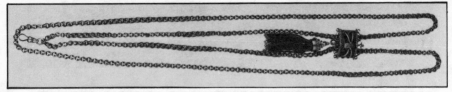

15

☐ **15** *Slide chain, loop-in-loop links, seed pearls set in fancy shape slide with fox tail tassel, 65 in. long, 14K gold, c. mid 19th* 1500.00 2000.00

☐ *Same as above but slide only* 300.00 400.00

1

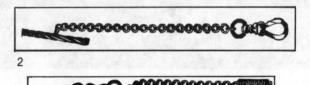

2

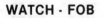

3

WATCH · FOB

PRICE RANGE

☐ **1** *Art Nouveau motif, two cabochon sardonyx stones in fob, gold, c. 1890* 600.00 650.00

☐ **2** *Barleycorn motif links, swivel loop, 14K gold, six in. long, American, , c. 1894-95* 65.00 85.00

☐ *Same as above but 10K gold* 45.00 50.00

☐ *Same as above but gold filled* 20.00 25.00

☐ **3** *Barleycorn motif link double chain with slide, seed pearls in slide, 14K gold, 12 in. long, American, c. 1894-95* 185.00 235.00

☐ *Same as above but 10K gold* 100.00 140.00

☐ *Same as above but gold filled* 65.00 85.00

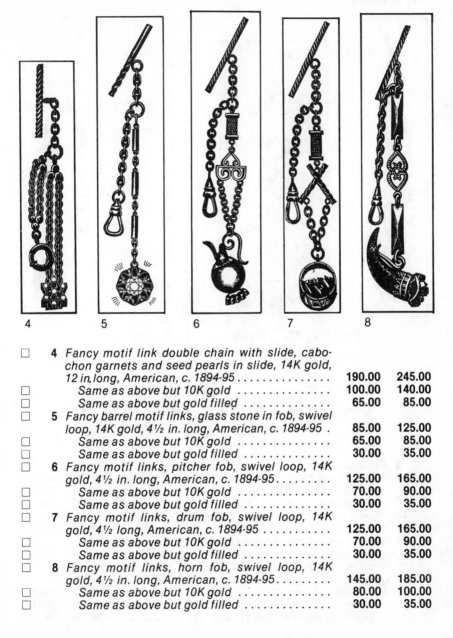

4   5   6   7   8

☐ **4** *Fancy motif link double chain with slide, cabo-*
chon garnets and seed pearls in slide, 14K gold,
12 in. long, American, c. 1894-95 . . . . **190.00**   **245.00**
☐   *Same as above but 10K gold* **100.00**   **140.00**
☐   *Same as above but gold filled* **65.00**   **85.00**
☐ **5** *Fancy barrel motif links, glass stone in fob, swivel*
loop, 14K gold, 4½ in. long, American, c. 1894-95 . **85.00**   **125.00**
☐   *Same as above but 10K gold* **65.00**   **85.00**
☐   *Same as above but gold filled* **30.00**   **35.00**
☐ **6** *Fancy motif links, pitcher fob, swivel loop, 14K*
gold, 4½ in. long, American, c. 1894-95 . . . . **125.00**   **165.00**
☐   *Same as above but 10K gold* **70.00**   **90.00**
☐   *Same as above but gold filled* **30.00**   **35.00**
☐ **7** *Fancy motif links, drum fob, swivel loop, 14K*
gold, 4½ long, American, c. 1894-95 . . . . **125.00**   **165.00**
☐   *Same as above but 10K gold* **70.00**   **90.00**
☐   *Same as above but gold filled* **30.00**   **35.00**
☐ **8** *Fancy motif links, horn fob, swivel loop, 14K*
gold, 4½ in. long, American, c. 1894-95 . . . . **145.00**   **185.00**
☐   *Same as above but 10K gold* **80.00**   **100.00**
☐   *Same as above but gold filled* **30.00**   **35.00**

9

10

11

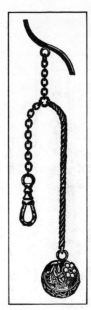

12

☐ **9** *Fetter and three motif links, pitcher fob, swivel
loop, 14K gold, 4½ in. long, American, c. 1894-95* **145.00** **185.00**
☐　　　*Same as above but 10K gold* **80.00** **100.00**
☐　　　*Same as above but gold filled* **30.00** **35.00**
☐ **10** *Flower motif, three oval cabochon garnets, gold,
c. 1850*.................................... **400.00** **500.00**
☐ **11** *Niello twisted links alternating with gold links,
swivel and round loops, sterling silver, c. 1920*... **125.00** **150.00**
☐ **12** *Rope motif links, flower fob with one cabochon
garnet and seed pearls, swivel loop, 14K gold,
4½ in. long, American, c. 1894-95* **100.00** **140.00**
☐　　　*Same as above but 10K gold* **65.00** **85.00**
☐　　　*Same as above but gold filled* **30.00** **35.00**

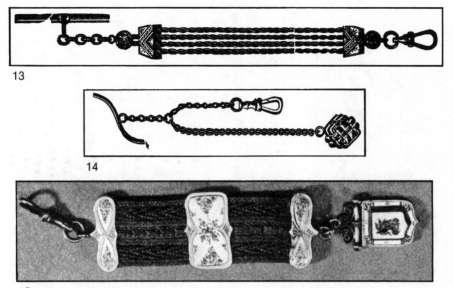

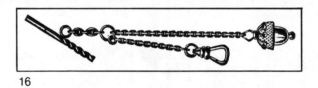

☐	**13**	Rope motif links, 6¾ in. long, chains extend to 11 in. long with center engraved slide, swivel loop, 14K gold, American, c. 1894-95	**265.00**	**325.00**
☐		Same as above but 10K gold	**145.00**	**165.00**
☐		Same as above but gold filled	**75.00**	**100.00**
☐	**14**	S-curb motif links, cube fob, swivel loop, 14K gold, 4½ in. long, American, c. 1894-95	**100.00**	**125.00**
☐		Same as above but 10K gold	**65.00**	**85.00**
☐		Same as above but gold filled	**30.00**	**35.00**
☐	**15**	Sardonyx intaglio of a warrior fob, engraved frame, end fittings and center slide, swivel loop, flat woven hair chain, gold, c. 1890	**100.00**	**125.00**
☐	**16**	Trace motif links, acorn fob, swivel loop, 14K gold, 4½ in. long, American, c. 1894-95	**85.00**	**125.00**
☐		Same as above but 10K gold	**65.00**	**85.00**
☐		Same as above but gold filled	**30.00**	**35.00**

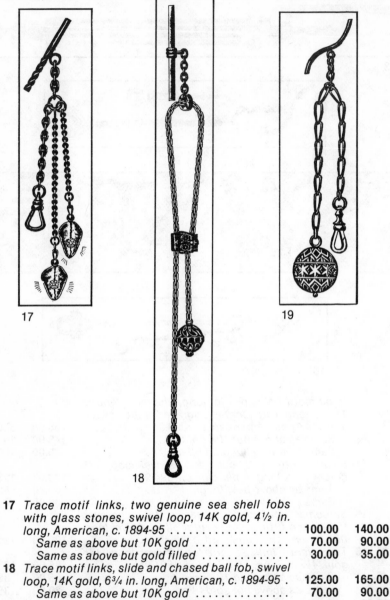

17

18

19

☐	**17**	*Trace motif links, two genuine sea shell fobs with glass stones, swivel loop, 14K gold, 4½ in. long, American, c. 1894-95*	**100.00**	**140.00**
☐		*Same as above but 10K gold*	**70.00**	**90.00**
☐		*Same as above but gold filled*	**30.00**	**35.00**
☐	**18**	*Trace motif links, slide and chased ball fob, swivel loop, 14K gold, 6¾ in. long, American, c. 1894-95* .	**125.00**	**165.00**
☐		*Same as above but 10K gold*	**70.00**	**90.00**
☐		*Same as above but gold filled*	**30.00**	**35.00**
☐	**19**	*Twisted oval motif links, openwork ball fob, swivel loop, 14K gold, 4½ long, American, c. 1894-95*	**85.00**	**125.00**
☐		*Same as above but 10K gold*	**65.00**	**85.00**
☐		*Same as above but gold filled*	**30.00**	**35.00**

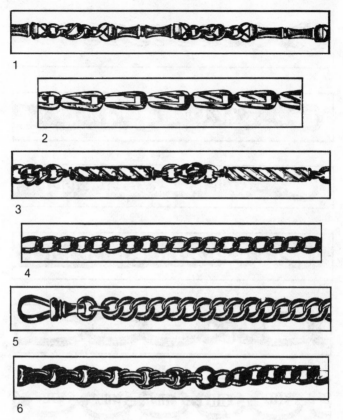

WATCH · VEST

<table>
<tr><td></td><td></td><td align="right">PRICE RANGE</td><td></td></tr>
<tr><td>☐</td><td>1 Bamboo motif mother-of-pearl links, fancy links, swivel loop, 14K gold, 12 in. long, American, c. 1894-95 . . . .</td><td align="right">275.00</td><td align="right">300.00</td></tr>
<tr><td>☐</td><td>2 Barleycorn links, swivel loop, 14K gold, 12 in. long, American, c. 1894-95 . . . .</td><td align="right">220.00</td><td align="right">265.00</td></tr>
<tr><td>☐</td><td>3 Barrel carved motif mother-of-pearl links, fancy links, swivel loop, 14K gold, 12 in. long, American, c. 1894-95 . . . .</td><td align="right">275.00</td><td align="right">300.00</td></tr>
<tr><td>☐</td><td>4 Curb links, swivel loop, 14K gold, 12 in. long, American, c. 1894-95 . . . .</td><td align="right">150.00</td><td align="right">165.00</td></tr>
<tr><td>☐</td><td>5 Curb links, swivel loops, 14K gold, 12 in. long, American, c. 1894-95 . . . .</td><td align="right">220.00</td><td align="right">265.00</td></tr>
<tr><td>☐</td><td>6 Curb link center, fancy oval link ends, swivel loop, 14K gold, 12 in. long, American, c. 1894-95 .</td><td align="right">250.00</td><td align="right">285.00</td></tr>
</table>

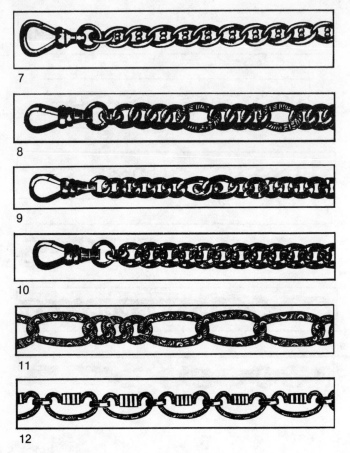

☐	**7**	*Curb and ball motif links, swivel loop, 14K gold, 12 in. long, American, c. 1894-95*	**220.00**	**265.00**
☐	**8**	*Curb links spaced with oval engraved links, swivel loop, 14K gold, 12 in. long, American, c. 1894-95* . .	**275.00**	**325.00**
☐	**9**	*Curb links spaced with fancy ball links, swivel loop, 14K gold, 12 in. long, American, c. 1894-95* .	**175.00**	**200.00**
☐	**10**	*Engraved fancy links, swivel loop, 14K gold, 12 in. long, American, c. 1894-95*	**220.00**	**265.00**
☐	**11**	*Engraved fancy links, swivel loop, 14K gold, 12 in. long, American, c. 1894-95*	**250.00**	**285.00**
☐	**12**	*Engraved fancy links, swivel loop, 14K gold, 12 in. long, American, c. 1894-95*	**200.00**	**235.00**

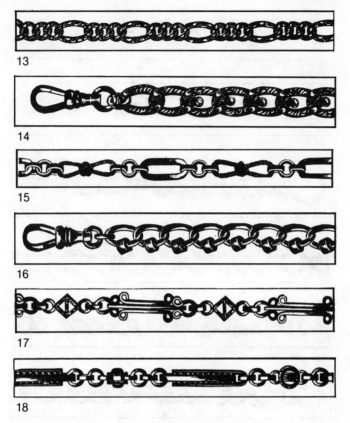

☐ **13** *Engraved fancy links, swivel loop, 14K gold, 12 in. long, American, c. 1894-95* **175.00**   **200.00**

☐ **14** *Engraved fancy links, swivel loop, 14K gold, 12 in. long, American, c. 1894-95* **275.00**   **325.00**

☐ **15** *Fancy links, swivel loop, 14K gold, 12 in. long, American, c. 1894-95* **200.00**   **235.00**

☐ **16** *Fancy links, swivel loop, 14K gold, 12 in. long, American, c. 1894-95* **220.00**   **265.00**

☐ **17** *Fancy links, swivel loop, 14K gold, 12 in. long, American, c. 1894-95* **275.00**   **325.00**

☐ **18** *Fancy links, swivel loop, 14K gold, 12 in. long, American, c. 1894-95* **200.00**   **235.00**

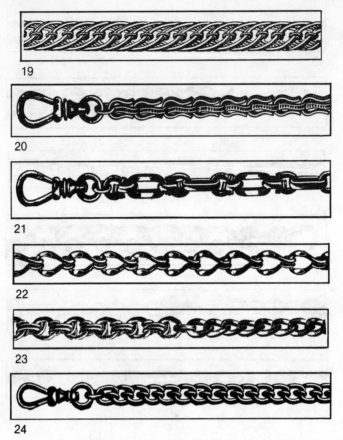

19

20

21

22

23

24

☐ **19** *Fancy links, swivel loop, 14K gold, 12 in. long, American, c. 1894-95* **325.00** **365.00**

☐ **20** *Fancy links, swivel loop, 14K gold, 12 in. long, American, c. 1894-95* **250.00** **285.00**

☐ **21** *Fancy links, swivel loop, 14K gold, 12 in. long, American, c. 1894-95* **220.00** **265.00**

☐ *Same as any of the above but gold filled* **35.00** **85.00**

☐ **22** *Fancy bell motif links, swivel loop, 14K gold, 12 in. long, American, c. 1894-95* **200.00** **235.00**

☐ **23** *Fancy oval link center, curb link ends, swivel loop, 14K gold, 12 in. long, American, c. 1894-95* . **275.00** **325.00**

☐ **24** *Fancy round links, swivel loop, 14K gold, 12 in. long, American, c. 1894-95* **175.00** **200.00**

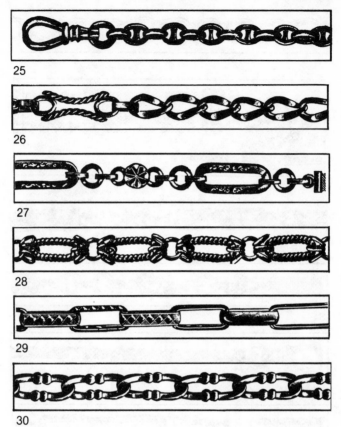

25

26

27

28

29

30

☐ **25** *Fancy round links, swivel loop, 14K gold, 12 in. long, American, c. 1894-95* **250.00** **285.00**

☐ **26** *Fancy twisted link center, trace link ends, swivel loop, 14K gold, 12 in. long, American, c. 1894-95* . **250.00** **285.00**

☐ **27** *Fetter and five modified links, swivel loop, 14K gold, 12 in. long, American, c. 1894-95* **275.00** **325.00**

☐ **28** *Flat fancy twisted links alternating with spiral links, swivel loop, 14K gold, 12 in. long, American, c. 1894-95* **300.00** **345.00**

☐ **29** *Half round plain and engraved square links, swivel loop, 14K gold, 12 in. long, American, c. 1894-95* **275.00** **325.00**

☐ **30** *Horseshoe links, swivel loop, 14K gold, 12 in. long, American, c. 1894-95* **300.00** **345.00**

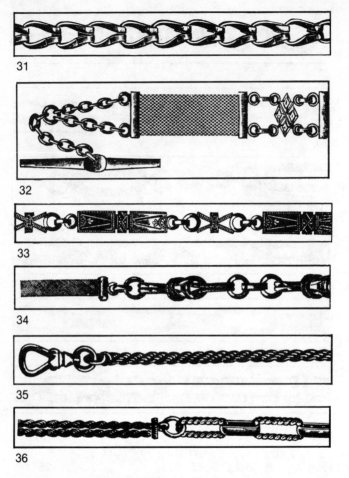

☐	**31**	*Loop-in-loop links, swivel loop, 14K gold, 12 in. long, American, c. 1894-95*	**175.00** **200.00**
☐	**32**	*Mesh woven alternating with fancy diamond-shape motif links, swivel loop, 14K gold, 12 in. long, American, c. 1894-95*	**325.00** **365.00**
☐	**33**	*Plaque and cross motif links, swivel loop, 14K gold, 12 in. long, American, c. 1894-95*	**300.00** **345.00**
☐	**34**	*Roman knot and trace links, mesh woven, swivel loop, 14K gold, 12 in. long, American, c. 1894-95* .	**250.00** **285.00**
☐	**35**	*Rope links, swivel loop, 14K gold, 12 in. long, American, c. 1894-95*	**150.00** **165.00**
☐	**36**	*Rope link center, trace flat and twisted link ends, swivel loop, 14K gold, 12 in. long, American, c. 1894-95*	**175.00** **200.00**

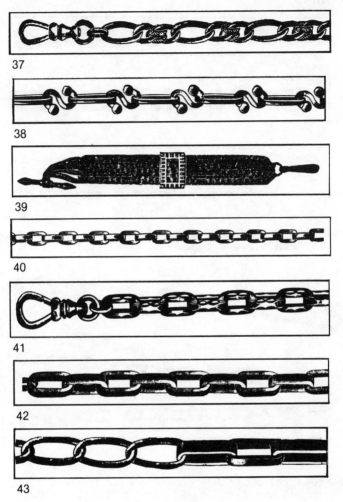

☐	**37**	*"S" curb links alternting with trace links, swivel loop, 14K gold, 12 in. long, American, c. 1894-95* .	**220.00** **265.00**
☐	**38**	*"S" links alternating with oblong links, swivel loop, 14K gold, 12 in. long, American, c. 1894-95* .	**275.00** **325.00**
☐	**39**	*Silk woven, American, c. 1894-95*	**35.00** **85.00**
☐	**40**	*Square links, swivel loop, 14K gold, 12 in. long, American, c. 1894-95*	**150.00** **165.00**
☐	**41**	*Square links, swivel loop, 14K gold, 12 in. long, American, c. 1894-95*	**160.00** **185.00**
☐	**42**	*Square (Boston) links, swivel loop, 14K gold, 12 in. long, American, c. 1894-95*	**220.00** **265.00**
☐	**43**	*Square link center, trace link ends, swivel loop, 14K gold, 12 in. long, American, c. 1894-95*	**275.00** **325.00**

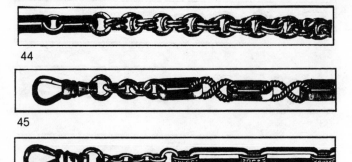

44

45

46

47

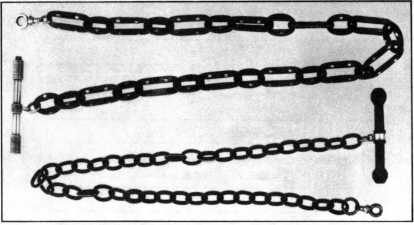

48

□ **44** *Square link center, fancy oval link ends, swivel loop, 14K gold, 12 in. long, American, c. 1894-95* . **250.00** **285.00**

□ **45** *Square links alternating with twisted figure eight links, swivel loop, 14K gold, 12 in. long, American, c. 1894-95* **250.00** **285.00**

□ **46** *Square links alternating with engraved oval links, swivel loop, 14K gold, 12 in. long, American, c. 1894-95* **200.00** **235.00**

□ **47** *Trace links, pique: tortoise shell inlaid with gold, swivel loop, bar with hidden watch key, gold, c. 1860* **300.00** **350.00**

□ **48** *Trace links, gutta percha with gold twisted edges, c. 1840* **150.00** **200.00**

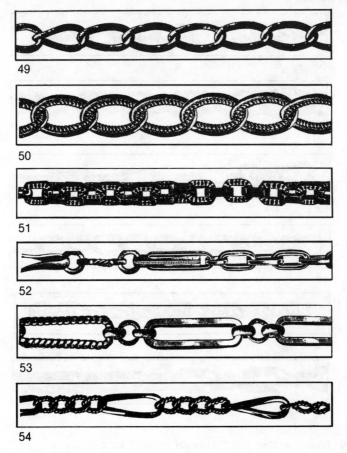

☐ **49** *Trace links, swivel loop, 14K gold, 12 in. long, American, c. 1894-95* **220.00** **265.00**

☐ **50** *Trace fancy links, swivel loop, 14K gold, 12 in. long, American, c. 1894-95* **325.00** **365.00**

☐ **51** *Trace hexagonal links, engraved, aluminum, swivel loop, 12 in. long, American, c. 1894-95* **30.00** **45.00**

☐ **52** *Trace and fancy links, swivel loop, 14K gold, 12 in. long, American, c. 1894-95* **175.00** **200.00**

☐ **53** *Twist and plain alternating links, swivel loop, 14K gold, 12 in. long, American, c. 1894-95* **220.00** **265.00**

☐ **54** *Trace links alternating with twisted curb links, swivel loop, 14K gold, 12 in. long, American, c. 1894-95* **250.00** **285.00**

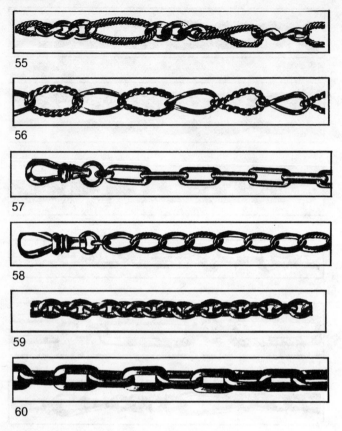

55

56

57

58

59

60

☐ **55** *Trace twisted links alternating with curb links, swivel loop, 14K gold, 12 in. long, American, c. 1894-95* **250.00** **285.00**

☐ **56** *Trace polished and twisted alternating links, swivel loop, 14K gold, 12 in. long, American, c. 1894-95* **275.00** **325.00**

☐ **57** *Trace long links, swivel loop, 14K gold, 12 in. long, American, c. 1894-95* **160.00** **185.00**

☐ **58** *Trace twisted links, swivel loop, 14K gold, 12 in. long, American, c. 1894-95* **150.00** **165.00**

☐ **59** *Trace round links, aluminum, swivel loop, 12 in. long, American, c. 1894-95* **25.00** **35.00**

☐ **60** *Trace square links, aluminum, swivel loop, 12 in. long, American, c. 1894-95* **30.00** **40.00**

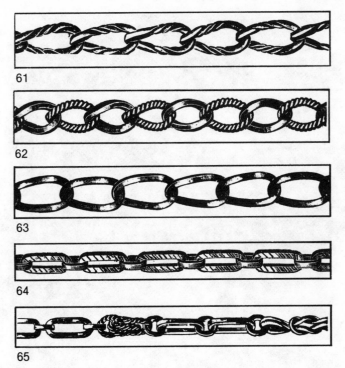

61

62

63

64

65

☐ **61** *Trace square and twisted links, swivel loop, 14K gold, 12 in. long, American, c. 1894-95* **275.00 325.00**

☐ **62** *Trace square links alternating with trace twisted links, swivel loop, 14K gold, 12 in. long, American, c. 1894-95* **325.00 365.00**

☐ **63** *Trace square links, swivel loop, 14K gold, 12 in. long, American, c. 1894-95* **300.00 345.00**

☐ **64** *Trace square and engraved links, swivel loop, 14K gold, 12 in. long, American, c. 1894-95* **220.00 265.00**

☐ **65** *Twisted knot links alternating with flat and oval trace links and loveknot links, swivel loop, 14K gold, 12 in. long, American, c. 1894-95* **250.00 285.00**

A young gentleman wearing a thick woven hair watch chain in the square and four-ribbed spiral pattern with an initial fob and a fraternal lapel pin. The watch chain is valued at $50-$75 on today's market.

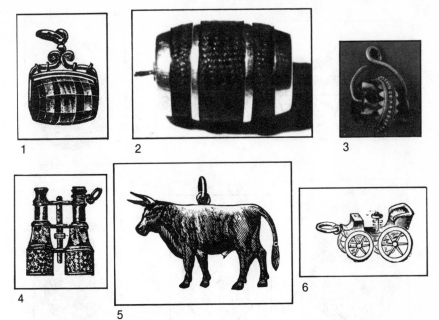

1
2
3
4
5
6

CHARMS, FOBS and SEALS

CHARMS

			PRICE	RANGE
☐	1	*Barrel, 14K gold, American, c. 1894-95*	65.00	90.00
☐		*Same as above but gold filled*	10.00	15.00
☐		*Same as above but sterling silver*	35.00	40.00
☐	2	*Barrel, woven hair, gold, c. 1880*	90.00	100.00
☐	3	*Barrel, Roman bead, Etruscan granulation on center band, gold, c. 1860*	175.00	200.00
☐	4	*Binoculars, 14K gold, American, c. 1894-95*	80.00	110.00
☐		*Same as above but gold filled*	15.00	25.00
☐		*Same as above but sterling silver*	35.00	40.00
☐	5	*Bull, 14K gold, American, c. 1894-95*	225.00	250.00
☐		*Same as above but gold filled*	20.00	30.00
☐		*Same as above but sterling silver*	50.00	60.00
☐	6	*Car, 14K gold, American, c. 1894-95*	100.00	135.00

7

8

9

10

11

12

☐	**7**	*Carriage, 14K gold, American, c. 1894-95*	**100.00**	**135.00**
☐		*Same as above but gold filled*	**20.00**	**30.00**
☐		*Same as above but sterling silver*	**50.00**	**60.00**
☐	**8**	*Cats in basket, gold, English, c. 1903-04*	**95.00**	**125.00**
☐		*Same as above but gold filled*	**15.00**	**25.00**
☐		*Same as above but sterling silver*	**40.00**	**45.00**
☐	**9**	*Compass, 14K gold, American, c. 1894-95*	**120.00**	**150.00**
☐		*Same as above but gold filled*	**20.00**	**30.00**
☐		*Same as above but sterling silver*	**50.00**	**60.00**
☐	**10**	*Compass, 14K gold, American, c. 1894-95*	**120.00**	**150.00**
☐		*Same as above but gold filled*	**20.00**	**30.00**
☐		*Same as above but sterling silver*	**50.00**	**60.00**
☐	**11**	*Compass, 14K gold, American, c. 1894-95*	**95.00**	**125.00**
☐		*Same as above but gold filled*	**15.00**	**25.00**
☐		*Same as above but sterling silver*	**40.00**	**50.00**
☐	**12**	*Compass and anchor, 14K gold, American, c. 1894*	**120.00**	**150.00**
☐		*Same as above but gold filled*	**20.00**	**30.00**
☐		*Same as above but sterling silver*	**50.00**	**60.00**

13

14

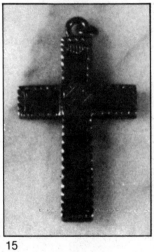

15

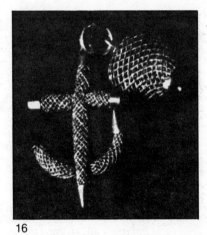

16

☐	**13** Compass and ship's wheel, 14K gold, American,		
	c. 1894-95	**120.00**	**150.00**
☐	Same as above but gold filled	**20.00**	**30.00**
☐	Same as above but sterling silver	**50.00**	**60.00**
☐	**14** Compass and watch motif, 14K gold, American,		
	c. 1894-95	**120.00**	**150.00**
☐	Same as above but gold filled	**20.00**	**30.00**
☐	Same as above but sterling silver	**50.00**	**60.00**
☐	**15** Cross, woven hair, gold, c. 1900	**65.00**	**95.00**
☐	**16** Cross, anchor and heart symbolizing faith, hope		
	and charity, woven hair, gold, c. 1840	**100.00**	**125.00**

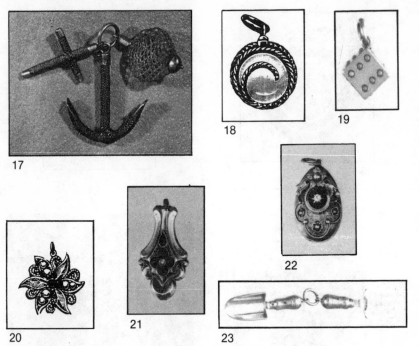

17

18

19

22

20

21

23

	17	Cross, anchor and heart symbolizing faith, hope and charity, woven hair, gold, c. 1860	100.00	125.00
☐	18	Crystal ball with rope motif, 14K gold, American, c. 1894-95	50.00	85.00
☐		Same as above but gold filled	10.00	15.00
☐		Same as above but sterling silver	25.00	30.00
☐	19	Die, cabochon turquoise marked numbers, 15K gold, one side opens to reveal three miniature sterling silver dice, c. 19th	350.00	375.00
☐	20	Flower motif, one garnet, seed pearls, 14K gold, American, c. 1894-95	75.00	100.00
☐	21	Flower motif, one seed pearl, garnets, hollow ware, gold, a former earring or dangle from a necklace, c. 1840	65.00	85.00
☐	22	Flower oval motif, one round diamond, gold, a former earring or dangle from a necklace, c. 1870	185.00	225.00
☐	23	Garden tools, 9K gold, English, c. early 20th	225.00	250.00

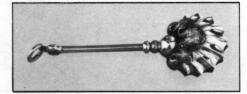

25

24

26

29

27

28

☐	**24**	Goat with Odd Fellow insignia, 14K gold, American, c. 1894-95	95.00	125.00
☐		Same as above but gold filled	15.00	25.00
☐		Same as above but sterling silver	40.00	50.00
☐	**25**	Hankerchief holder, gold, English, c. 1840	225.00	250.00
☐	**26**	Hardstone scarab, Etruscan granulation on frame, c. 1860	300.00	400.00
☐	**27**	Heart, two garnets, one seed pearl, 14K gold, American, c. 1894-95	50.00	85.00
☐		Same as above but gold filled	10.00	15.00
☐		Same as above but sterling silver	25.00	35.00
☐	**28**	Heart, chased, 14K gold, American, c. 1894-95	45.00	65.00
☐		Same as above but gold filled	10.00	15.00
☐		Same as above but sterling silver	20.00	30.00
☐	**29**	Heart, one garnet, chased, 14K gold, American, c. 1894-95	50.00	85.00
☐		Same as above but gold filled	10.00	15.00
☐		Same as above but sterling silver	20.00	35.00

30

31

32 33 35

34

36

☐	**30**	*Heart, one seed pearl, 14K gold, American, c. 1894-95*	**45.00**	**65.00**
☐		*Same as above but gold filled*	**10.00**	**15.00**
☐		*Same as above but sterling silver*	**20.00**	**30.00**
☐	**31**	*Heart and clover, one round sapphire, gold, English, c. 1903-04*	**80.00**	**110.00**
☐	**32**	*Heart, woven hair, gold, c. 1860*	**75.00**	**90.00**
☐	**33**	*Lyre, woven hair, gold, c. 1860*	**75.00**	**90.00**
☐	**34**	*Horn, mother-of-pearl, 14K gold, American, c. 1894-95*	**45.00**	**65.00**
☐		*Same as above but gold filled*	**10.00**	**15.00**
☐		*Same as above but sterling silver*	**20.00**	**30.00**
☐	**35**	*Horn, woven hair, gold, c. 1880*	**90.00**	**100.00**
☐	**36**	*Horse's leg, carved ivory, gold horseshoe, c. 1870*	**285.00**	**325.00**

37

38

39

40

41

42

☐	**37**	Horseshoe, 14K gold, American, c. 1894-95	80.00	110.00
☐		*Same as above but gold filled*	15.00	25.00
☐		*Same as above but sterling silver*	35.00	40.00
☐	**38**	Hourglass, 14K gold, American, c. 1894-95	100.00	135.00
☐		*Same as above but gold filled*	20.00	30.00
☐		*Same as above but sterling silver*	50.00	55.00
☐	**39**	Hourglass, 9K gold, English, c. 1900	65.00	75.00
☐	**40**	Initial motif, 14K gold, American, c. 1894-95	45.00	65.00
☐		*Same as above but gold filled*	10.00	15.00
☐		*Same as above but sterling silver*	20.00	30.00
☐	**41**	Ladies shoe, 14K gold, American, c. 1894-95	65.00	90.00
☐		*Same as above but gold filled*	10.00	15.00
☐		*Same as above but sterling silver*	25.00	30.00
☐	**42**	Locket, Prince of Wales feathers of hair under		
		glass, seed pearls, gold, English, c. 1880	100.00	125.00

43

44

45

46

47

48

49

☐	**43**	Locket, hair with miniature feather pen under glass, chased case, gold, English, c. 1880	100.00	125.00
☐	**44**	Locket with photo, gold filled, c. 1900	40.00	50.00
☐	**45**	Lyre, woven hair, gold, English, c. 1820	275.00	300.00
☐	**46**	Medallion of Venus and Cupid, sterling silver, American, c. 1920	85.00	95.00
☐	**47**	Monkey with stick, two seed pearls, gold, English, c. 1894-95	75.00	100.00
☐	**48**	Mother-of-pearl intaglio, 14K gold, American, c. 1894-95	75.00	100.00
☐		Same as above but gold filled	15.00	20.00
☐		Same as above but sterling silver	40.00	50.00
☐	**49**	Oval motif, three gemstones, 15K gold, American, c. 1894-95	65.00	90.00

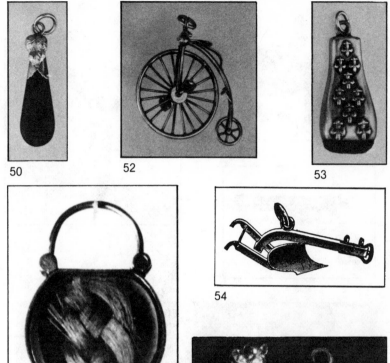

☐	**50**	*Paddle, green jade, gold, c. 20th*	**125.00**	**145.00**
☐	**51**	*Padlock, braided hair under glass, gold, c. 1880* .	**120.00**	**135.00**
☐	**52**	*Penny Farthing bicycle, all movable parts, 15K gold, c. early 20th*	**325.00**	**375.00**
☐	**53**	*Pin cushion with fleur-de-lys motif, sterling silver, former chatelaine part, c. 20th*	**65.00**	**85.00**
☐	**54**	*Plow, 14K gold, American, c. 1894-95*	**80.00**	**110.00**
☐		*Same as above but gold filled*	**15.00**	**20.00**
☐		*Same as above but sterling silver*	**35.00**	**40.00**
☐	**55**	*Pug, diamonds in harness, gold, c. late 19th*	**450.00**	**550.00**

56

58

57

59   60   61   62

☐	**56**	*Ram, 14K gold, American, c. 1894-95*	**225.00**	**250.00**
☐		*Same as above but gold filled*	**20.00**	**30.00**
☐		*Same as above but sterling silver*	**50.00**	**60.00**
☐ ′	**57**	*Revolver, 14K gold, American, c. 1894-95*	**75.00**	**100.00**
☐		*Same as above but gold filled*	**15.00**	**25.00**
☐		*Same as above but sterling silver*	**40.00**	**45.00**
☐	**58**	*Saw, mallet and plane, gold, English, c. 19th*	**300.00**	**350.00**
☐	**59**	*Scottish Terrier, gold, c. early 20th*	**150.00**	**175.00**
☐	**60**	*Bulldog, gold, c. early 20th*	**175.00**	**200.00**
☐	**61**	*Scottish Terrier, gold, c. early 20th*	**250.00**	**300.00**
☐	**62**	*Mastiff, rose diamonds in collar, gold, c. early 20th*	**200.00**	**225.00**

63

64

65

66

70

67

68

69

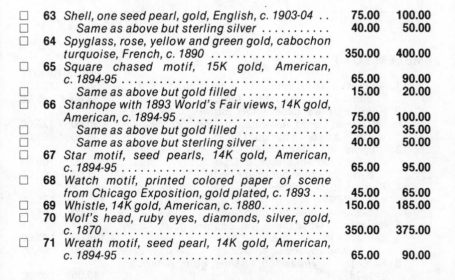
71

☐	**63**	Shell, one seed pearl, gold, English, c. 1903-04 ..	75.00	100.00
☐		Same as above but sterling silver	40.00	50.00
☐	**64**	Spyglass, rose, yellow and green gold, cabochon turquoise, French, c. 1890	350.00	400.00
☐	**65**	Square chased motif, 15K gold, American, c. 1894-95	65.00	90.00
☐		Same as above but gold filled	15.00	20.00
☐	**66**	Stanhope with 1893 World's Fair views, 14K gold, American, c. 1894-95	75.00	100.00
☐		Same as above but gold filled	25.00	35.00
☐		Same as above but sterling silver	40.00	50.00
☐	**67**	Star motif, seed pearls, 14K gold, American, c. 1894-95	65.00	95.00
☐	**68**	Watch motif, printed colored paper of scene from Chicago Exposition, gold plated, c. 1893 ...	45.00	65.00
☐	**69**	Whistle, 14K gold, American, c. 1880.	150.00	185.00
☐	**70**	Wolf's head, ruby eyes, diamonds, silver, gold, c. 1870.	350.00	375.00
☐	**71**	Wreath motif, seed pearl, 14K gold, American, c. 1894-95	65.00	90.00

1

2

3

4

5

6

EMBLEM FOBS

			PRICE	RANGE
☐	**1**	*A.O.U.W. fob, enamel, gold, American, c. 1896...*	**90.00**	**125.00**
☐		*Same as above but gold filled*	**35.00**	**65.00**
☐	**2**	*Knights of Maccabees fob, mother-of-pearl center, enamel, gold, American, c. 1896*	**90.00**	**125.00**
☐		*Same as above but gold filled*	**35.00**	**65.00**
☐	**3**	*Knights of Maccabees fob, mother-of-pearl, enamel, gold, American, c. 1896*	**80.00**	**100.00**
☐		*Same as above but gold filled*	**35.00**	**65.00**
☐	**4**	*Knights of Maccabees fob, enamel, gold, American, c. 1896*................................	**125.00**	**160.00**
☐		*Same as above but gold filled*	**35.00**	**65.00**
☐	**5**	*Knights of Maccabees fob, enamel, gold, American, c. 1896*................................	**125.00**	**160.00**
☐		*Same as above but gold filled*	**35.00**	**65.00**
☐	**6**	*Knights of Pythias fob, enamel, gold, American, c. 1896*................................	**140.00**	**180.00**
☐		*Same as above but gold filled*	**35.00**	**45.00**

7

8

9

10

11

12

	7	Knights of Pythias fob, mother-of-pearl, enamel, gold, American, c. 1896	80.00	100.00
		Same as above but gold filled	35.00	65.00
	8	Knights of Pythias fob, mother-of-pearl, enamel, gold, American, c. 1896	90.00	125.00
		Same as above but gold filled	35.00	65.00
	9	Knights of Pythias fob, enamel, gold, American, c. 1896	140.00	180.00
		Same as above but gold filled	65.00	85.00
	10	Knights of Pythias fob, enamel, gold, American, c. 1896	150.00	200.00
		Same as above but gold filled	65.00	85.00
	11	Knight Templar fob, enamel, gold, American, c. 1896	140.00	180.00
		Same as above but gold filled	65.00	85.00
	12	Knight Templar fob, 32d degree, enamel, gold, American, c. 1896	200.00	225.00
		Same as above but gold filled	65.00	85.00

13

14

15

16

17

18

☐	**13**	*Knight Templar fob, enamel, gold, American, c. 1896*	**150.00**	**200.00**
☐		*Same as above but gold filled*	**65.00**	**85.00**
☐	**14**	*Knight Templar fob, four rose diamonds, enamel, gold, American, c. 1896*	**250.00**	**300.00**
☐		*Same as above but with ten round rubies in cross*	**350.00**	**400.00**
☐	**15**	*Masonic fob, enamel, gold, American, c. 1896* . . .	**115.00**	**140.00**
☐		*Same as above but gold filled*	**35.00**	**65.00**
☐	**16**	*Masonic fob, mother-of-pearl center, enamel, gold, American, c. 1896*	**90.00**	**125.00**
☐		*Same as above but gold filled*	**35.00**	**65.00**
☐	**17**	*Masonic fob, gold, American, c. 1896*	**125.00**	**160.00**
☐		*Same as above but gold filled*	**35.00**	**65.00**
☐	**18**	*Masonic fob, mother-of-pearl, enamel, gold, American, c. 1896*	**80.00**	**100.00**

19

20

21

22

23

24

☐		*Same as above but gold filled*	**35.00**	**65.00**
☐	**19**	*Masonic fob, enamel, gold, American, c. 1896* . . .	**125.00**	**160.00**
☐		*Same as above but gold filled*	**35.00**	**65.00**
☐	**20**	*Modern Woodmen fob, enamel, gold, American, c. 1896*	**140.00**	**180.00**
☐		*Same as above but gold filled*	**35.00**	**65.00**
☐	**21**	*Modern Woodmen fob, enamel, gold, American, c. 1896*	**90.00**	**125.00**
☐		*Same as above but gold filled*	**35.00**	**65.00**
☐	**22**	*Modern Woodmen fob, enamel, gold, American, c. 1896*	**90.00**	**125.00**
☐		*Same as above but gold filled*	**35.00**	**65.00**
☐	**23**	*Odd Fellows fob, enamel, gold, American, c. 1896*	**90.00**	**125.00**
☐		*Same as above but gold filled*	**35.00**	**65.00**
☐	**24**	*Odd Fellows fob, enamel, gold, American, c. 1896*	**150.00**	**200.00**
☐		*Same as above but gold filled*	**65.00**	**85.00**

25

26

☐	**25**	*Plain fob, enamel, gold, American, c. 1896*	125.00	160.00
☐		*Same as above but gold filled*	35.00	65.00
☐	**26**	*Royal Arcanum fob, enamel, gold, American, c. 1896*	125.00	160.00
☐		*Same as above but gold filled*	35.00	65.00

1

2

3

SEALS

			PRICE RANGE	
☐	**1**	*Blackamoor motif, diamonds in collar, square amethyst seal, gold, c. 1750*	2000.00	2200.00
☐	**2**	*Dog motif, hardstone seal, gold, c. 19th*	800.00	1000.00
☐	**3**	*Flower motif, amethyst intaglio inscribed "Though Lost to Sight to Memory Dear" on hidden hinge with glass locket inside, gold, c. 1840 .*	800.00	900.00

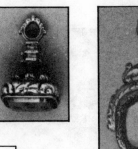

4

5

6

7

8

☐	**4**	Flower motif, chased, hardstone seal, gold, c. 19th	**400.00**	**500.00**
☐	**5**	Leaf motif, citrine swivel, gold, c. 1840	**600.00**	**800.00**
☐	**6**	Polished motif, intaglio of a monogram or a carnelian seal, gold, c. 1850	**250.00**	**300.00**
☐	**7**	Ribbed motif, onyx intaglio, seal, gold, c. 1850 . .	**275.00**	**300.00**
☐	**8**	Scroll motif, intaglio hardstone seal, yellow metal, c. 19th	**300.00**	**325.00**

CHATELAINES

		Item	PRICE RANGE	
☐	**1**	*Angel and wreath plaque with swivel, sterling silver, American, c. 1896*	**75.00**	**85.00**
☐	**2**	*Angel plaque with swivel, sterling silver, American, c. 1896*	**65.00**	**75.00**
☐	**3**	*Angel repoussé plaque with four fancy link chains, sterling silver, c. 1900*	**200.00**	**250.00**

☐ **4** Chain motif with round pin cusion, memo pad with mother-of-pearl cover, pick, pencil and square pin cushion, contemporary loop at top, sterling silver, c. 1880 .... **185.00   225.00**

☐ **5** Chain motif with implements for cleaning and operating on opium pipe, fancy link chains, silver, Near Eastern, c. 19th **145.00   165.00**

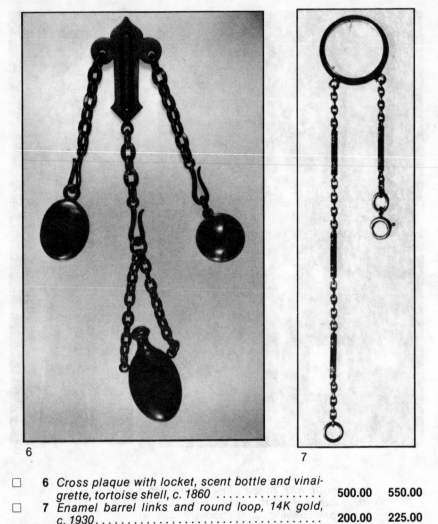

6

7

☐ **6** Cross plaque with locket, scent bottle and vinaigrette, tortoise shell, c. 1860 . . . .   500.00   550.00

☐ **7** Enamel barrel links and round loop, 14K gold, c. 1930 . . . .   200.00   225.00

8

9

☐ **8** *Enamel flower and Greek key plaque and chain motif with American 1861 gold dollar, padlock locket with hair, watch, religious locket and heart, rose diamonds in watch, cobalt blue enamel, 7 in. long, gold, c. 1840* **24000.00 26000.00**

☐ **9** *Griffin and snake pin plaque with sliding mirror, scissors case and scent bottle, chased and repoussé, sterling silver, c. 1890* **325.00   350.00**

10

11

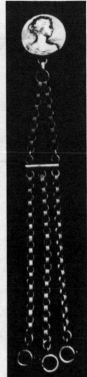

12

☐ **10** *Heart plaque with swivel, sterling silver, American, c. 1896.* **45.00   65.00**

☐ **11** *Heart plaque with thimble in case and pencil, sterling silver, c. 1880* **150.00   165.00**

☐ **12** *Lady head medallion plaque with three modified trace link chains, silver plated, c. 1900* **85.00   100.00**

13

14

☐ **13** *Lady head plaque with memo pad, scissors case, thimble case and pencil, yellow metal, c. 1870*. . . **150.00 175.00**

☐ **14** *Leather motif with purse, memo pad and pencil, scissors with case, mirror and scent bottle, English, c. 1900* **300.00 350.00**

16

15

17

☐ **15** *Macaroni chatelaine, guilloche red, blue, white, green and yellow enamel, watch: quarter-hour repeater, enamel dial, gold hands, pendant and clasp set with rose diamond, gilt engraved movement, verge escapement, chain and fusee, two translucent red enamel hearts and matching watch key, gold watch and chains, signed: Geo Prior London, c. 1825* **35000.00 40000.00**

☐ **16** *Macaroni chatelaine, guilloche cobalt-blue enamel, seed pearls, rose diamonds, watch: quarter-hour repeater, enamel dial, gold hands, verge escapement, chain and fusee, gold watch and chains, English, c. 1810* **25000.00 30000.00**

☐ **17** *Macaroni chatelaine, guilloche polychrome enamel, two goldstone teardrop charms, watch: quarter-hour repeater, enamel dial, steel hands, pendant set with rose diamond, gilt movement, verge escapement, chain and fusee, gold watch and chains, signed: George Prior London, c. 1825* **35000.00 40000.00**

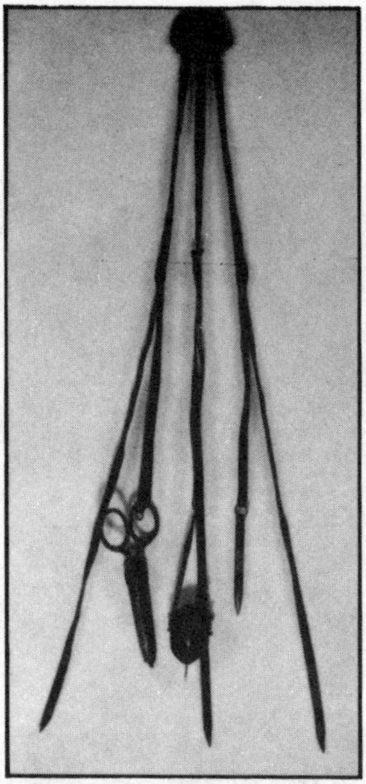

18

19

20

☐	**18**	*Leather motif with scissors with case, thimble holder with pencil, English, c. 1900*	**150.00**	**175.00**
☐	**19**	*Mesh motif plaque, gold, c. 1860*	**250.00**	**300.00**
☐	**20**	*Morning glory plaque with memo pad, pencil and glass scent bottle, white metal, Art Nouveau, c. 1895*	**150.00**	**180.00**

21

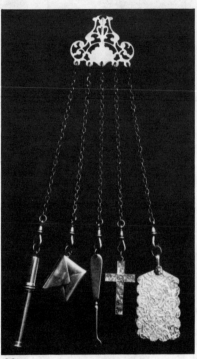

22

☐ **21** *Mourning sewing motif with pencil holder, memo pad, scissors with case, pin cushion and thimble with holder, faceted polished jet, black metal, c. 1865* **350.00** **400.00**

☐ **22** *Openwork plaque with pencil, stamp envelope, button hook, cross and memo pad, sterling silver, English, c. 1900* **265.00** **300.00**

23

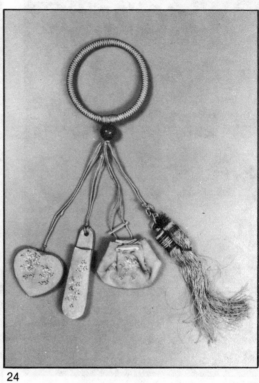

24

☐ **23** *Openwork plaque with pin cushion, needle case in holder and scissors with case, yellow metal, c. 1870* **145.00** **165.00**

☐ **24** *Oriental painted silk with heart pin cushion, needle case and purse, c. 19th* **150.00** **200.00**

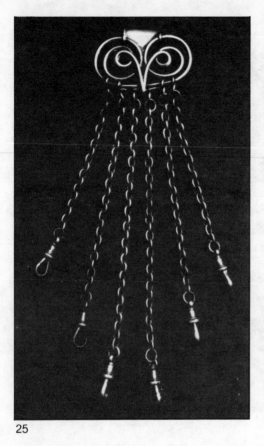

25

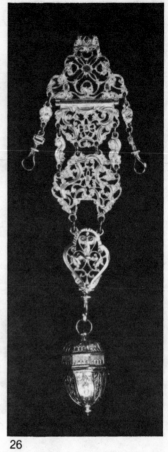

26

☐	**25** *Owl wire plaque with six trace link chains, silver plated, c. 1900*	**125.00**	**150.00**
☐	**26** *Plaque openwork motif with thimble case, pinchbeck, English, c. 1780*	**350.00**	**375.00**

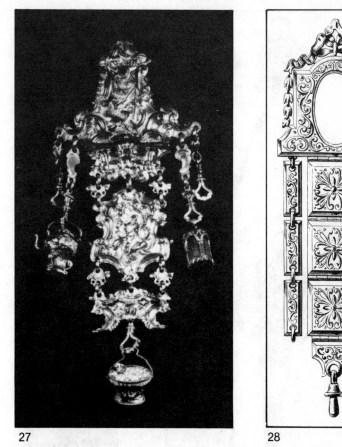

27   28

☐ **27** *Plaque repoussé and chased motif, three hard-*
      stone seal charms, gold, 5¾ in. long, c. 1790 .... **3000.00   3500.00**
☐ **28** *Plaque repoussé and chased motif, gold, design-*
      er: A. Leroy, Paris, France, c. 1868-83 .... **2400.00   2600.00**

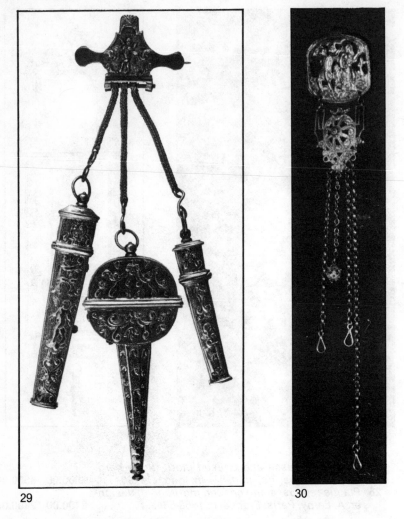

29

30

☐ **29** Repoussé shield pin with two needle cases and scissors case, pinchbeck, c. 1790 . . . . 400.00   450.00
☐ **30** Scenic repoussé plaque with four chains, sterling silver, c. 1870 . . . . 150.00   165.00

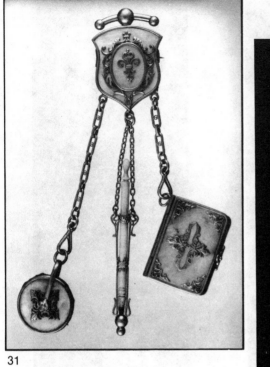

31

32

☐ **31** *Shield pin plaque with pin cushion, pencil and memo pad, mother-of-pearl inserts, gold filled, c. 1880* **265.00** **300.00**

☐ **32** *Single purpose dance card motif, ivory, c. late 19th* **175.00** **225.00**

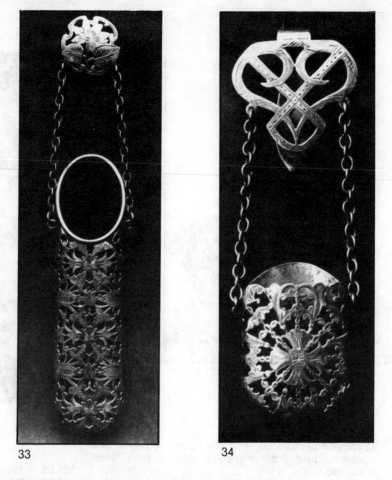

33

34

☐ **33** *Single purpose eyeglass case motif, openwork flower designs, sterling silver, velvet lined, c. 1880* **140.00 160.00**

☐ **34** *Single purpose folding eyeglass case motif, openwork designs, sterling silver, c. 1880* **125.00 140.00**

35

36

37

☐ **35** *Single purpose mesh purse motif, sterling silver,
c. 1900* **125.00   150.00**
☐ **36** *Single purpose watch motif, family crest plaque,
gold, designer: G. Huot, Paris, France, c. 1868-83* . . **4000.00 5000.00**
☐ **37** *Single purpose scarf clip motif, white metal,
enamel flowers, c. late 19th* **100.00   125.00**

39

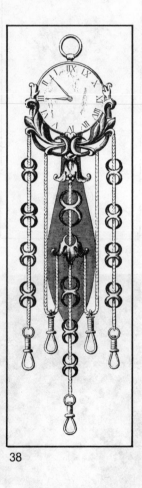

38

40

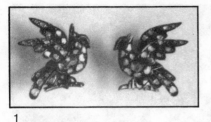

1

2

4

3

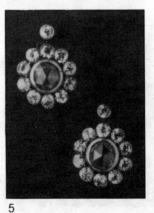

5

EARRINGS

DIAMOND

			PRICE RANGE	
☐	**1**	*Bird motif, rose diamonds, ruby eyes, silver gilt, c. 1820*	600.00	700.00
☐	**2**	*Button loveknot motif, round diamonds, gold, American, c. 1895*	165.00	185.00
☐	**3**	*Cluster motif, 42 round and rose diamonds, gold, silver, c. mid 19th*	1000.00	1400.00
☐	**4**	*Cluster motif, 18 round diamonds approx. 3.50 cts., silver topped gold, c. late 19th*	3000.00	3200.00
☐	**5**	*Cluster motif, two center rose diamonds and 22 old mine diamonds approx. 4.50 cts., silver, gold, c. early to mid 19th*	3000.00	3500.00

6

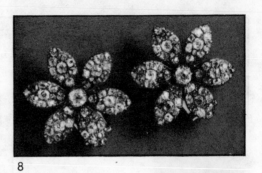

8

7

9

10

11

☐ **6** *Dangle motif, rose diamonds, black enamel border, gold, c. 1870* 1400.00 1500.00
☐ **7** *Dangle flower motif, rose diamonds, collet-set, silver topped gold, c. early 19th* 600.00 800.00
☐ **8** *Flower motif, old mine diamonds, silver, converted to clips, c. 1820-40* 3500.00 4500.00
☐ **9** *Flower dangle motif, round diamonds, gold, maker: M. Baugrand, Paris, France, c. 1868-83* ... 2500.00 3500.00
☐ **10** *Flower round motif, rose diamonds, silver gilt, c. 1840* 500.00 600.00
☐ **11** *Hand motif, rose diamonds, ruby set as ring on pinky finger, c. 1820* 1200.00 1500.00

12

14

13

15

☐ **12** *Leaf and flower dangle motif, rose diamonds, silver, c. 1820-40* **1000.00 1200.00**

☐ **13** *Leaf and flower motif, two pear-shape rose diamonds, round rose diamonds, silver back gold, c. 1790* **3500.00 4000.00**

☐ **14** *Leaf and flower dangle motif, rose diamonds, gold topped silver, c. 1820-40* **1600.00 1800.00**

☐ **15** *Pendants with cluster motif, old mine diamonds and four rose diamonds approx. 2.50 cts., gold, platinum, c. 1900* **2200.00 2600.00**

16

17

18

21

20

19

22

☐	**16**	Round Etruscan granulation motif, two old mine diamonds, gold, c. 1860	350.00	450.00
☐	**17**	Single stone motif, old mine diamonds, 14K gold, c. 1900....................................	250.00	300.00
☐	**18**	Spade motif, 12 round diamonds, 14K gold, c. early 20th	800.00	1000.00
☐	**19**	Star dangle motif, round diamonds, gold, maker: M. Baugrand, Paris, France, c. 1868-83	5000.00	6000.00
☐	**20**	Star motif, blue enamel, rose diamonds, gold, c. 1850....................................	850.00	1000.00
☐	**21**	Straight line dangle motif, rose diamonds, gold, c. 1800....................................	1200.00	1500.00
☐	**22**	Wreath motif, two old mine diamonds, rose diamonds, silver, c. 18th........................	1000.00	1200.00

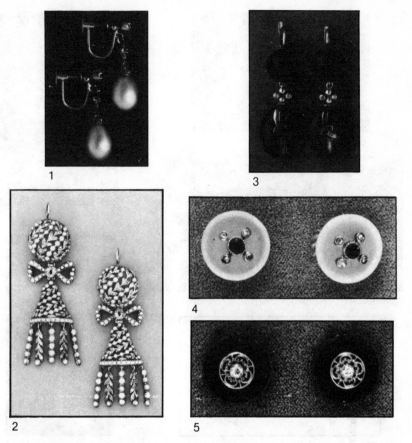

1

3

4

2

5

DIAMOND and GEMSTONE

PRICE RANGE

- [ ] **1** *Baroque natural pearls, diamonds, gold topped silver, contemporary conversion, c. 1860* 1500.00 2000.00
- [ ] **2** *Bell and bow openwork motif, seed pearls, diamonds, gold, c. early 20th* 2600.00 3000.00
- [ ] **3** *Belt motif, enamel, rose diamonds, 18K gold, c. late 19th* 500.00 600.00
- [ ] **4** *Button motif, white onyx circle with emeralds, rose diamonds, gold, c. late 19th* 350.00 500.00
- [ ] **5** *Button motif, amethyst circle with round diamond in openwork white gold frame, c. early 20th* 250.00 300.00

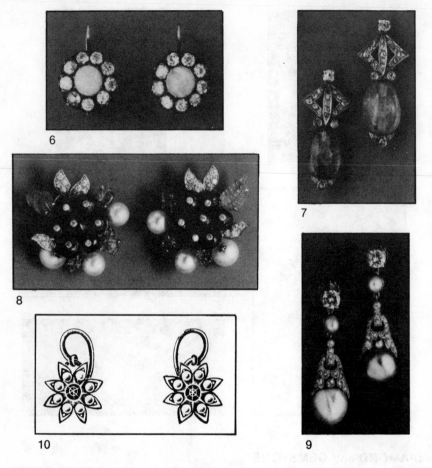

6

7

8

10

9

☐ **6** *Cluster motif, cabochon white opal in center, 18
diamonds approx. 3.0 cts., gold, c. mid 19th* 2000.00 2500.00
☐ **7** *Emerald beads, rose diamonds, gold, c. 1920-30* . 1200.00 1400.00
☐ **8** *Flower and berry motif, 14 ruby beads, eight
carved emerald leaves, six pearls, diamonds,
platinum, c. 1930-40.* 1800.00 2200.00
☐ **9** *Flower motif, baroque natural pearls, round and
rose diamonds, platinum, c. 1910* 4000.00 4500.00
☐ **10** *Flower motif, pearls, round diamonds, gold,
American, c. 1885* 200.00 250.00

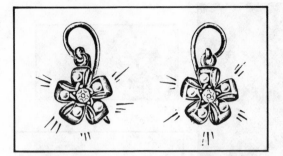

11

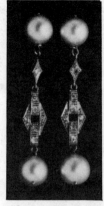

13

12

14

15

☐	**11**	*Flower motif, pearls, round diamonds, gold, American, c. 1895*	**225.00**	**275.00**
☐	**12**	*Fly and shell motif, rubies, rose diamonds, gold, silver, fitted leather box inscribed: E. Emanuel, c. late 19th*	**1200.00**	**1600.00**
☐	**13**	*Geometric motif, 14 round diamonds, four pearls, approx. 9MM to 9.5MM, platinum, c. 1915-30*	**600.00**	**900.00**
☐	**14**	*Geometric motif, sapphire, round diamonds, gold, platinum, c. 1930*	**600.00**	**800.00**
☐	**15**	*Jade, gold, c. 20th*	**2000.00**	**2200.00**

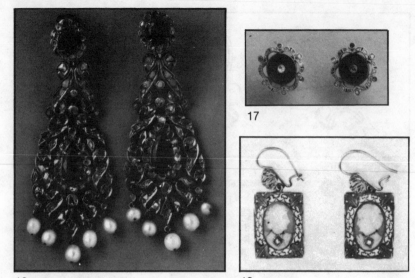

16

17

18

☐ **16** *Ribbon dangle motif, two round and two pear-shape emeralds, ten seed pearls, rose diamonds, silver, gold, c. 19th* **1400.00 1500.00**

☐ **17** *Ribbon motif, black onyx, rose diamonds, gold, c. 19th* **600.00 650.00**

☐ **18** *Shell cameo motif, filigree frame, diamond in necklaces, gold, c. 1920-30* **350.00 400.00**

1

GEMSTONE

PRICE RANGE

☐ **1** *Angel dangle motif, cabochon opals, gold, c. late 19th* **850.00 900.00**

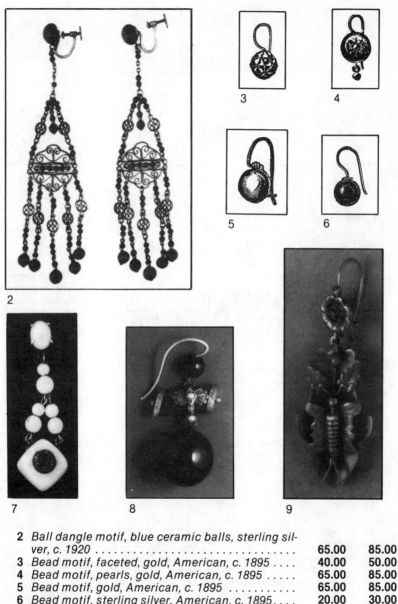

☐	**2**	*Ball dangle motif, blue ceramic balls, sterling silver, c. 1920*	**65.00**	**85.00**
☐	**3**	*Bead motif, faceted, gold, American, c. 1895*	**40.00**	**50.00**
☐	**4**	*Bead motif, pearls, gold, American, c. 1895*	**65.00**	**85.00**
☐	**5**	*Bead motif, gold, American, c. 1895*	**65.00**	**85.00**
☐	**6**	*Bead motif, sterling silver, American, c. 1895*....	**20.00**	**30.00**
☐	**7**	*Bead dangle motif, opals, round rubies in square opal, gold, c. 1890*	**1000.00**	**1200.00**
☐	**8**	*Black onyx ball and bar motif, seed pearls, gold, c. 1860-80*	**450.00**	**500.00**
☐	**9**	*Butterfly and flower dangle motif, seed pearls, gold, c. 1860-80*	**800.00**	**900.00**

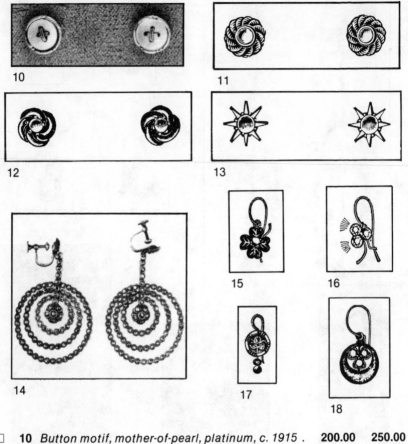

☐	**10**	*Button motif, mother-of-pearl, platinum, c. 1915* .	**200.00**	**250.00**
☐	**11**	*Button motif, pearls, gold, American, c. 1895*	**65.00**	**85.00**
☐	**12**	*Button loveknot motif, opals, gold, American, c. 1895*	**90.00**	**110.00**
☐	**13**	*Button star motif, opals, gold, American, c. 1895*	**65.00**	**85.00**
☐	**14**	*Circle dangle motif, marcasites, sterling silver, c. 1920-30*	**65.00**	**85.00**
☐	**15**	*Clover motif, pearls, gold, American, c. 1895*	**90.00**	**110.00**
☐	**16**	*Clover motif, white sapphires, gold, American, c. 1895*	**90.00**	**110.00**
☐	**17**	*Clover and bead motif, gold, American, c. 1895* . .	**50.00**	**60.00**
☐	**18**	*Clover and hoop motif, pearls, gold, American, c. 1895*	**100.00**	**125.00**

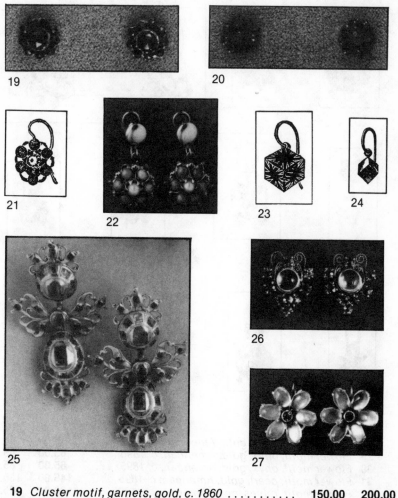

19

20

21

22

23

24

25

26

27

☐	**19**	*Cluster motif, garnets, gold, c. 1860*	**150.00**	**200.00**
☐	**20**	*Cluster motif, garnets, gold, c. 1860*	**150.00**	**200.00**
☐	**21**	*Cluster motif, garnets, gold, American, c. 1895* . .	**165.00**	**185.00**
☐	**22**	*Cluster motif, cabochon turquoise, seed pearl center, enamel, gold, contemporary posts, c. 1860*	**150.00**	**200.00**
☐	**23**	*Cube motif, engraved, onyx, gold, American, c. 1895*.	**45.00**	**65.00**
☐	**24**	*Cube motif, gold, American, c. 1895*	**40.00**	**50.00**
☐	**25**	*Emeralds: step-cut, gold, c. 1790*	**1500.00**	**2000.00**
☐	**26**	*Filigree motif, round moonstone centers, round sapphires, white gold, maker: Tiffany & Co.*	**350.00**	**450.00**
☐	**27**	*Flower motif, oval moonstone petals, round sapphire center, white gold, maker: Tiffany & Co.* . . .	**350.00**	**450.00**

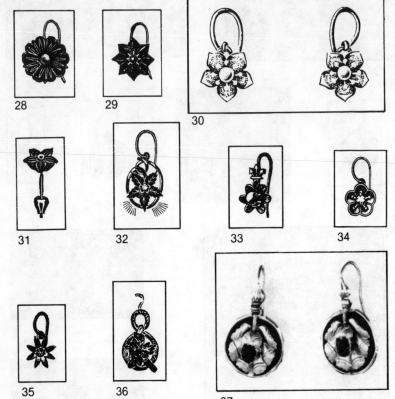

☐	**28**	*Flower motif, onyx, gold, American, c. 1895*	**65.00**	**85.00**
☐	**29**	*Flower motif, onyx, gold, American, c. 1895*	**65.00**	**85.00**
☐	**30**	*Flower motif, onyx, gold, American, c. 1895*	**65.00**	**85.00**
☐	**31**	*Flower motif, pearl, gold, American, c. 1895*	**145.00**	**165.00**
☐	**32**	*Flower motif, rubies, gold, American, c. 1895*	**100.00**	**125.00**
☐	**33**	*Flower motif, pearl, gold, American, c. 1895*	**90.00**	**110.00**
☐	**34**	*Flower motif, pearls, gold, American, c. 1895*	**65.00**	**85.00**
☐	**35**	*Flower motif, rubies, gold, American, c. 1895*	**90.00**	**110.00**
☐	**36**	*Flower motif, coral, gold, American, c. 1895*	**100.00**	**125.00**
☐	**37**	*Flower motif, garnets, gold, c. 1850-60*	**300.00**	**400.00**

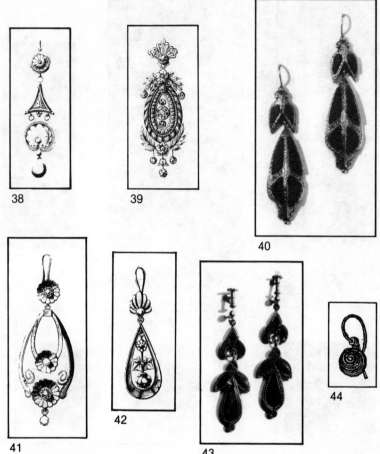

38

39

40

41

42

43

44

☐	**38**	*Flower dangle motif, pearls, gold, German, c. 1860-80*	**350.00**	**400.00**
☐	**39**	*Flower dangle motif, garnets, gold, maker: G. Ehni, Stuttgart, Germany, c. 1870-80*	**600.00**	**650.00**
☐	**40**	*Flower dangle motif, green malachite, engraved silver, c. 1850*	**150.00**	**200.00**
☐	**41**	*Flower dangle motif, pearls, gold, German, c. 1860-80*	**400.00**	**450.00**
☐	**42**	*Flower dangle motif, pearls, gold, Stuttgart, Germany, c. 1870-80*	**350.00**	**400.00**
☐	**43**	*Flower dangle motif, bloodstone, carnelian, engraved silver, contemporary conversion, c. 1860* .	**175.00**	**225.00**
☐	**44**	*Genuine sea shell motif, gold, American, c. 1895.*	**50.00**	**60.00**

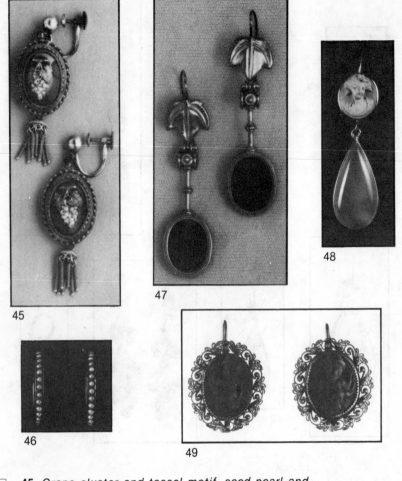

45

46

47

48

49

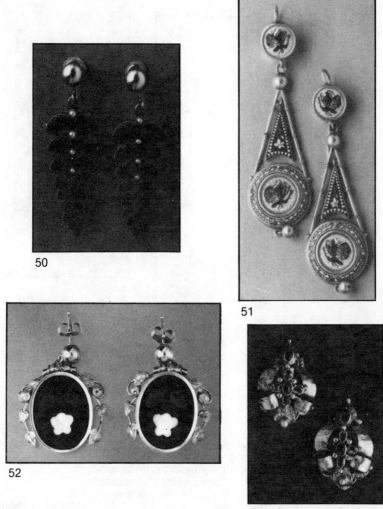

50

51

52

53

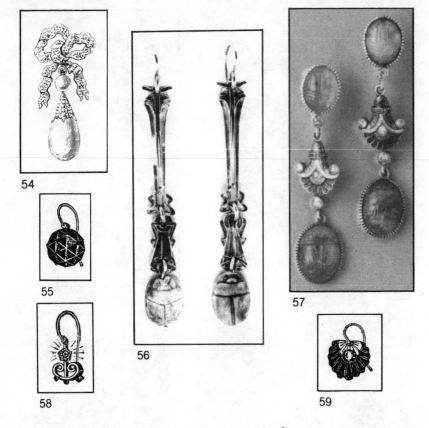

54

55

56

57

58

59

☐ **54** *Ribbon dangle motif, pearls, gold, German, c. 1860-80* 500.00 600.00

☐ **55** *Rose cut, onyx, gold, American, c. 1895* 45.00 65.00

☐ **56** *Scarab motif, faience scarabs, reverse: one carved hieroglyphics, one Royal cartouche of 18th Dynasty Pharaoh: Tuthmosis, translucent blue-green enamel links, gold, Art Nouveau, maker: Rene Lalique, French, c. 1890* 1500.00 1600.00

☐ **57** *Scarab motif, four carved emerald scarabs, translucent red, blue and apple green enamel, ten round diamonds, gold, Faberge, workmaster: Henrik Wigstrom, c. 1900, Russian* 6500.00 7000.00

☐ **58** *Scroll motif, garnets, gold, American, c. 1895* ... 90.00 110.00

☐ **59** *Sea shell motif, pearls, gold, American, c. 1895* .. 90.00 110.00

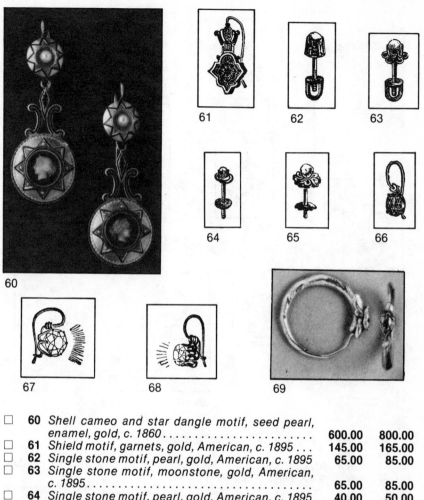

60

61   62   63

64   65   66

67   68   69

	60	Shell cameo and star dangle motif, seed pearl, enamel, gold, c. 1860	600.00	800.00
	61	Shield motif, garnets, gold, American, c. 1895	145.00	165.00
	62	Single stone motif, pearl, gold, American, c. 1895	65.00	85.00
	63	Single stone motif, moonstone, gold, American, c. 1895	65.00	85.00
	64	Single stone motif, pearl, gold, American, c. 1895	40.00	50.00
	65	Single stone motif, pearl, gold, American, c. 1895	50.00	60.00
	66	Single stone motif, amethyst, gold, American, c. 1895	100.00	125.00
	67	Single stone motif, white sapphires, gold, American, c. 1895	100.00	125.00
	68	Single stone motif, white sapphires, gold, American, c. 1895	90.00	110.00
	69	Snake motif, pear-shape diamond in head, gold, c. 19th	900.00	1200.00

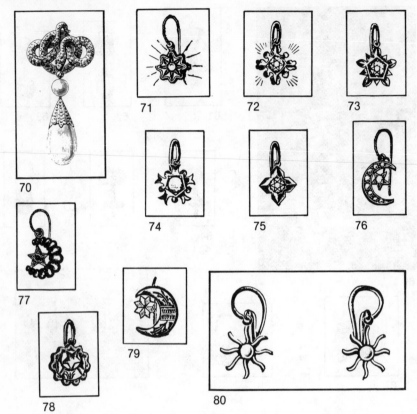

81

82

☐ **81** *Teardrop motif, lapis lazuli, seed pearls, gold, c. 1890*................................. 375.00 425.00

☐ **82** *Tiger claws, filigree gold motif, 15K gold, English, c. 1870* 350.00 450.00

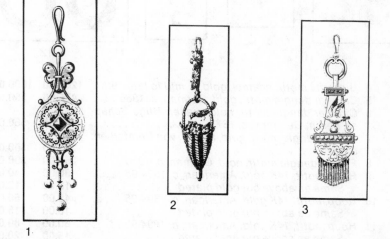

1

2

3

GOLD

		PRICE RANGE	
☐	**1** *Ball and butterfly wing dangle motif, gold, German, c. 1871*	500.00	600.00
☐	**2** *Bird, nest and flower motif, gold, French, c. 1860-80*	650.00	750.00
☐	**3** *Bird and tassel motif, gold, French, c. 1860-80* ...	650.00	750.00

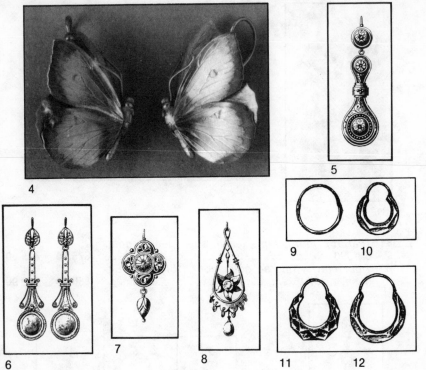

4

5

9　　　10

7

8

11　　　12

6

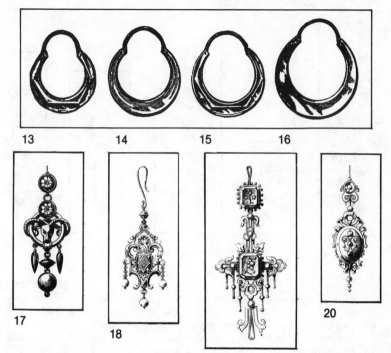

13   14   15   16

17

18

19

20

☐	**13**	*Hoop motif, 14K gold, American, c. 1894-95*	**85.00**	**110.00**
☐		*Same as above but gold plated*	**25.00**	**35.00**
☐	**14**	*Hoop motif, 14K gold, American, c. 1894-95*	**100.00**	**120.00**
☐		*Same as above but gold plated*	**35.00**	**45.00**
☐	**15**	*Hoop motif, 14K gold, American, c. 1894-95* .	**110.00**	**130.00**
☐		*Same as above but gold plated*	**35.00**	**45.00**
☐	**16**	*Hoop motif, 14K gold, American, c. 1894-95*	**125.00**	**145.00**
☐		*Same as above but gold plated*	**40.00**	**50.00**
☐	**17**	*Rams' head dangle motif, gold, German, c. 1869* .	**500.00**	**600.00**
☐	**18**	*Renaissance revival motif, pearls, gold, c.1840-60*	**500.00**	**600.00**
☐	**19**	*Renaissance revival motif, gold, c. 1840-60*	**500.00**	**600.00**
☐	**20**	*Ribbon dangle motif, gold, German, c. 1872*	**350.00**	**400.00**

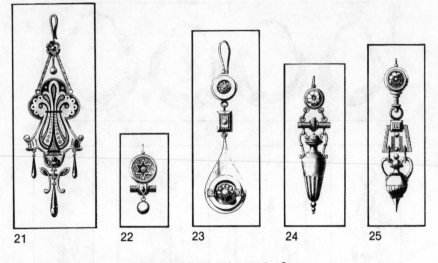

21   22   23   24   25

☐ **21** *Scroll teardrop dangle motif, gold, German, c. 1871.....................................*   650.00   750.00

☐ **22** *Star dangle motif, gold, maker: von Demfelben, c. 1870.......................................*   250.00   300.00

☐ **23** *Teardrop circle dangle motif, gold, Stuttgart, Germany, c. 1870..........................*   350.00   400.00

☐ **24** *Urn dangle motif, gold, German, c. 1866........*   500.00   600.00

☐ **25** *Urn dangle motif, gold, Italian, c. 1840-60.......*   350.00   400.00

1

HUMAN HAIR - GOLD
All items made from hair referred to throughout this section are of brunette human hair unless stated otherwise.

PRICE RANGE

☐ **1** *Ball motif, woven hair in beehive pattern, gold fittings, c. 1840-60 ....*   55.00   65.00

2

4

3

5

1

2

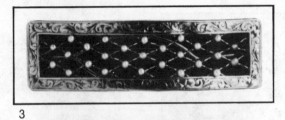

3

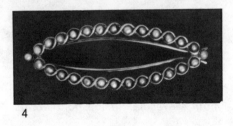

4

HAIR COMBS, HATPINS and BARRETTES

BARRETTES

		PRICE RANGE	
☐	**1** *Floral motif barrette, half pearls, gold, c. 1920* ...	85.00	140.00
☐	**2** *Greek key motif barrette or brooch, 200 round diamonds approx. 9.0 cts., platinum topped gold, c. 1870*	6000.00	8000.00
☐	**3** *Lattice motif barrette, seed pearls, engraved, gold, c. 1925*	325.00	425.00
☐	**4** *Vine motif barrette, seed pearls, gold, c. 1920* ...	250.00	285.00

HAIR COMBS

			PRICE RANGE	
☐	1	*Axe filigree motif, tortoise hair ornament, gold plated, c. 1890-1900*	35.00	50.00
☐	2	*Filigree wreath motif, tortoise shell hair comb, sterling silver, American, c. 1896*	100.00	200.00
☐	3	*Filigree swirl motif, tortoise shell hair comb, sterling silver, American, c. 1896*	125.00	135.00
☐	4	*Filigree swirl motif, tortoise shell hair comb, sterling silver, American, c. 1896*	100.00	120.00
☐	5	*Filigree flower motif, tortoise shell hair comb, sterling silver, American, c. 1896*	125.00	135.00

6

7

8

9

☐ **6** *Filigree leaf motif, tortoise shell hair comb, sterling silver, American, c. 1896* **125.00** **135.00**

☐ **7** *Filigree axe motif, tortoise shell hair ornament, sterling silver, American, c. 1896* **100.00** **120.00**

☐ **8** *Filigree flower motif, tortoise shell hair comb, sterling silver, American, c. 1896* **125.00** **135.00**

☐ **9** *Flower and leaf motif, hair ornament, sterling silver, c. 1860-70* **110.00** **135.00**

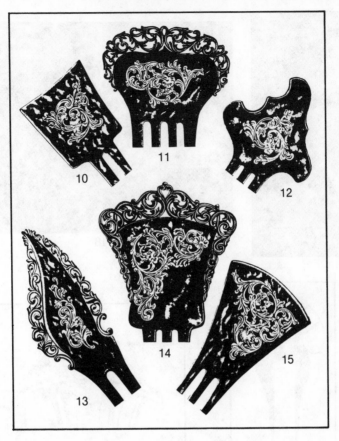

□	**10**	*Flower swirl motif, tortoise shell hair comb, 14K gold, American, c. 1896*	50.00	65.00
□	**11**	*Flower swirl motif, tortoise shell hair comb, 14K gold, American, c. 1896*	75.00	100.00
□	**12**	*Flower swirl motif, tortoise shell hair comb, 14K gold, American, c. 1896*	50.00	65.00
□	**13**	*Flower swirl motif, tortoise shell hair comb, 14K gold, American, c. 1896*	60.00	85.00
□	**14**	*Flower swirl motif, tortoise shell hair comb, 14K gold, American, c. 1896*	100.00	125.00
□	**15**	*Flower swirl motif, tortoise shell hair comb, 14K gold, American, c. 1896*	60.00	85.00

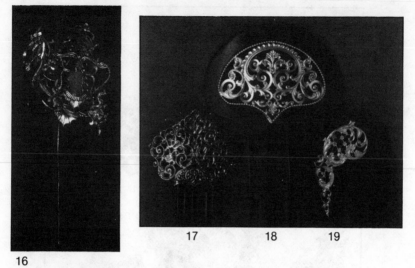

17   18   19

16

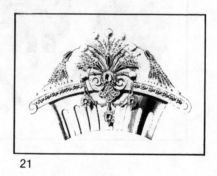

21

20

☐	**16**	*Flower and jade mouse motif, hair comb, king-fisher feathers, silver, Oriental, c. 1840*	200.00	250.00
☐	**17**	*Openwork motif, tortoise shell hair comb, gold, c. 1870*	325.00	350.00
☐	**18**	*Flower swirl motif, tortoise hair comb, gold, c. 1890-1900*	340.00	360.00
☐	**19**	*Flower swirl motif, tortoise hair ornament, gold, c. 1890-1900*	175.00	200.00
☐	**20**	*Flower motif, sterling silver, Art Nouveau, c. 1890*	165.00	200.00
☐	**21**	*Lotus flower motif, tortoise shell hair comb, ru-bies, sapphires, pearls, gold, maker: O. Weber, Hanau, Germany, c. 1860-80*	800.00	1200.00

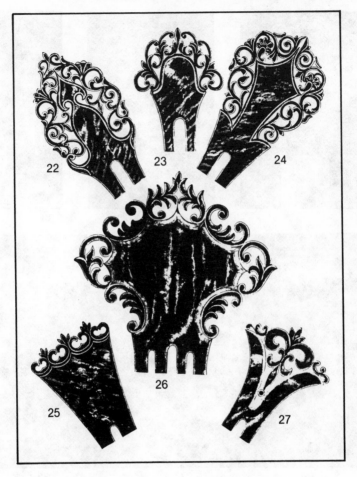

28   29   30

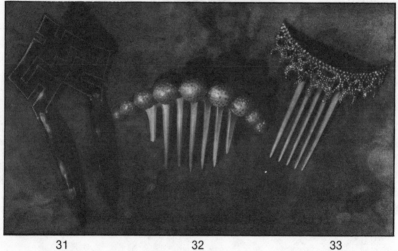

31   32   33

☐ **28** *Openwork flower motif, tortoise shell hair comb, sterling silver, American, c. 1896* **85.00   100.00**

☐ **29** *Openwork swirl motif, tortoise shell hair comb, sterling silver, American, c. 1896* **85.00   100.00**

☐ **30** *Oriental cloud motif rim, tortoise shell hair comb, seed pearls, gold, maker: Pickslay & Co., New York, c. 20th* **200.00   225.00**

☐ **31** *Geometric motif, pique tortoise shell hair comb, gold, c. 1920-30* **50.00   75.00**

☐ **32** *Star and ball motif, blond tortoise shell hair comb, gold, c. 19th* **65.00   85.00**

☐ **33** *Cresent motif, blond tortoise shell hair comb, cut steel, c. 19th* **85.00   125.00**

1

2

3

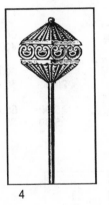

4

5

HATPINS

		PRICE RANGE	
☐	**1** *Ball cutout motif hatpin, 14K gold top, American, c. 1896*	50.00	60.00
☐	*Same as above but sterling silver top*	25.00	35.00
☐	**2** *Ball cutout swirl motif hatpin, 14K gold top, American, c. 1896*	50.00	60.00
☐	*Same as above but sterling silver top*	25.00	35.00
☐	**3** *Calla lily flower motif hatpins and hair pin, translucent white and green enamel, gold, Art Nouveau, c. 1910. Set*	400.00	500.00
☐	**4** *Dome cutout motif hatpin, 14K gold top, American, c. 1896*	50.00	60.00
☐	*Same as above but sterling silver top*	25.00	35.00
☐	**5** *Loop motif hatpin, 14K gold top, American, c. 1896*	35.00	55.00
☐	*Same as above but sterling silver top*	30.00	40.00

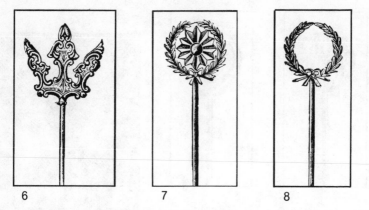

6   7   8

☐	**6** *Shield motif hatpin, 14K gold top, American, c. 1896*	50.00	60.00
☐	*Same as above but sterling silver top*	30.00	40.00
☐	**7** *Wreath and star motif hatpin, 14K gold top, American, c. 1896*	50.00	60.00
☐	*Same as above but sterling silver top*	20.00	30.00
☐	**8** *Wreath and star motif hatpin, 14K gold top American, c. 1896*	45.00	55.00
	Same as above but sterling silver top	25.00	35.00

1   2   3

LOCKETS

			PRICE RANGE	
☐	**1** *Baby locket, oval engraved, one round diamond, 14K gold, American, c. 1896*		85.00	100.00
☐	**2** *Baby locket, oval engraved, 14K gold, American, c. 1896*		35.00	50.00
☐	*Same as above but gold filled*		15.00	20.00
☐	**3** *Baby locket, oval with half pearl, 14K gold, American, c. 1896*		25.00	50.00
☐	*Same as above but gold filled*		15.00	20.00

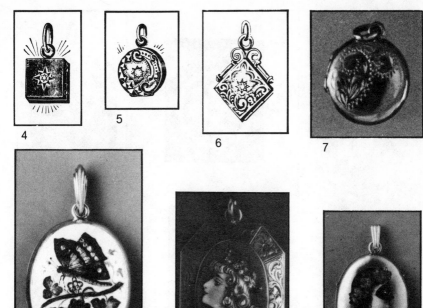

☐ **4** Baby locket, square with one round diamond, 14K gold, American, c. 1896 .... **65.00** **85.00**

☐ **5** Baby locket, round engraved, one round diamond, 14K gold, American, c. 1896 .... **85.00** **100.00**

☐ **6** Baby locket, square engraved, one round diamond, 14K gold, American, c. 1896 .... **100.00** **115.00**

☐ Same as above but gold filled and one round paste.................................... **20.00** **35.00**

☐ **7** Baby locket, engraved, sterling, c. 1940 .... **12.00** **15.00**

☐ **8** Butterfly and grape vine motif, enamelled, rose diamonds, gold, c. late 19th **2400.00** **2800.00**

☐ **9** Enamel miniature portrait of a lady, diamonds, rubies, gold, c. 1900....................... **1000.00** **1500.00**

☐ **10** Enamel portrait of a masked lady, diamond in eye, gold, c. 1860 .... **500.00** **600.00**

11

12

13

14

15

16

☐ **11** *Enameled oval locket, slides open, brass, c. late 19th* 85.00   150.00

☐ **12** *Fleur-de-lys motif, pearl and diamonds in silver, opaque white and translucent green enamel, gold, c. late 19th* 500.00   600.00

☐ **13** *Floral motif, square engraved, three round diamonds, 14K gold, American, c. 1896* 350.00   400.00

☐   *Same as above but gold filled and glass stones* 75.00   90.00

☐ **14** *Floral engraved motif, 14K gold, American, c. 1896.* 100.00   125.00

☐   *Same as above but gold filled* 20.00   30.00

☐ **15** *Floral and scenic engraved motif, 14K gold, American, c. 1896* 200.00   250.00

☐   *Same as above but gold filled* 60.00   75.00

☐ **16** *Floral and scenic engraved motif, 14K gold, American, c. 1896* 200.00   250.00

☐   *Same as above but gold filled* 60.00   75.00

18

20

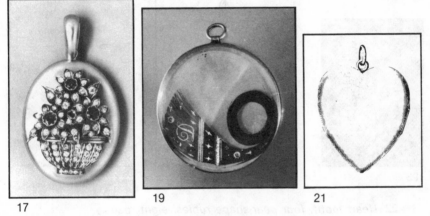

17

19

21

- □ **17** *Flower basket motif, 57 round diamonds, three round rubies, gold, c. 19th* **2600.00 3000.00**
- □ **18** *Flower and triangle motif, square-cut emeralds, one old mine diamond, rose diamonds, gold, c. 1860.* **800.00 1000.00**
- □ **19** *Hair curl behind beveled glass, seed pearls and gold wire glued onto hair, gold frame, c. 1860* ... **400.00 600.00**
- □ **20** *Heart, floral and letter "F" motif, turquoise, flower rosettes, signed: JB, fitted leather box marked: John Brogden, Goldsmith, gold, c. 1860.* **1000.00 1200.00**
- □ **21** *Heart motif, sterling, American, c. 1896* **85.00 100.00**

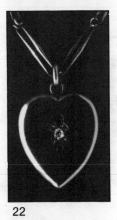

22

24

26

23

25

27

☐ **22** *Heart motif, four pear-shape rubies, eight rose diamonds, one round diamond, fancy link chain, gold, c. 1915* **1000.00   1400.00**

☐ **23** *Heart motif, pavé with 44 old mine diamonds approx. 3.0 cts., one old mine diamond approx. .50 ct., reverse: crystal locket, gold, c. late 19th* **5000.00   6000.00**

☐ **24** *Heart engraved floral motif, sterling, American, c. 1896* **100.00   125.00**

☐ **25** *Heart engraved angel motif, sterling, American, c. 1896* **125.00   145.00**

☐ **26** *Horseshoe motif, pearls, turquoise, gold, c. 1870* **350.00   450.00**

☐ **27** *Indian, obverse: cushion-cut yellow sapphire in center, rubies, seven diamonds approx. 3.0 cts.; reverse: floral motif in blue, green, red and white opaque champlevé enamel, c. 19th* **2600.00   3200.00**

28

30

31

29

29

☐ **28** *Indian, obverse: rose diamond wreath with photograph portrait of Indian gentleman; reverse: Jaipur blue, green, gold, red and white enamel of tiger, gazelle and floral motif; gold, c. 19th* 600.00   700.00

☐ **29** *Intaglios, obverse: crest, reverse: initials, triple hinged frame inside, gold, c. late 19th* 600.00   800.00

☐ **30** *Leaf motif, cabochon turquoise in center, gold, c. mid 19th* 1000.00 1200.00

☐ **31** *Leaf motif, sterling, English, c. late 19th* 65.00   85.00

32

34

33

35

36

☐ **32** *Lion motif, one round diamond in mouth, emeralds in eyes, 14K gold, Art Nouveau, American, c. 1910* **350.00** **450.00**

☐ **33** *Medallion portrait of a lady and birds, 14K gold, Art Nouveau, c. 1900* **350.00** **450.00**

☐ **34** *Medallion portrait of a lady, 14K gold, Art Nouveau, c. 1890-1910* **250.00** **300.00**

☐ **35** *Medallion portrait of a lady, rose diamonds, slides to open, gold, Art Nouveau, maker: Diolot, c. 1890* **1800.00** **2000.00**

☐ **36** *Memorial motif, black and white enamel, gold filled, c. mid 19th* **85.00** **125.00**

37

39

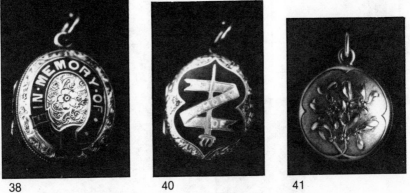

38   40   41

☐	**37**	*Memorial motif, black and white enamel, gold front and back covers, gold filled locket, c. mid 19th*	110.00	150.00
☐	**38**	*Memorial motif, black and white enamel, gold front and back covers, gold filled locket, c. mid 19th*	100.00	125.00
☐	**39**	*Memorial motif, black and white enamel, gold, c. mid 19th*	200.00	225.00
☐	**40**	*Memorial motif, black and white enamel, gold filled, c. mid 19th*	80.00	100.00
☐	**41**	*Mistletoe motif, slides open, gold, c. early 20th* . .	350.00	450.00

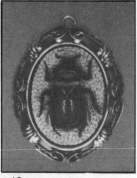

42

44

43

45

46

☐	**42**	*Mosaic beetle motif, 15K gold, c. 1860*	**385.00**	**425.00**
☐	**43**	*Octagonal wreath and ribbon motif, 14K green gold, c. 1930*	**400.00**	**500.00**
☐	**44**	*Open double-sided locket with woven hair under glass, rose gold, English, c. mid 19th*	**250.00**	**350.00**
☐	**45**	*Oval motif, 14K gold, c. late 19th to early 20th* ...	**200.00**	**300.00**
☐	**46**	*Oval motif, Etruscan granulation, one seed pearl, gold, c. 1880*	**1000.00**	**1200.00**

47

48

49

50

51

52

☐ **47** *Oval cutout motif, 55 round diamonds approx. 2.25 cts., platinum, signed: J.E.C. & Co., c. 1900* 3000.00 3500.00

☐ **48** *Oval engraved motif, one round diamond, 14K gold, American, c. 1896* 250.00 300.00

☐   *Same as above but gold filled and glass stone* 75.00 90.00

☐ **49** *Oval engraved motif, 14K gold, American, c. 1896* 200.00 250.00

☐   *Same as above but gold filled* 60.00 75.00

☐ **50** *Oval and flower motif, green gold flower, yellow gold locket, Etruscan granulation, c. 1860* 500.00 600.00

☐ **51** *Oval and star motif, blue enamel, half pearl, 14K gold, c. late 19th* 350.00 400.00

☐ **52** *Oval motif with Knights of Pythias insignia, enamelled, 14K gold, American, c. 1896* 200.00 250.00

☐   *Same as above but gold filled* 60.00 75.00

53

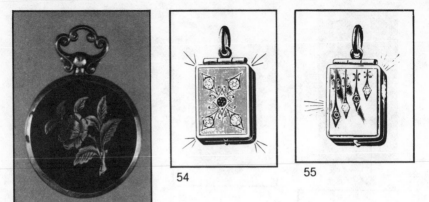

54

55

56

57

58

☐ **53** *Piqué, tortoise shell with gold rose, reverse: glass locket, 9K gold, maker: C & Co., Edinburgh, Scotland, c. 1947* **150.00   200.00**

☐ **54** *Rectangular motif, one round ruby, four round diamonds, 14K gold, American, c. 1896* **350.00   400.00**

☐ *Same as above but gold filled and glass stones* **75.00   90.00**

☐ **55** *Rectangular motif, one round ruby, one round sapphire, two round diamonds, 14K gold, American, c. 1896* **250.00   300.00**

☐ *Same as above but gold filled and glass stones* **75.00   90.00**

☐ **56** *Rectangular engraved motif, 14K gold, American, c. 1896* **100.00   125.00**

☐ *Same as above but gold filled* **30.00   35.00**

☐ **57** *Rectangular engraved motif, one round diamond, 14K gold, American, c. 1896* **275.00   325.00**

☐ *Same as above but gold filled and glass stone* **75.00   90.00**

☐ **58** *Rectangular floral motif, one round diamond, 14K gold, American, c. 1896* **200.00   250.00**

☐ *Same as above but gold filled and glass stones* **60.00   75.00**

59

60

61

62

63

64

☐	**59**	Rectangular moon and star motif, one round emerald, seven round diamonds, 14K gold, American, c. 1896	350.00	400.00
☐		Same as above but gold filled and glass stones	75.00	90.00
☐	**60**	Rectangular moon and star motif, six round diamonds, 14K gold, American, c. 1896	300.00	350.00
☐		Same as above but gold filled and glass stones	75.00	90.00
☐	**61**	Round motif, interior two-sided glass hinged locket, gold, English, c. 1870	400.00	500.00
☐	**62**	Round floral motif, 14K gold, American, c. 1896 . .	85.00	100.00
☐		Same as above but gold filled	20.00	30.00
☐	**63**	Round floral motif, 14K gold, American, c. 1896 . .	100.00	125.00
☐		Same as above but gold filled	30.00	35.00
☐	**64**	Round motif with a single initial, 14K gold, American, c. 1896	85.00	100.00
☐		Same as above but gold filled	20.00	30.00

65

67

69

66

68

70

☐	**65**	Shell motif, gold, English, c. 19th	225.00	275.00
☐	**66**	Shield motif, Etruscan granulation, one old mine diamond, link chain, gold, c. 1860	1400.00	1500.00
☐	**67**	Square motif, one round emerald, four round diamonds, 14K gold, American, c. 1896	350.00	400.00
☐		Same as above but gold filled and glass stone	75.00	90.00
☐	**68**	Square motif with Masonic insignia, enamelled, 14K gold, American, c. 1896	200.00	250.00
☐		Same as above but gold filled	60.00	75.00
☐	**69**	Square engraved motif, one round diamond, 14K gold, American, c. 1896	250.00	300.00
☐		Same as above but gold filled and glass stone	75.00	90.00
☐	**70**	Square engraved floral motif, one round diamond, 14K gold, American, c. 1896	250.00	300.00
☐		Same as above but gold filled and glass stone	75.00	90.00

71

73

75

72

74

76

 71 Square engraved motif, 14K gold, American, c. 1896.................................... 200.00 250.00
Same as above but gold filled 60.00 75.00
72 Square floral motif, 14K gold, American, c. 1896 . 100.00 125.00
Same as above but gold filled 30.00 35.00
73 Star motif, gold, c. 19th...................... 300.00 350.00
74 Swirl motif, one round diamond, 14K gold, Art Nouveau, American, c. 1900 .... 300.00 400.00
75 Sword and leaf motif, round engraved, one round ruby, three round diamonds, 14K gold, American, c. 1896.................................... 350.00 400.00
Same as above but gold filled and glass stones................................... 75.00 90.00
76 Wreath motif, round engraved, sterling, American, c. 1896.............................. 50.00 65.00

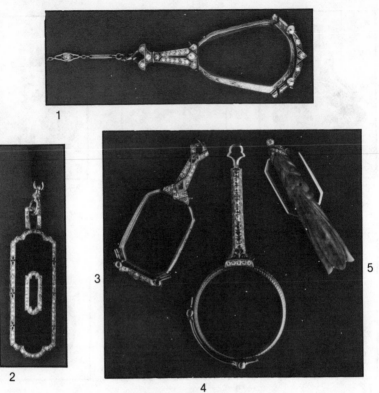

LORGNETTES

			PRICE RANGE	
☐	**1**	*Fancy shape retractable lenses, 38 round diamonds approximately 1.0 ct. in frame and chain, platinum, c. 1915*	**2500.00**	**3000.00**
☐	**2**	*Fancy shape retractable lenses in closed black onyx case, round diamonds, platinum, c. 1919* ...	**3500.00**	**4000.00**
☐	**3**	*Octagonal retractable lenses, numerous round diamonds, two trapezoid diamonds, platinum, c. 1925*....................................	**2500.00**	**3000.00**
☐	**4**	*Round retractable lenses, 11 French-cut diamonds and five round diamonds approx. 1.75 cts., platinum, c. 1925*	**2000.00**	**2500.00**
☐		*Similar to above without diamonds, gold not platinum*	**600.00**	**800.00**
☐	**5**	*Octagonal retractable lenses, 15 round diamonds, leaf motif handle of carved jade, platinum, c. 1915*	**3200.00**	**4200.00**

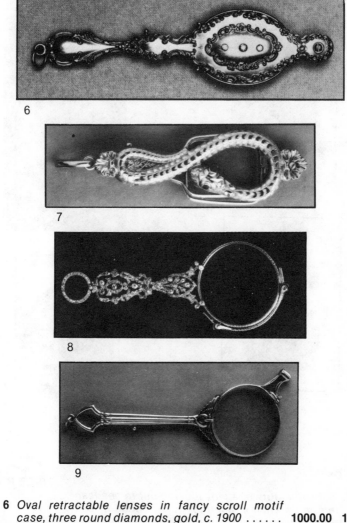

6

7

8

9

MINIATURES

MEMORIAL

PRICE RANGE

☐ **1** Ivory miniature of a lady looking out to sea leaning on an anchor, painted, gold, brooch or pendant, c. 1790 . . . .   325.00   375.00

☐ **2** Ivory miniature of a lady looking out to sea holding an anchor at gravesite, painted, gold, brooch or pendant, c. 1790 . . . .   350.00   450.00

☐ **3** Ivory miniature of children weeping at urn, painted, gold, brooch or pendant, c. 1800 . . . .   400.00   450.00

☐ **4** Ivory miniature of lovebirds and urn, painted, dissolved hair, inscribed: "His Hair I wear whose Friendship is Sincere," c. 1820, contemporary frame, 14K gold 300.00   350.00

5

6

5 *Ivory miniature of religious scene, painted, star motif frame, silver, inscribed: Presented to P.G.L.M.G.E. Hawkes.June.for Meritorious services Sept. 1853," maker: MS, London, England, c. 1852* 275.00 325.00

6 *Porcelain miniature of two angels with urn, painted, dissolved hair, gold wire, ivory cutout pieces, black enamel, gold, c. 1830* 175.00 225.00

1

2

PORTRAIT

PRICE RANGE

1 *Enamel miniatue portrait of a gentleman in Turkish garb by Christian Frederick Zinke, 1683/4-1767, 1¾ in. high, gilt* 2500.00 2800.00

2 *Enamel miniature portrait of a Medieval warrior, nine round diamonds, American, 1.25 cts., pendant or brooch, gold, c. late 19th* 2500.00 2800.00

3

4

6

5

7

☐	**3** *Enamel miniature portrait of a lady and a bunny, locket, gold, c. 1840*	**600.00**	**800.00**
☐	**4** *Enamel miniature portrait of a lady, 12 round diamonds, gold, c. 1870*	**1200.00**	**1400.00**
☐	**5** *Enamel miniature portrait of a lady, 36 rose diamonds, gold, French, c. mid 19th*	**1500.00**	**2000.00**
☐	**6** *Enamel miniature portrait of a lady, round diamonds in border, 18K gold, Art Nouveau, signed: Gollay Fils & Stah, Geneve, c. 1890*	**2000.00**	**2500.00**
☐	**7** *Enamel miniature portrait of a Turkish lady, rose diamonds in cloak, seed pearls, six old mine diamonds approx. .75 ct. in frame, gold, c. 1880*	**1000.00**	**1500.00**

8

10

11

9

12

☐ **8** *Ivory miniature portrait of a baby, reverse: woven hair locket, gold, English, c. 1900.* 150.00   200.00

☐ **9** *Ivory miniature portrait of a child, Swiss-cut sapphires set in silver backed gold, gold pendant, c. 1915.* 900.00 1100.00

☐ **10** *Ivory miniature portrait probably of Dante, sterling, c. 1840* 350.00   450.00

☐ **11** *Ivory miniature portrait of a gentleman, rose, green, white and yellow gold frame, miniature c. 1815-30, frame c. 1840* 600.00   800.00

☐ **12** *Ivory miniature portrait of a gentleman by Jeremiah Meyer, 1735-89, 1⅝ in. high, reverse: plaited hair, gold* 2300.00 2600.00

13

14

15   16

☐ **17** *Ivory miniature portrait of a gentleman by John Bogle, 1746-1803, 2³/₄ in. high, reverse: hair under glass with enamel border, gold, fitted leather case, dated 1796* 6500.00 7000.00

☐ **18** *Ivory miniature portrait of Archibald Douglas by John Bogle, 1746-1803, 1³/₈ in. high, gold, dated 1776.* 3000.00 3400.00

☐ **19** *Ivory miniature portrait of a lady by John Bogle, 1746-1803, 2¹/₈ in. high, half pearl border, gold, dated 1787* 2500.00 2800.00

☐ **20** *Ivory miniature portrait of a gentleman by Gervase Spencer, 1⁷/₈ in. high, gilt, English, mid 18th* . 3000.00 3300.00

21

22

23

24

25

☐ **21** *Ivory miniature portrait of a lady by Gervase Spencer, 1⅝ in. high, gilt, English, dated 1759* ... 1500.00 1800.00

☐ **22** *Ivory miniature portrait of a wench by Samuel Finney, 1718/9-1798, 2 in. high, gold, English* 1000.00 1200.00

☐ **23** *Ivory miniature portrait of Lady Mary King Cooper by Gervase Spencer, gold, half pearl border, reverse: hair under glass, English, dated 1754* 1500.00 1800.00

☐ **24** *Ivory miniature portrait of a gentleman by John Downman, 1750-1824, 1¾ in. high, gold, English. One of a pair with following portrait. Pair* 2500.00 3000.00

☐ **25** *Ivory miniature portrait of a lady by John Downman, 1750-1824, 1¾ in. high, gold, English. One of a pair with above portrait. Pair* 2500.00 3000.00

□ **26** *Ivory miniature portrait of a lady by Thomas Hull, 2¼ in. high, reverse: plaited hair, gold, English, c. 1775-1827* **3400.00 3600.00**

□ **27** *Ivory miniature portrait of a gentleman by Samuel Rickards, 1735-1823, 1¼ in. high, gilt, English* **1000.00 1200.00**

□ **28** *Ivory miniature portrait of a lady by R. B. de Chair, 1⅝ in. high, reverse: mother-of-pearl, gilt, English, dated 1783. One of a pair with following portrait. Pair* **1500.00 1800.00**

□ **29** *Ivory miniature portrait of a gentleman by R. B. de Chair, 1⅝ in. high, reverse: mother-of-pearl, gilt, English, dated 1783. One of a pair with above portrait. Pair* **1500.00 1800.00**

□ **30** *Ivory miniature portrait of a gentleman by Peter Paillou, 2¾ in. high, reverse: plaited hair with "B" composed of seed pearls, gold, dated 1813* . **1000.00 1200.00**

□ **31** *Ivory miniature portrait of an infantry officer by Richard Bull, reverse: plaited hair with cutout "J N" and inscribed: "Born 30 June 1760", gold, dated 1787* **500.00 650.00**

☐ **32** *Ivory miniature portrait of a gentleman by Thomas Richmond, Jr., 1802-74, 2⅜ in. high, gilt, English, dated 1822* **600.00 800.00**

☐ **33** *Ivory miniature portrait of a gentleman by William John Thomson, 1771/3-1845, 2⅜ in. high, gilt, dated 1800* **450.00 650.00**

☐ **34** *Ivory miniature portrait of a gentleman by Charles G. Dillon, 2⅞ in. high, gold, c. 1810-30* ... **600.00 800.00**

☐ **35** *Ivory miniature portrait of a lady by Abraham Daniel, 2 in. high, silver, c. 1806* **1100.00 1400.00**

☐ **36** *Ivory miniature portrait of a gentleman by Joseph Daniel, 1760-1803, 2¾ in. high, gold* **1100.00 1400.00**

COLOR PLATE #1

COLOR PLATE #2

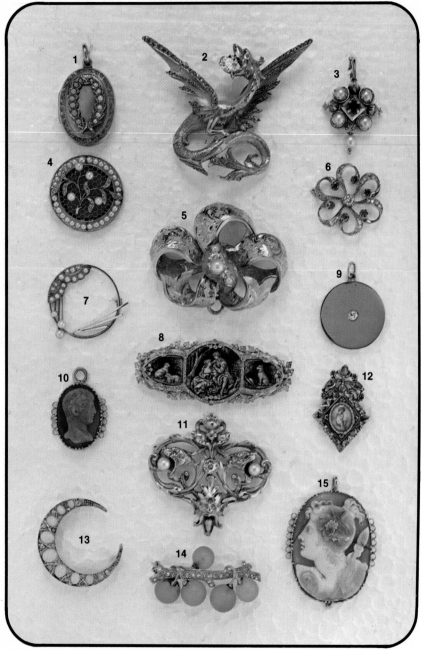

Courtesy: N. Bloom & Son (Antiques) Limited, London, England.

COLOR PLATE #3

Courtesy: N. Bloom & Son (Antiques) Limited, London, England.

GEMSTONE PLATE #1

GEMSTONE PLATE #2

COLOR PLATE #4

NECKLACE, *dyed horse-*
hair, c. 1860 . . . . 300.00 350.00

HAIR PENDANT, *Prince of*
Wales, c. 1865 . . . . 400.00 450.00

BROOCH, *stuffed humming bird, gold beak, ruby eyes, c. mid-Victorian.* 450.00 500.00

BROOCH OR PENDANT,
enamel portrait of a lady   1400.00 1600.00

☐ **37** *Ivory miniature portrait of a gentleman by J. T. Mitchell, 2⅞ in. high, gold, English, c. 1798-1830* . **700.00** **1000.00**

☐ **38** *Ivory miniature portrait of an officer by Abraham Daniel, 2¾ in. high, reverse: hair under glass, gilt, ivory cracked, c. 1806* **500.00** **650.00**

☐ **39** *Ivory miniature portrait of a gentleman by John Barry, 2⅝ in. high, reverse: hair under glass with initials "JH," gold, c. 1784-1827* **700.00** **900.00**

☐ **40** *Ivory miniature portrait of an officer of the 2nd Dragoon Guards by J. Burman, 2⅝ in. high, gold, c. 1802* **1000.00** **1250.00**

☐ **41** *Ivory miniature portrait of an officer of the 42nd Royal Highland Regiment, Black Watch, by Stephen Denney, 1⅝ in. high, gold, dated 1814* **1200.00** **1500.00**

☐ **42** *Ivory miniature portrait of a lady by Adam Buck, 1759-1833, 2¾ in. high, gold, dated 1802* **1600.00** **2000.00**

☐ **43** *Ivory miniature portrait of Master George Forrester by William Wood, 1769-1810, 3¼ in. high, gilt* **2500.00** **3000.00**

☐ **44** *Ivory miniature portrait of a gentleman by Andrew Plimer, 1763-1837, 2⅞ in. high, reverse: hair under glass, gold* **2200.00** **2600.00**

☐ **45** *Ivory miniature portrait of two sisters by Thomas Hobday, 3¼ in. high, reverse: plaited hair with "ED" and "AMD," gold* **2000.00** **2400.00**

☐ **46** *Ivory miniature portrait of Dr. and Mrs. James by Peter Stroeby, 1768-1826, 3¼ in. high, half-pearl border, gold* **6000.00** **6400.00**

47

48

49

49

50

51

52

53

54

☐ **50** *Ivory miniature portrait of a lady, four seed pearls, c. late 19th* **450.00** **650.00**

☐ **51** *Ivory miniature portrait of a lady, pavé rose diamonds in gold frame, signed: "Henri/28 Moi/1887"* **900.00** **1200.00**

☐ **52** *Ivory miniature portrait of a lady, flower motif frame, gold, c. mid to late 19th* **500.00** **600.00**

☐ **53** *Porcelain miniature portrait of a lady, diamonds and seed pearls in frame, pendant or brooch, silver, Hungarian, c. late 19th* **800.00** **900.00**

☐ **54** *Porcelain miniature portrait of Empress Marie-Louise, metal frame, inscribed on reverse: "To Ella-Esther Cohen 1901"* **40.00** **60.00**

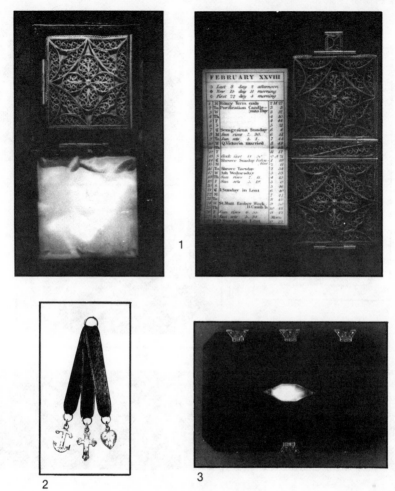

1

2

3

MISCELLANEOUS

		PRICE RANGE	
☐	**1** *Almanac miniature, silver filigree cover, fitted leather box, London, England, c. 1847*	350.00	400.00
☐	**2** *Bookmark, anchor, cross and heart in sterling silver, satin ribbon, 9 in. long, American, c. 1896* . . .	50.00	60.00
☐	**3** *Box, faceted black onyx, moonstone on top and thumbpiece, rose diamonds, platinum, Art Deco, c. 1930*	1500.00	1600.00

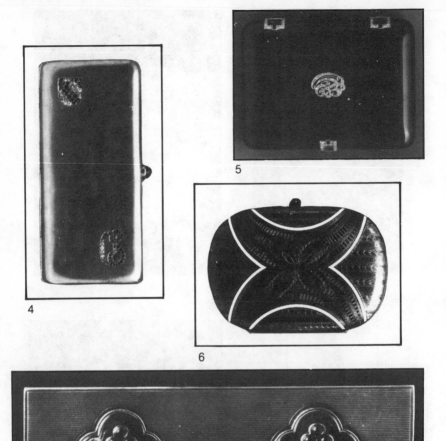

8

9

10

11

□ **8** Compact, translucent blue enamel, engraved, cabochon sapphire thumb-piece, gold, maker: Cartier, c. 1900-20 .... **1200.00 1500.00**

□ **9** Compact, engraved geometric motif, champlevé black enamel border, rose diamond square, cabochon sapphire thumb-piece, gold, c. 1910 .... **1000.00 1200.00**

□ **10** Diary, leather cover, finger shape, "De La Rue's Improved Condensed Diary and Engagement Book, edited by Edward Roberts, F.R.A.S., Chief Assistant at the 'Nautical Almanac' office," sterling silver holder made in Birmingham, England, registration number 320421, maker: HM, holder c. 1897, almanac c. 1899 .... **225.00 250.00**

□ **11** Earring covers or opera caps, , black enamel, gold, c. 1850 .... **400.00 450.00**

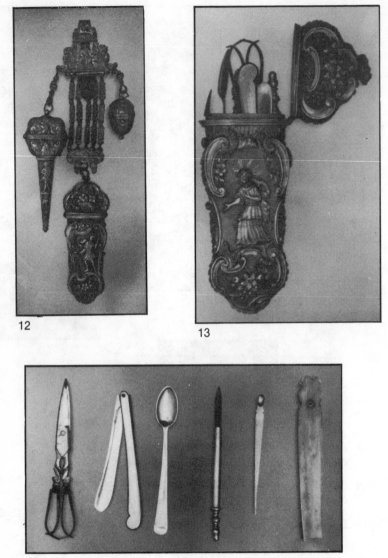

12

13

14

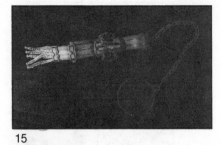

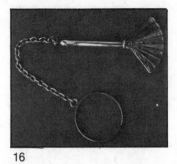

15

16

17

18

19

☐ **15** *Handkerchief or dress train holder, woven mesh bracelet motif, one seed pearl, black enamel, gold, c. 1850* **275.00** **325.00**

☐ **16** *Handkerchief or dress train holder, fan motif, gold, c. 1869* **100.00** **125.00**

☐ **17** *Lipstick holder with ring attached to chain, spinach green nephrite, 14K gold, c. 1920* **300.00** **400.00**

☐ **18** *Match safe, beaver motif lid, maple leaf motif container, obverse: shield for initials, reverse: Canadian crest, sterling silver, c. 1900* **250.00** **300.00**

☐ **19** *Match safe, cigar cutter base, Art Nouveau engraved initials, sterling silver, c. 1910* **150.00** **200.00**

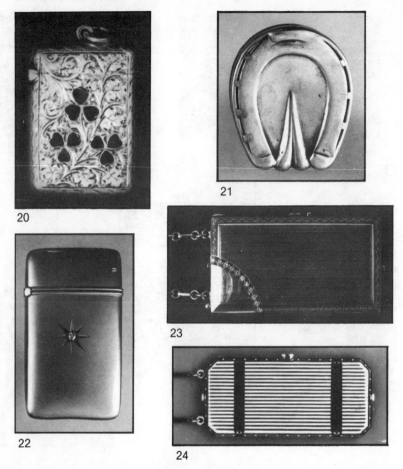

20

21

23

22

24

<table>
</table>

☐ **20** *Match safe, clover motif of green marble, en-graved case, silver, English, c. 1925* **100.00**   **150.00**

☐ **21** *Match safe, horseshoe motif, coin silver, Ameri-can, c. 1930*. **125.00**   **175.00**

☐ **22** *Match safe, star motif on plain case, one round diamond, 14K gold, American, c. 1920*. **400.00**   **600.00**

☐ **23** *Minaudiere, geometric motif, three compart-ments with mirror and money clip, engraved, 11 round diamonds, 20 calibre sapphires, platinum corner, 18K gold, c. 1920* **2400.00**   **2600.00**

☐ **24** *Minaudiere, geometric motif, engraved, cham-plevé black and white enamel, diamond thumb-piece, gold, c. 1920-30* **2500.00**   **3000.00**

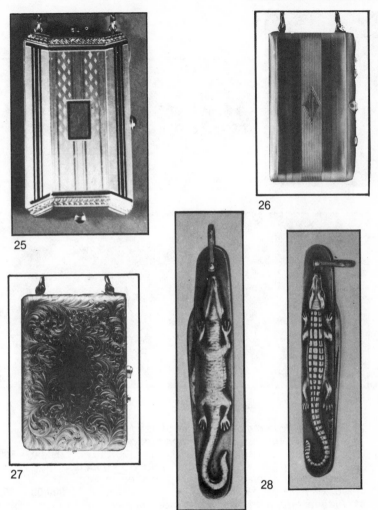

25

26

27

28

33   34   35   36

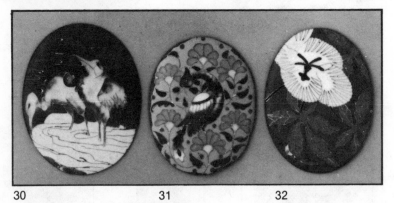

30   31   32

☐ **29** *Pill box, flower motif, mother-of-pearl top, colored stone flowers, rose diamond leaves, gold, c. 1900* **750.00   800.00**

☐ **30** *Plaque, bird motif, cloissoné enamel, copper with silver cloisonne wire, probable maker: Alexis Falize, c. 1870* **900.00   1000.00**

☐ **31** *Plaque, bird and flower motif, cloisonné enamel, copper with silver cloisonne wire, probable maker: Alexis Falize, c. 1870* **900.00   1000.00**

☐ **32** *Plaque, flower motif, cloissoné enamel, copper with silver cloisonne wire, probable maker: Alexis Falize, c. 1870* **900.00   1000.00**

☐ **33** *Plaque, warrior motif, translucent enamel on copper, c. 1870* **145.00   165.00**

☐ **34** *Plaque, bird motif, translucent enamel on copper, c. 1870* **135.00   155.00**

☐ **35** *Plaque, bird motif, translucent enamel on copper, c. 1870* **135.00   155.00**

☐ **36** *Plaque, lake motif, enamel on copper, c. 1870* ... **120.00   130.00**

37

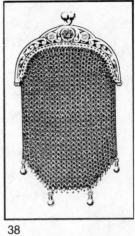

38

39

40

☐ **37** *Purse, leather, basket and flower motif, rose diamonds, gold, c. 1930* 300.00   400.00

☐ **38** *Purse, mesh, three round diamonds in openwork frame, 14K gold, c. 1903-04* 400.00   600.00

☐ **39** *Purse, mesh, hinged expandable frame, 14K gold, c. 1903-04* 450.00   500.00

☐   *Same as above but sterling silver* 125.00   150.00

☐ **40** *Purse, mesh, seven cabochon turquoise and four round diamonds in openwork ribbon motif frame, gold, Art Nouveau, maker: Black, Star and Frost, American, c. 1900* 3000.00   3500.00

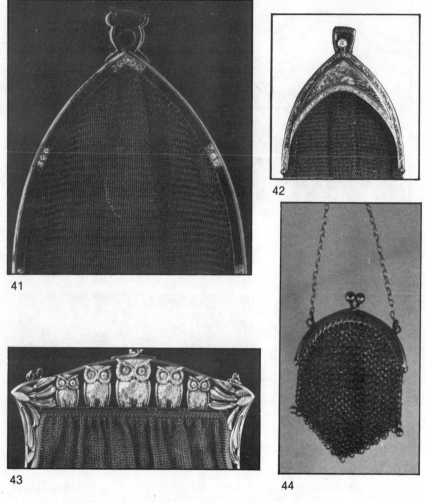

41

42

43

44

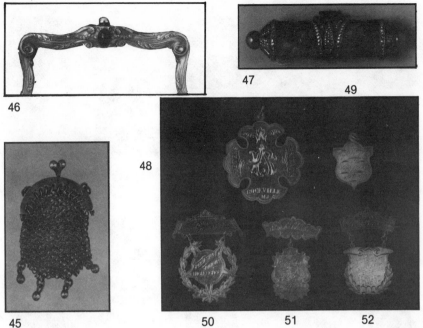

46

47

49

48

45

50   51   52

☐ **45** *Purse, mesh miniature, sterling silver, American, c. early 20th* **35.00   65.00**

☐ **46** *Purse frame, scroll motif, moonstones, half pearls, round diamonds, orange tourmaline scarab, gold, maker: Spaulding & Co., Art Nouveau, c. 1902* **1800.00   1900.00**

☐ **47** *Purse handle, lapis lazuli, green onyx, cut steel, sterling silver, Art Deco, c. 1930* **200.00   225.00**

☐ **48** *School award, gold, pendant, Rockville, Maryland, American, c. 1900* **65.00   75.00**

☐ **49** *School award, obverse: "For regular attendance at Sunday School 1905 to 1920," reverse: "Presented to Dora E. Grimes by First Lutheran S.S. Dec. 25, 1919," gold, charm, American, c. 1920* .. **30.00   35.00**

☐ **50** *School award, obverse: "General Excellency, Green Street Junior High School," reverse: "Queen City Council No. 49 Jr. O.V.A.M.," gold, brooch, maker: Peters, American, c. 1900* **65.00   80.00**

☐ **51** *School award, obverse: "Blanche Schlichter, Presented by Prof. H. M. Bell May 7, 1901," gold, brooch, American, c. 1901* **40.00   45.00**

☐ **52** *School award, obverse: "C.E.L.S.S. Geo. E. Emmerich Regular Attendance 1902 1903 1904," reverse: "With approval of Miss Cora Wraver, Baltimore," gold, brooch, American, c. 1904* **45.00   50.00**

53

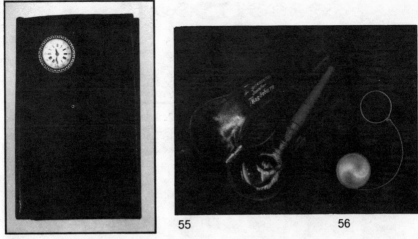

54

55   56

<table>
<tr><td>☐</td><td>54</td><td>Wallet, leather, keywind watch, white porcelain face, one diamond set in minute hand, c. 1890...</td><td>350.00</td><td>425.00</td></tr>
<tr><td>☐</td><td>55</td><td>Pipe, carved tiger-eye bowl, sterling silver eagle claw stem, amber mouthpiece, fitted leather box, English, c. early 20th ....</td><td>250.00</td><td>300.00</td></tr>
<tr><td>☐</td><td>56</td><td>Yo-Yo miniature, gold filled, ¾ in. diameter, fitted leather box, c. 20th ....</td><td>200.00</td><td>250.00</td></tr>
</table>

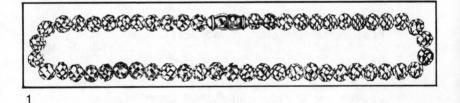

1

NECKLACES

BEADS

PRICE RANGE

☐ **1** *Amber, round faceted beads, screw clasp, c. 1896.....................................*   85.00   125.00

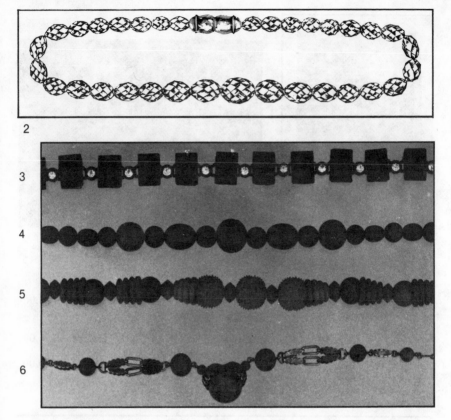

☐ **2** *Amber, graduated oval faceted beads, screw clasp, c. 1896* **120.00** **150.00**

☐ **3** *Art Deco, faceted black glass rectangles, oval faceted pastes, black metal mountings, 15 in. long, Czechoslovakian, c. 1920-30* **35.00** **45.00**

☐ **4** *Art Deco, oval and round bittersweet amber colored plastic beads, 15½ in. long, c. 1920-30* **15.00** **25.00**

☐ **5** *Art Deco, fancy shaped pumpkin, orange and amber colored plastic beads, 16½ in. long, c. 1920-30* **25.00** **35.00**

☐ **6** *Art Deco, round jade green ceramic beads spaced with white metal fancy links, 15½ in. long, c. 1920-30* **25.00** **35.00**

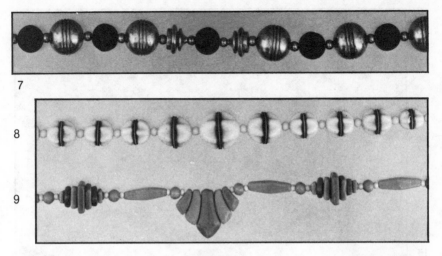

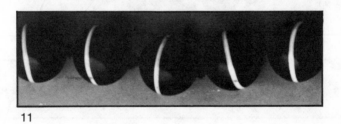

☐	7	Art Deco, fancy shape aluminum and round black glass beads, 16½ in. long, c. 1920-30	85.00	125.00
☐	8	Art Deco, fancy shape green and white plastic beads, 20 in. long, c. 1920-30	35.00	45.00
☐	9	Art Deco, geometric motif, beige, apple green and white plastic beads, 17 in. long, c. 1920-30 . .	25.00	35.00
☐	10	Art Deco, three pendants of round pastes sandwiched between two round amber glass beads, chain of small cherry red plastic tubes, 22½ in. long, c. 1920-30	20.00	30.00
☐	11	Banded black and white onyx beads, c. 19th	350.00	400.00

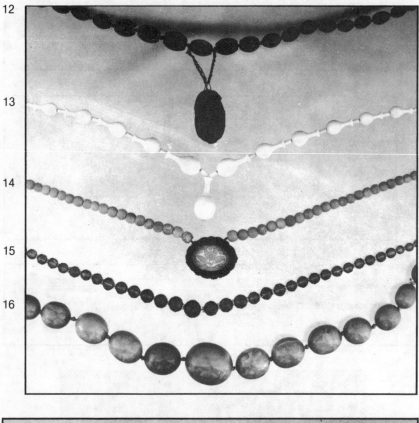

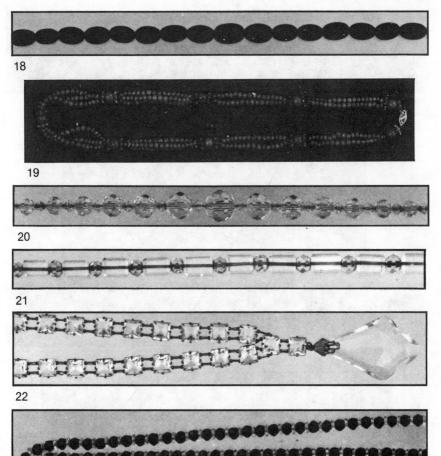

24

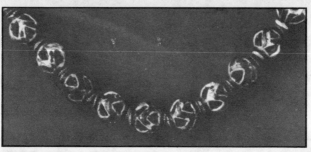

25

26

27

☐ **24** *Faceted beads, flower motif clasp, gold, c. 19th* . **600.00** **800.00**
☐ **25** *Indian champlevé translucent red, green and blue enamel beads, gold, c. 19th* **800.00** **1000.00**
☐ **26** *Jade beads spaced with carved carnelian beads, c. early 20th* **400.00** **550.00**
☐ **27** *Jade beads, 73 ranging from 6MM to 7MM, c. early 20th* **1600.00** **2200.00**

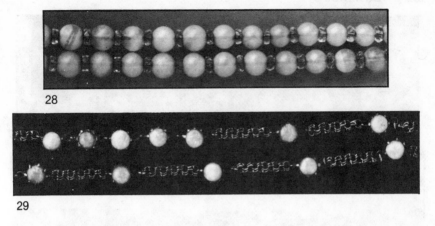

28

29

☐ **28** Opal beads, 43 alternating with faceted crystal
   rondelles, opal bead clasp, c. 1890 .... **1200.00 1500.00**
☐ **29** Opal beads in silver, spaced with contemporary
   curb link chain, gold, c. 1820 .... **1000.00 1200.00**

1

CHOKERS

PRICE RANGE

☐ **1** Art Nouveau scroll links, lozenge-shape peridots,
   54 old mine diamonds approximately 4.50 cts.,
   forms two bracelets, maker: Harvey & Gore, English, c. late 19th **5500.00 6000.00**

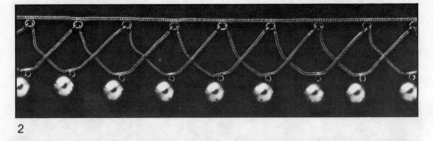

2

3

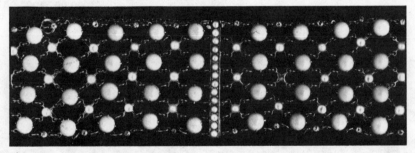

4

☐ **2** *Festoon and ball choker, foxtail link chain, gold,*
c. 1860 . . . . **1200.00 1500.00**

☐ **3** *Fire opal choker, 25 faceted marquise, emerald*
and hexagonal-shape fire opals alternating with
rose diamonds **3000.00 3600.00**

☐ **4** *Open mesh choker, round cabochon turquoise,*
button pearls, round diamonds, gold, forms two
bracelets, c. 1895 . . . . **3000.00 3200.00**

5

6

7

□ **5** *Seed pearl choker, 14 strands, three gold bars with half pearls, c. 1900* **1200.00 1400.00**

□ **6** *Snake choker, one pear-shape pink sapphire, two half-pearls and two rose diamonds set in enamelled head, scale-link chain, gold, English, c. 1840* **1400.00 1800.00**

□ **7** *Snake choker, cabochon turquoise body, cabochon ruby eyes, rose diamonds in head, gold, English, c. early 19th* **6000.00 8000.00**

8

9

10

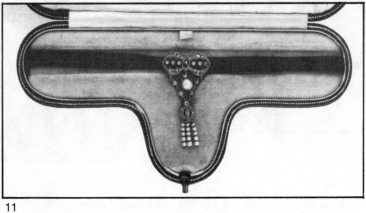

11

- ☐ **8** *Snake choker, snake link chain, ruby eyes, contemporary baroque pearl pendant, gold, c. 1870* . **1500.00 1800.00**
- ☐ **9** *Velvet ribbon choker with cut-out slide, 39 round diamonds, platinum, c. early 1870* **1200.00 1600.00**
- ☐ **10** *Velvet ribbon choker with cut-out slide and tassel, rose diamonds, one baroque pearl and 15 seed pearls, fitted leather box, platinum, English, c. 1900* **1400.00 1800.00**
- ☐ **11** *Velvet ribbon choker with floral cutout slide, one round diamond approx. 2.25 cts., rose and round diamonds, platinum, c. 1900* **20000.00 23000.00**

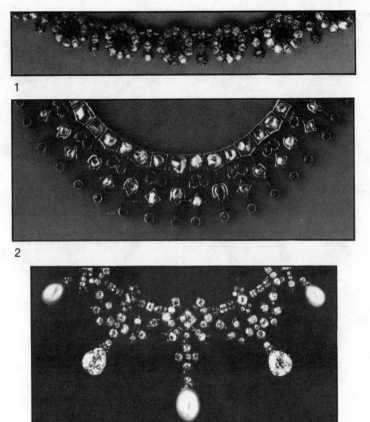

1

2

3

DIAMOND

PRICE RANGE

☐ **1** *Cluster motif, 24 clusters of old mine diamonds surrounding one round blue sapphire per cluster, three old mine diamonds between each cluster, a total of 264 old mine diamonds approx. 14.75 cts., silver, gold, maker: Frazier & Haws, c. mid 19th . . .* **25000.00 30000.00**

☐ **2** *Collar necklace, rose diamonds, rubies, forms pair of bracelets, gold, silver, c. 1840 . . . .* **2600.00 3200.00**

☐ **3** *Flower and bow motif, seven pearl pendants, two pear-shape diamonds approx. 5.25 cts., two smaller pear-shape, 189 round and old mine diamonds approx. 19.50 cts., rose diamonds, silver, gold, c. mid 19th . . . .* **19500.00 20500.00**

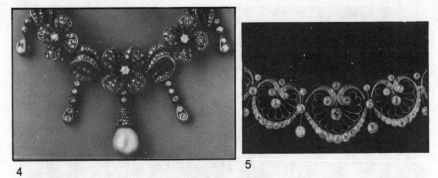

4 5

6

☐ **4** *Flower motif, one large baroque cultured pearl
     approx. 13.5MM by 15.3MM, rose diamonds, 25
     old mine diamonds, silver, gold, c. mid 19th* **6000.00 8000.00**

☐ **5** *Openwork motif, 199 old mine, rose and round
     diamonds, platinum, detachable tiara support,
     c. late 19th* **7000.00 9000.00**

☐ **6** *Renaissance motif, 21 clusters with large rose
     diamonds surrounded with round diamonds,
     translucent enamelled mermaids and angels, re-
     verse: openwork and pierced, forms choker,
     brooch or pendant, 32 in. long, maker: Tiffany &
     Co., French, c. late 19th* **80000.00 90000.00**

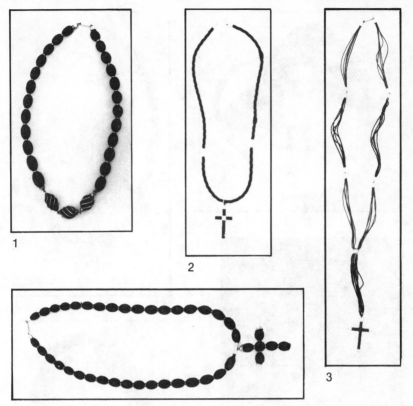

HAIR
All items made from hair referred to throughout this section are of brunette human hair unless stated otherwise.

			PRICE RANGE	
☐	1	*Ball motif chain, woven hair, gold fittings and barrel clasp, c. 1850-70*	110.00	140.00
☐	2	*Cross motif, woven and braided hair, gold fittings and barrel clasp, 17 in. long, c. 1850-70*	100.00	125.00
☐	3	*Cross motif, tightly woven chains of different brunette shades of hair, engraved gold fittings and barrel clasp, 22½ in. long, c. 1800-40*	300.00	325.00
☐	4	*Cross motif, wooden molds removed from woven hair to form ball motif chain, gold fittings and barrel clasp, 21 in. long, c. 1850-70*	125.00	150.00

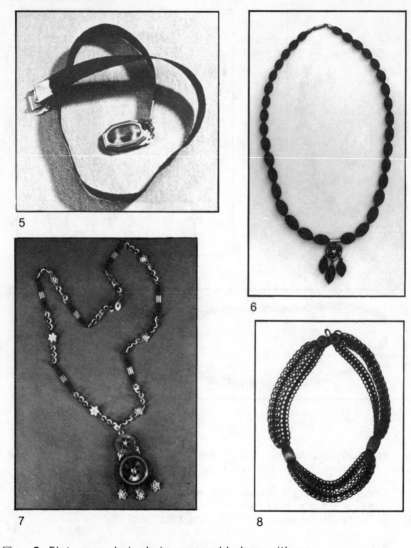

5

6

7

8

1

2

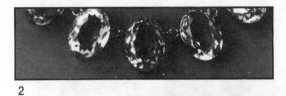

3

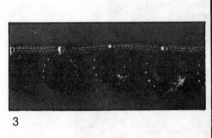

4

MISCELLANEOUS

PRICE RANGE

☐ **1** *Agate tubular motif, wide trace link chain, 15K gold, English, c. 1880* 375.00 450.00
☐ **2** *Amethyst necklace, oval amethysts, gold, c. 1860* 800.00 1000.00
☐ **3** *Amethyst necklace, round amethysts suspended from a foxtail chain, gold, c. 1850* 1200.00 1400.00
☐ **4** *Amethyst necklace, cushion-cut amethysts surrounded by seed pearls, one pear-shape amethyst surrounded by seed pearls and small round amethysts drops, foxtail chain, gold, fitted leather box inscribed: D. Sapio, Nice, France, hallmarks, c. 1830* 4000.00 4500.00

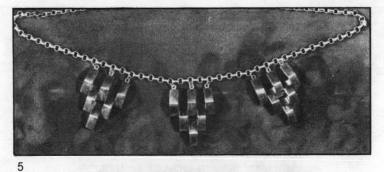

5

6

7

☐ **5** *Art Deco triple pendant necklace, 14K gold, American, c. 1930* **650.00   800.00**

☐ **6** *Bacchantes and grape cluster motif, carved coral, gold, c. 1860* **2500.00   3000.00**

☐ **7** *Bird and flower motif, 26 openwork panels in green, yellow and rose gold, maker: Tiffany, New York, c. 1875* **20000.00 22000.00**

8

9

10

☐ **8** Black onyx carved rectangular link alternating with gold link chain, oval faceted medallion with glass locket reverse, gold sheaf of wheat motif with seed pearls centered on medallion, gold, c. 1880 . . . . **600.00   900.00**

☐ **9** Bog oak motif, ovals carved with scenes of Irish castles, c. 1850-70 . . . . **250.00   350.00**

☐ **10** Cabochon emerald, surrounded by nine cabochon rubies in each of 15 panels with enamelled sides and back, plaited thread chain, gold, Indian, c. 19th **1500.00 2000.00**

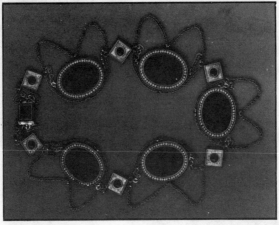

11

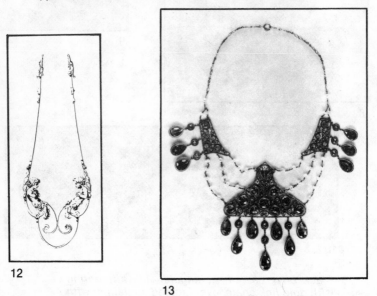

12

13

☐ **11** *Carnelian plaque motif, seed pearls, cabochon carnelians in square links, gold, English, c. 1830 .* **2800.00 3000.00**

☐ **12** *Cherubs with leaf feet on scroll motif, silver, designed by: A. Ortwein, Germany, c. 1873 . . . .* **1500.00 2000.00**

☐ **13** *Citrine pear-shape pendants dangling from three plaques, ten fancy-cut peridots and six round diamonds in center plaque, fancy link chains spaced with baroque pearls, 18K gold, c. late 19th . . . .* **3000.00 3500.00**

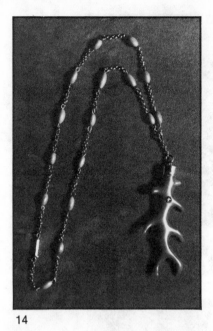

14

15

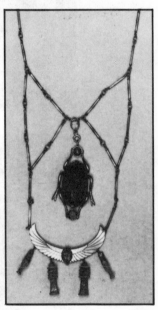

16

17

☐	**14** Coral egg-shape beads spaced in simple 18 in. link chain, branch coral pendant with one round diamond, gold, English, c. 1870	**265.00**	**365.00**
☐	**15** Crown and festooned motif, two round, one oval and one pear-shape amethyst, 14K gold, American, c. late 19th	**650.00**	**850.00**
☐	**16** Egyptian motif, carved lapis lazuli scarab, turquoise, gold, c. 1920	**850.00**	**1000.00**
☐	**17** Emeralds, buff-top emeralds, table-cut diamonds, baroque pearls, champleve enamelled red flowers with green and white background on the reverse of the links, gold, Indian, c. 19th	**5500.00**	**6500.00**
☐	Same as above, along with similar ear pendants in fitted leather box	**6000.00**	**7000.00**

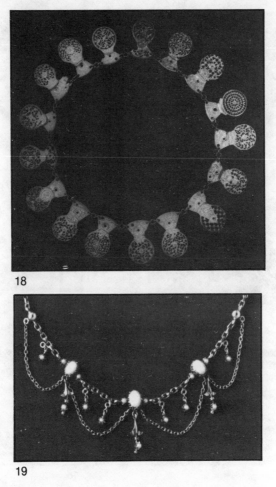

18

19

20

22

21

☐ **20** *Festoon motif, 15 cabochon turquoise in fancy links with seed pearls spaced in chains and as clusters, ten fresh water pearl pendants, 14K gold, American, c. 1890* **1500.00 1800.00**

☐ **21** *Festoon and pendant motif, 789 rose and old mine diamonds approx. 26 cts., ten oval, four pear-shape and three round amethyst approx. 20 cts., gold, French, c. 1850* **20000.00 25000.00**

☐ **22** *Floral wreath motif, enamel blue center plaque surrounded by 23 old mine diamonds, three round faceted garnet drops surrounded with rose diamonds, 14K gold, American, c. 19th* **1600.00 2000.00**

23

24

25

☐ **23** *Flower motif, oval cabochon opals, demantoid garnets, Art Nouveau, c. 1900* 4000.00 4200.00
☐ **24** *Flowers and fleur-de-lys motif, enameled, seven pearls, gold, Art Nouveau, c. 1890-1910* 550.00 800.00
☐ **25** *Flower and leaf motif links, hanging pearls, gold pendants, gold, German, c. 1866* 1800.00 2200.00

26

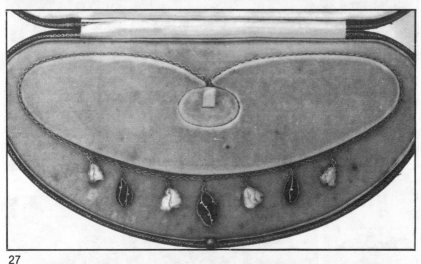

27

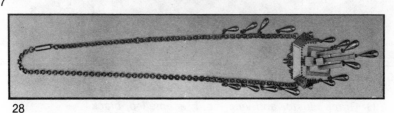

28

☐ **26** *Flower and leaf motif collar necklace, robin-egg blue enamel panels with applied gold asters and leaves joined by flowers with diamond, ruby or pearl centers, gold, signed: S. Grunfeld, c. late 19th* **3300.00 3800.00**

☐ **27** *Fresh water pearls and amethyst pendants in gold cages on a plain link chain in fitted leather box marked: "Weedon, 164 Sloan St., S.W.," 15K gold, English, c. early 20th* **475.00 575.00**

☐ **28** *Geometric hinged pendant motif, 14 teardrops on link chain, gold, c. late 19th* **600.00 800.00**

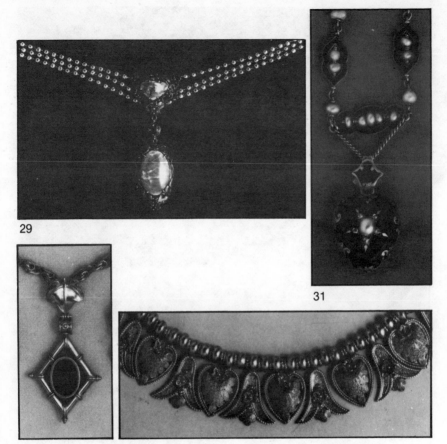

29

30   32

☐ **29** *Grape cluster and vine motif, enamelled, black
        opals, sapphires and demantoid garnets in cen-
        ter pendant and necklace, gold bead chains,
        gold, Arts and Crafts style, signed: Tiffany & Co.,,
        American, c. late 19th* **35000.00 40000.00**
☐ **30** *Hardstone intaglio in square tubular frame at-
        tached with carved leaf to fancy link chain, gold,
        c. 1860-80* **2000.00   2500.00**
☐ **31** *Heart motif, blue enamel, five rose diamonds
        around one half-pearl, gold chain spaced with
        pearls and three blue enamel modified oval
        frames around pearls, c. mid 19th* **2800.00   3500.00**
☐ **32** *Heart and flower motif links on gold bead neck-
        lace, double-heart clasp, c. 1850* **3200.00   3800.00**

33

34

35

☐ **33** Heart pendant with angel head motif, curb chain, gold, German, c. 1870 .... **2000.00** **2500.00**

☐ **34** Ivory medallion and curved links, silver, Chinese, c. 1900-20 .... **250.00** **400.00**

☐ **35** Jade, seven pierced and carved oval medallions separated by rose diamonds in oval scroll motif links, white gold, c. early 20th **3500.00** **3800.00**

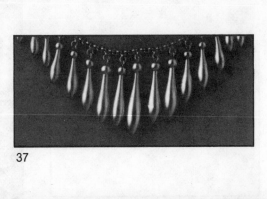

37

38

36

☐	**36** *Japanese motif locket, book link chain, silver, maker: S. Bros., Birmingham, England, c. 1883* ..	**350.00**	**400.00**
☐	**37** *Juggling pin motif, 41 graduated juggling pin shaped pendants, gold, c. late 19th*	**1200.00**	**1500.00**
☐	**38** *Ladies and birds motif, carved coral, teardrop pendants, floral motif links, gold, c. 1860*	**2000.00**	**2500.00**

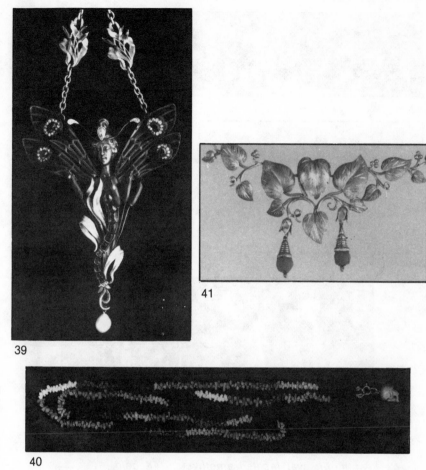

39

41

40

□ **39** Lady with dragonfly wing motif, green and blue
plique-a-jour wings with one calibre sapphire surrounded by rose diamonds, one Holland-rose diamond set in hair of lady, 11 calibre sapphires in
tail, two baroque pearls, opaque enamelled cat-
tails, detachable pin and chain, gold, Art Nou-
veau, c. late 19th **18000.00 22000.00**

□ **40** Lava carved as crossbones with short branch
coral, 29 in. long, carved grey lava skull pendant,
Italian, c. mid 19th **300.00   350.00**

□   Same as above but carved grey lava skull
charm only **75.00   100.00**

□ **41** Leaf motif, two faceted coral beads, 15K gold,
English, c. 1850 . . . . **900.00   1100.00**

42

43

44

45

☐ **42** *Leaf motif, oval faceted amethysts, 14K gold, American, c. 1900* **1200.00** **1500.00**

☐   *Same as above, along with similar bracelet and earrings* **2500.00** **2800.00**

☐ **43** *Leaf and heart motif, one heart-shape and one pear-shape peridot with baroque pearls set in center, two round and one pear-shape peridot with baroque pearls on either side of center, 14K gold, American, c. 1900* **750.00** **850.00**

☐ **44** *Leaf and swirl motif, translucent green and yellow enamel, one oval and two round faceted peridots, one large baroque pearl suspended from center, smaller baroque pearls spaced in chain, 14K gold, Art Nouveau, American, c. 1890-1910* .. **600.00** **800.00**

☐ **45** *Malachite necklace, malachite beads and six malachite pendants in gold caps with Etruscan granulation, gold, c. mid 19th* **800.00** **1000.00**

46

47

48

49

☐ **46** *Micro mosaic of two angels with blue enamel border and seed pearls c. 18th, scroll motif neck-lace with seed pearls, gold, c. 19th* **4000.00** **4800.00**

☐ **47** *Moonstones, oval cabochon moonstones in pen-dant and spaced in chain, round sapphires sur-rounding pendant and spaced in chain, white gold, signed: Tiffany & Co., American, c. early 20th* **3500.00** **4000.00**

☐ **48** *Mosaic beetle motif, silver gilt, c. early 20th* **250.00** **300.00**

☐ **49** *Mosaic motif, oval and pear-shape pendants, fox-tail chain, gold-plated metal, Italian, c. mid 20th* .. **150.00** **300.00**

50

51

52

53

55

54

□ **52** *Onyx cameos of 12 Roman Senators, 48 round diamonds approx. 2.50 cts., gold, c. 1870* **5500.00 6000.00**

□ **53** *Openwork flower motif, one round peridot in each link and pendant, seed pearls, gold, c. 1915* **1400.00 1600.00**

□ **54** *Pink topaz necklace, fancy scroll motif links, each with one oval foil-back pink topaz, c. 1810* .. **1800.00 2200.00**

□ **55** *Priestess motif, green and blue enamel, bar link chain, gold, 3¾ in. long, Art Nouveau, maker: Rene Lalique, French, c. late 19th* **30000.00 35000.00**

56

57

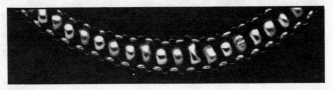

58

☐ **56** Rock crystal carved discs alternating with carnelian carved discs, gold links, c. 1920 . . . . **600.00   800.00**

☐ **57** Rosette motif, seven cabochon turquoise rosettes, gold, forms pair of bracelets, gold, c. 1840 **1600.00   2000.00**

☐ **58** Round large engraved links sandwiched between small oval links, gold, Russian, c. 1875-1900 . . . . **1200.00   1500.00**

59

60

62

61

□ **59** *Sapphires, four cabochon sapphires surrounded with seed pearls, four half-pearls in center pendant, white gold, c. 19th* **2000.00 3000.00**

□ **60** *Satsuma medallions depicting birds, flowers and butterflies, each link marked "FS," white metal, Oriental, c. 19th* **600.00 800.00**

□ **61** *Scotch agate, various colors, 15K gold mounts, English, c. 1860* **700.00 800.00**

□ **62** *Shell broad collar motif, whole and cut shell, brass beads, hand-knotted with silk thread, Pacific Islands, c. early 20th* **150.00 250.00**

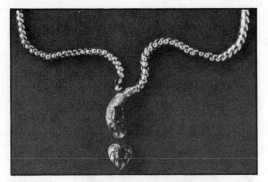

63

64

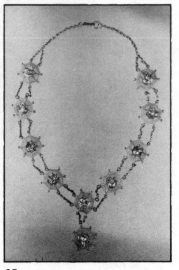

65

☐ **63** *Snake motif, oval-cut garnet in head with cabochon garnet eyes, square-cut garnet in heart pendant, scale link chain, c. 1840* **1200.00 1800.00**

☐ **64** *Snake and heart motif, two pear-shape garnets, seed pearls, ruby eyes, gold, c. 1840* **1400.00 1800.00**

☐ **65** *Spider and spiderweb motif, ten spiderwebs connected with simple link chain, 16½ in. long, silver, English, c. late 19th* **150.00 250.00**

66

67

68

69

☐ **66** *Teardrop motif, corals suspended from fancy gold links, c. 1900* 600.00 800.00

☐ **67** *Topaz, 30 graduated topaz, collet-set, gold, c. 1860* 2000.00 2500.00

☐ **68** *Turquoise baroque beads, 9K gold, English, c. 20th* 250.00 300.00

☐ **69** *Turquoise baroque beads, 18K gold, English, c. 20th* 350.00 375.00

70

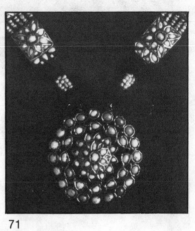

71

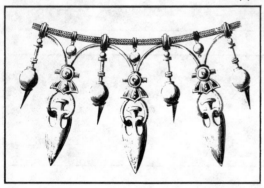

72

1

2

3

PEARLS

		PRICE RANGE	
☐	**1** *Crescent and flower links, seed pearls, rope twist chain, gold, c. 1850*	**800.00**	**900.00**
☐	**2** *Cultured pearls, single strand, small round diamond in gold clasp, c. late 19th*	**1600.00**	**1800.00**
☐	**3** *Emerald drop and emerald beads with button-shape pearls spaced on 2.0MM seed pearl strands, gold, c. 1920*	**2300.00**	**2800.00**

4

5

6

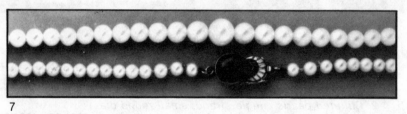

7

☐ **8** Moonstones, cabochon cut, in center, seed pearls, gold beads, c. mid 19th	**1000.00**	**1300.00**
☐ **9** Openwork pendant with one small round diamond and a fresh water pearl drop attached to a double link chain spaced with seed pearls, Art Nouveau motif circle, gold, c. 1900	**400.00**	**500.00**
☐ **10** Ribbon motif woven seed pearl necklace with rose diamonds in ends, large cushion-cut aquamarine pendant with rose diamonds, gold, platinum, necklace c. 1870, pendant c. 1920	**4500.00**	**5500.00**
☐ **11** Ribbon motif woven seed pearl necklace, gold clasp, c. 1870	**600.00**	**800.00**

12

13

14

☐ **12** *Single strand motif, 96 graduated natural pearls, eight old mine diamonds approximately .75 ct. set in clasp, silver topped gold, c. 19th* **2000.00   2500.00**

☐ **13** *Star and flower motif, pave seed pearls, round diamonds in center of stars and flowers approx. 2.0 cts., seed pearl link chain, 15K gold, two pendants or brooches with detachable pins, English, c. 1870-80* **4800.00   5600.00**

☐ **14** *Tassels of seed pearls, 14 strands of seed pearls, rose diamonds, colored stones, silver.* **3400.00   4000.00**

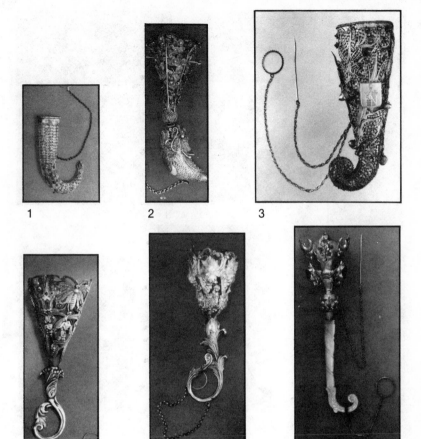

NOSEGAY HOLDERS

		PRICE RANGE	
☐	**1** *Filigree circle motif, miniature converted to pin, silver, c. 19th*	50.00	75.00
☐	**2** *Filigree fish motif handle, silver, c. 19th*	500.00	550.00
☐	**3** *Filigree oak leaf and acorn motif, shield with crest, silver, c. 19th*	400.00	450.00
☐	**4** *Cutout butterfly motif, silver, c. 19th*	200.00	250.00
☐	**5** *Cutout grape leaf motif, silver, c. 19th*	200.00	250.00
☐	**6** *Cutout motif, two round amethysts, carved mother-of-pearl handle, 18K gold, c. 19th*	1200.00	1400.00

1

2

3

4

5

6

PENDANTS

DIAMOND

PRICE RANGE

☐ **1** *Black onyx center border, missing marquise-shape diamond center, round diamonds, platinum, c. 1900* **2000.00 2500.00**

☐ **2** *Cross, 95 round diamonds approx. 10.0 cts., fancy link chain, gold, c. 1850* **8000.00 10000.00**

☐ **3** *Cross, 11 old mine diamonds approx. 11.0 cts., gold, pendant or brooch, c. 1870* **7000.00 9000.00**

☐ **4** *Cross, 11 foil-back rose diamonds, gold, c. 1840 .* **350.00 400.00**

☐ **5** *Cross, one oval sapphire, 39 old mine diamonds approx. 2.0 cts., silver, gold, c. 1840* **1700.00 1800.00**

☐ **6** *Cultured pearl center, openwork motif, 13 rose diamonds in leaf design, 36 round diamonds set around pearl and border, platinum, c. 1900* **1500.00 1800.00**

7

8

9

10

11

12

13

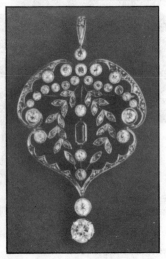

14

15

☐ **12** *Openwork flower motif, 201 round diamonds, two marquise-shape diamonds, all approx. 3.50 cts., platinum, brooch or pendant, c. 1900* **2500.00 3500.00**

☐ **13** *Openwork leaf motif, two old mine diamonds approx. 2.40 cts., 102 small old mine diamonds, gold, platinum, brooch or pendant, c. 1900* **8000.00 10000.00**

☐ **14** *Openwork leaf motif, 27 round diamonds approx. 2.40 cts., one emerald-cut emerald, pendant or brooch, gold, platinum, c. 1910* **3500.00 4000.00**

☐ **15** *Openwork leaf motif, four marquise-shape and 136 round diamonds approx. 3.0 cts., platinum, c. 1910* **5500.00 6500.00**

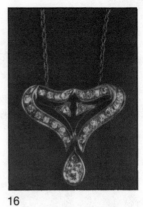

16

17

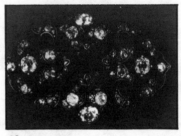

18

19

☐ **16** *Ribbon motif, 28 round diamonds approx. 1.10 cts., pendant or brooch, gold, c. 1900* **1200.00 1400.00**

☐ **17** *Scroll motif, 31 round diamonds, platinum, c. 1900* **600.00 800.00**

☐ **18** *Scroll motif, one round diamond approx. .60 ct., 93 old mine diamonds approx. 2.75 cts., platinum topped gold, c. 1880* **2800.00 3800.00**

☐ **18** *Shield motif, scissor-cut emerald approx. 2.75 cts. in center, four old mine diamonds approx. 3.75 cts., 30 rose diamonds, gold topped silver, c.1840* **5000.00 6000.00**

☐ **19** *Sunburst motif, 38 round diamonds approx. 3.50 cts., gold topped silver, c. 1840* **3000.00 3500.00**

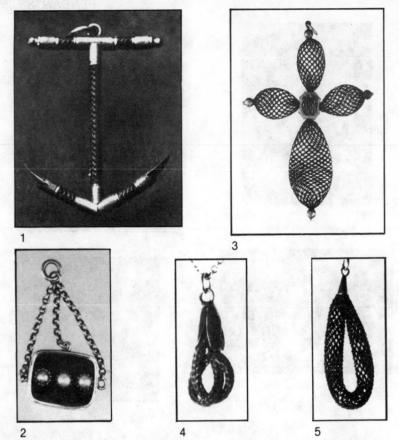

1

3

2

4

5

HUMAN HAIR

All items made from hair referred to throughout this section are of brunette human hair unless stated otherwise.

PRICE RANGE

☐ **1** *Anchor motif, woven hair over metal tube, engraved gold fittings, c. 19th* **160.00** **180.00**

☐ **2** *Black enamel motif with three half seed pearls on obverse, reverse: black enamel "It Is The Lord 22 Sep. 1823," inside: Prince of Wales feathers of hair and gold wire, hinged glass cover and inscription: "Set not your affections on the things of this World," gold, English, c. 1823* **600.00** **650.00**

☐ **3** *Cross motif, woven hair, gold ball tips and center plaque with cobalt-blue enamel monogram, English, c. 1850-70* **140.00** **160.00**

☐ **4** *Flower motif, woven and braided hair, gold filled cap, c. 1850-70* **20.00** **30.00**

☐ **5** *Loop motif, woven hair, gold filled cap, c. 1850-70* **30.00** **40.00**

6

7

8

9

☐ **6** *Miniature of doves symbolizing love and peace, branches and arrows painted with dissolved and cut and paste hair on ivory plaque, sterling silver, English, c. 1860* 350.00 400.00

☐ **7** *Miniature of gravesite by river with trees, cross and heart painted with dissolved hair and sepia paint on porcelain plaque, faceted black onyx frame, gold fittings, English, c. 1860-80* 500.00 550.00

☐ **8** *Ribbed dangle with shield motif, gold, French, c. mid 19th* 275.00 350.00

☐ **9** *Seed pearl border and monogram, basket weave hair under glass, pendant or brooch, leather covered boxwood box, English, c. 1790-1800* 450.00 500.00

1

3

2

4

5

MISCELLANEOUS

PRICE RANGE

☐ **1** *Agate cameo of a lion, lion is yellow with grey background, gold, c. late 17th* **4500.00 5000.00**

☐ **2** *Amethyst: emerald-cut and marquise-shape, round diamonds, white gold, c. 1915* **2400.00 2600.00**

☐ **3** *Amethyst: cushion-cut, carved oak leaf frame, fancy link chain, gold, maker: Tiffany & Co., American, c. 1900* **3000.00 3500.00**

☐ **4** *Anchor motif, 11 seed pearls, 12 in. chain, 14K gold, American, c. 1894-95* **90.00 120.00**

☐ **5** *Bell motif, opaque white enamel, two round corn-flower blue sapphires, seed pearls, gold, c. 1915 .* **325.00 375.00**

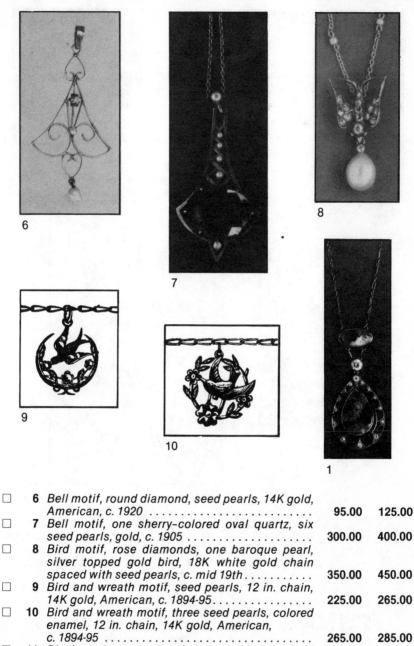

6

7

8

9

10

1

12

13

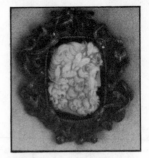

14

15

16

☐	**12**	Bow and cross motif, square and calibre-cut emeralds, gold, Spanish, c. mid 18th	1600.00	1800.00
☐	**13**	Cameo of a mythological figure, carved snake frame, gold, c. 19th	2200.00	2500.00
☐	**14**	Circle motif, cabochon turquoise, 15K gold, English, c. early 20th	300.00	335.00
☐	**15**	Circle cutout motif, two half pearls, one oval cabochon opal, one faceted Mexican opal, gold, Arts & Crafts MVT., c. 1905	600.00	650.00
☐	**16**	Citizenship medal, red and white opaque enamel, silver, Eastern European, c. 1891	250.00	300.00

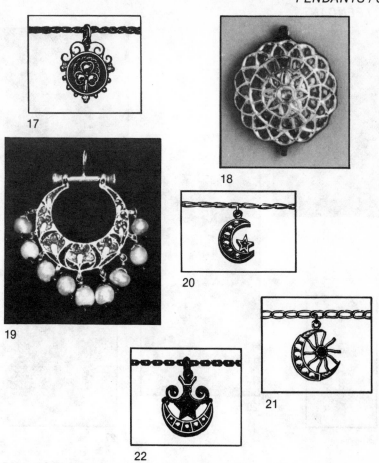

17

18

20

21

22

☐ **17** *Clover flower motif, three seed pearls, 12 in.*
chain, 14K gold, American, c. 1894-95 .... **125.00** **150.00**

☐ **18** *Cluster motif, cabochon rubies, diamonds, re-*
verse: opaque white enamel with translucent red
and green enamel flowers, Indian, c. 19th **450.00** **550.00**

☐ **19** *Crescent motif, nine rose diamonds, nine ba-*
roque pearls, reverse: red and green enamel, 20K
gold, Indian, c. 19th **1400.00** **1600.00**

☐ **20** *Crescent and star motif, one turquoise, six seed*
pearls, 12 in. chain, 14K gold, American, c. 1894-95 **125.00** **150.00**

☐ **21** *Crescent and star motif, one round ruby, six seed*
pearls, 12 in. chain, 14K gold, American, c. 1894-95 **90.00** **120.00**

☐ **22** *Crescent and star motif, one round ruby, five*
seed pearls, 12 in. chain, 14K gold, American,
c. 1894-95 .... **200.00** **245.00**

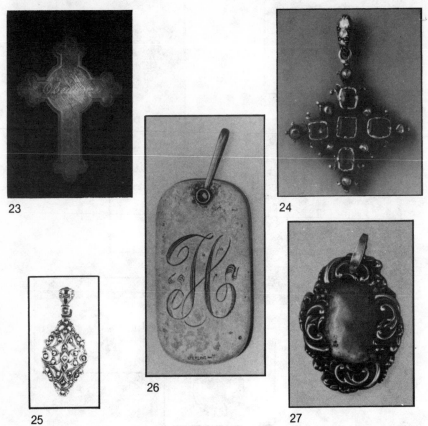

23

24

25

26

27

☐	**23** Cross motif, silver, French, c. 19th	**90.00**	**125.00**
☐	**24** Cruciform motif, five emerald-cut emeralds, rose diamonds, silver, gold, c. late 18th	**1200.00**	**1400.00**
☐	**25** Cutout swirl motif, marcasites, sterling silver, American, c. 1920	**25.00**	**35.00**
☐	**26** Dance card holder, sterling silver front and back with celluloid cards inside, formerly part of a chatelaine, American, c. 1910	**45.00**	**55.00**
☐	**27** Dance card holder, repoussé sterling silver front and back with celluloid cards inside, formerly part of a chatelaine, American, c. 1900	**60.00**	**70.00**

28

29

30

31

32

☐	**28** *Dragonfly motif, pink and blue plique-á-jour wings, green enamel body, ruby eyes, old mine and rose diamonds, gold, Art Nouveau, c. 1890* ..	3000.00	3300.00
☐	**29** *Eye miniature on ivory, gold frame, c. late 18th* ..	850.00	1000.00
☐	**30** *Fire opal: cabochon, rose diamonds, silver, gold, c. mid 19th*	1500.00	1700.00
☐	**31** *Flower motif, foil-back jargoons, rose diamonds, reverse: Jaipur enamel, Indian, c. 19th*	800.00	900.00
☐	**32** *Flower motif, carved amethyst, one round diamond in center, rose diamonds, gold, c. 19th*	800.00	850.00

33

34

35

36

38

37

□ **33** *Flower motif, two cabochon moonstones, 11 ca-*
bochon opals, 830 silver, maker: RRCi, Copen-
hagen, c. early 20th **300.00   350.00**

□ **34** *Flower motif, translucent colored enamel, one*
round diamond, 12 in. chain, 14K gold, American,
c. 1894-95 .... **200.00   245.00**

□ **35** *Flower motif, one round ruby, seed pearls, 12 in.*
chain, 14K gold, American, c. 1894-95 .... **160.00   190.00**

□ **36** *Flower motif, seed pearls, 12 in. chain, 14K gold,*
American, c. 1894-95 .... **145.00   165.00**

□ **37** *Flower motif, 20 old mine diamonds, 16 pearls,*
gold, platinum, pendant or brooch, c. early 20th . **800.00   1000.00**

□ **38** *Flower motif, repoussé, one oval pink sapphire,*
four seed pearls, gold, c. 1840 .... **600.00   650.00**

39

40

41

42

43

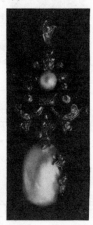

44

☐ **39** *Flower motif, one emerald-cut amethyst approx. 20.0 cts., rose diamonds, gold, silver, c. 1860* **1200.00 1500.00**

☐ **40** *Flower motif, marcasites, sterling silver, American, c. 1920.* **50.00 60.00**

☐ **41** *Flower motif, translucent pea green enamel, 930 silver, French, c. 1920* **75.00 95.00**

☐ **42** *Flower basket motif, faceted sardonyx, marcasites, sterling silver, American, c. 1920* **65.00 85.00**

☐ **43** *Flower motif, carved amethyst, one round diamond in each, gold, c. 20th. Pair* **700.00 800.00**

☐ **44** *Flower openwork motif, 20 round diamonds approx. 1.0 ct., one round pearl, one baroque pearl approx. 12MM by 18MM, gold, platinum, c. 1860* . **2400.00 2600.00**

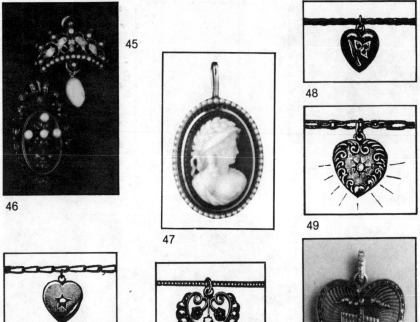

45

46

47

48

49

50

51

52

☐	**45**	Crown motif, seed pearls, one baroque pearl, gold, c. mid 19th..........................	225.00	275.00
☐	**46**	Flower and ribbon motif, four seed pearls, rose diamonds, gold, c. mid 19th	400.00	450.00
☐	**47**	Hardstone cameo of a lady, half seed pearl border, gold, pendant or brooch, c. 1880..........	1200.00	1500.00
☐	**48**	Heart motif, three cabochon turquoise, 12 in. chain, 14K gold, American, c. 1894-95	90.00	120.00
☐	**49**	Heart motif, chased, one round diamond, 12 in. chain, 14K gold, American, c. 1894-95	160.00	190.00
☐	**50**	Heart motif, one seed pearl, 12 in. chain, 14K gold, American, c. 1894-95	65.00	85.00
☐	**51**	Heart motif, two round rubies, seed pearls, 12 in. chain, 14K gold, American, c, 1894-95	200.00	245.00
☐	**52**	Heart motif, green and blue translucent enamel, rose diamonds, silver, gold, c. 19th	600.00	750.00

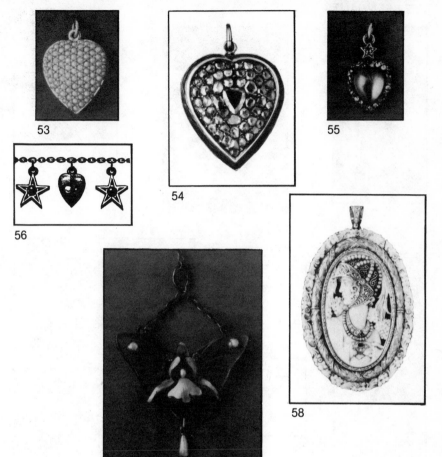

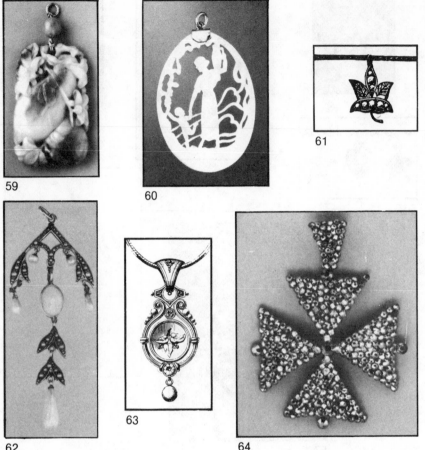

59

60

61

62

63

64

☐	**59**	*Jade, carved, gold fitting*		450.00	550.00
☐	**60**	*Lady and child motif, cutout ivory, gold, c. 1925* .		65.00	90.00
☐	**61**	*Leaf motif, engraved, eight seed pearls, 12 in.* *chain, 14K gold, American, c. 1894-95*		140.00	165.00
☐	**62**	*Leaf dangle motif, cabochon opal, seed pearls,* *gold, c. 1900*		350.00	400.00
☐	**63**	*Leaf and shield motif, gold, Italian, c. 1869*		550.00	650.00
☐	**64**	*Maltese cross motif, cut steel, c. early 19th*		250.00	275.00

65

66

68

67

69

☐	**65**	*Maltese cross motif, engraved, gold, c. 1800 . . . .*	**700.00**	**800.00**
☐	**66**	*Maltese cross, filigree, cannetille, gold, c. 1820 .*	**500.00**	**550.00**
☐	**67**	*Medalion motif, obverse: warrior with griffin, reverse: a lady, gold, Art Nouveau, maker: RL, c. 1900. . . . .*	**900.00**	**1000.00**
☐	**68**	*Mermaid motif, carved lava, c. 1840. . . . .*	**300.00**	**400.00**
☐	**69**	*Mirror, repousse lady and flower motif, sterling silver, Art Nouveau, American, c. 1900 . . . .*	**85.00**	**110.00**

70

71

72

73

74

☐ **70** Mirror, scenic motif on both sides, slides with mirror interior, sterling silver, artist: B. Wicker, French, c. 19th 300.00   350.00

☐ **71** Monkey motif, carved ivory, "See no evil, Hear no evil, Speak no evil," sterling silver reverse, c. 19th   300.00   400.00

☐ **72** Moonstones, one cushion-cut sapphire approx. 7.50 cts., round sapphires, filigree, white gold, maker: Tiffany & Co., American, c. late 19th 1000.00   1200.00

☐ **73** Mosaic motif of a lady, Etruscan granulation, gold, pendant or brooch, c. mid 19th 1000.00   1200.00

☐ **74** Mosaic architectual motif, white metal fittings, c. late 19th 45.00   65.00

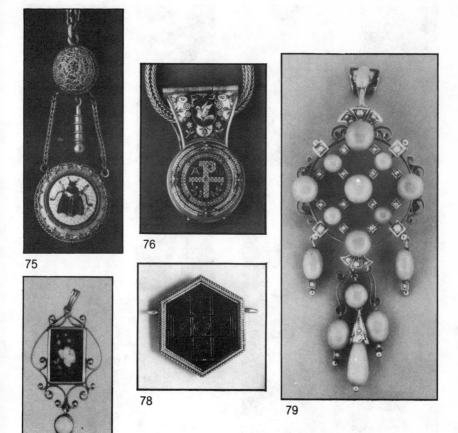

75

76

78

79

77

- [ ] **75** Mosaic beetle motif, Etruscan granulation, gold, c. 1860 . . . . 400.00 500.00
- [ ] **76** Mosaic bulla pendant, dove and religious motif, pendant and locket, foxtail chain, gold, Italian, c. 1870 . . . . 1800.00 2400.00
- [ ] **77** Mosaic flower motif, one round cabochon opal, 14K gold, American, c. 1920 . . . . 325.00 375.00
- [ ] **78** Mosaic religious motif, silver cloisonné wire, gold, maker: Castellani, Italian, c. 1860 . . . . 2200.00 2500.00
- [ ] **79** Openwork motif, coral, pearls, gold, silver, c. 1850 1000.00 1200.00

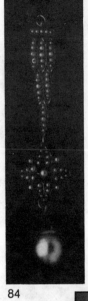

80

82

85

84

81

83

86

☐	**80**	*Openwork motif, one faceted emerald, pearls, rose and round diamonds, gold, c. mid 19th*	**900.00**	**1000.00**
☐	**81**	*Oval center of frosted crystal, marcasites, sterling silver, American, c. 1920*	**50.00**	**75.00**
☐	**82**	*Oval flower motif, cabochon black and white banded agate, seed pearls, gold, c. 1850*	**600.00**	**750.00**
☐	**83**	*Pearls: seed pearls and one baroque pearl approx. 9.5M by 11MM, gold, c. 1850*	**700.00**	**900.00**
☐	**84**	*Pearls: seed pearls and one baroque pearl approx. 10MM by 11MM, gold, c. 1850*	**800.00**	**1000.00**
☐	**85**	*Ribbon motif, five round diamonds, one baroque pearl, gold, c. late 19th*	**350.00**	**450.00**
☐	**86**	*Round motif, translucent blue guilloche enamel, rose diamonds, gold, silver, c. 1900*	**550.00**	**650.00**

87

89

91

88

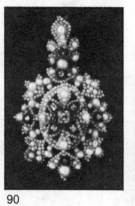

90

92

☐ **87** *Round motif, chased, one round diamond, 12 in. chain, 14K gold, American, c. 1894-95* **160.00**   **190.00**

☐ **88** *Sardonyx cameo of a lady, pearls, Etruscan granulation, gold, pendant or brooch, c. 1820* **600.00**   **800.00**

☐ **89** *Scallop and swirl motif, seed pearls, rubies, 12 in. chain, 14K gold, American, c. 1894-95* **200.00**   **245.00**

☐ **90** *Seed pearl motif, strung with white horsehair on mother-of-pearl templets, ten diamonds, silver, fitted leather box inscribed: "Read & Son, London," c. 1880* **350.00**   **400.00**

☐ **91** *Shield motif, guilloche cream, red and blue enamel, rose diamonds, gold, c. 1900* **2600.00**   **2800.00**

☐ **92** *Shield openwork motif, opaque black and white enamel, seven oval cabochon opals, three old mine diamonds, silver, gold, c. 1840* **1000.00**   **1200.00**

93

95

97

94

96

98

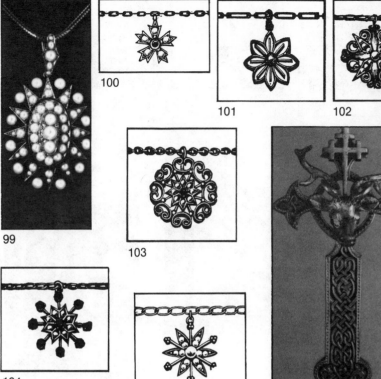

99

100

101

102

103

104

105

106

107

108

109

110

112

111

113

☐	**107**	*Star motif, filigree, seed pearls, gold, c. 19th . . . .*	**400.00**	**450.00**
☐	**108**	*Star motif, seed pearls, 12 in. chain, 14K gold,*		
		American, c. 1894-95	**150.00**	**175.00**
☐	**109**	*Star coin motif, 14K gold, American, c. 1920 . . . .*	**350.00**	**375.00**
☐	**110**	*Star and fleur-de-lys motif, one seed pearl, 12 in.*		
		chain, 14K gold, American, c. 1894-95	**125.00**	**145.00**
☐	**111**	*Star and leaf motif, engraved, seed pearls, 12 in.*		
		chain, 14K gold, American, c. 1894-95	**225.00**	**265.00**
☐	**112**	*Star oval motif, opaque black and white enamel,*		
		one oval amethyst in center, other gemstones,		
		silver gilt, Hungarian, c. 1860	**650.00**	**700.00**
☐	**113**	*Tassel motif, seed pearls, diamonds in cap, 14K*		
		white gold, c. 1920	**600.00**	**650.00**

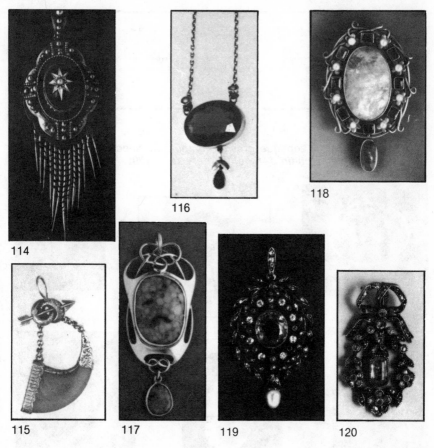

114

116

118

115   117   119   120

☐ **114** Tassel motif, one oval cabochon garnet, one seed pearl, Etruscan granulation, gold, fitted leather box, c. 1850 . . . .   600.00   700.00

☐ **115** Tiger claw and arrow motif, engraved, 15K gold, English, c. 1870 . . . . ,,   300.00   325.00

☐ **116** Tourmaline: one oval and one pear-shape, seed pearls, 15K gold, English, c. early 20th 450.00   500.00

☐ **117** Turquoise, gold, Arts & Crafts MVT., maker: Murrle Bennett, English, c. 1910 . . . .   750.00   850.00

☐ **118** Wreath motif, eight emerald-cut emeralds, eight seed pearls, two oval cabochon opals, gold pendant or brooch, c. 1900 . . . .   1500.00 1600.00

☐ **119** Wreath motif, one oval sapphire, one baroque pearl, diamonds, gold, silver, c. 19th 3300.00 3500.00

☐ **120** Wreath and bow motif, one emerald-cut emerald, round emeralds, rose diamonds, gold, silver, c. 1860. . . . .   475.00   575.00

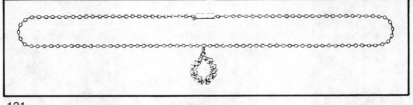

121

☐ **121** *Wreath motif, opaque green enamel, nine seed pearls, 12 in. chain, 14K gold, American, c. 1896* .   **160.00**   **190.00**

1

2

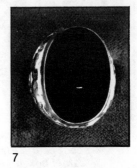

3

4

5

6

7

RINGS

CAMEO and INTAGLIO

		PRICE RANGE	
☐	**1** *Ancient malachite cameo of a mythological scene, remounted in 15K gold, c. 1860*	**600.00**	**700.00**
☐	**2** *Ancient Roman intaglio, setting c. 18th*	**2000.00**	**2400.00**
☐	**3** *Coral cameo of a lady, 14K gold, c. 1930*	**100.00**	**150.00**
☐	**4** *Coral cameo of a lady, gold, c. 1850*	**125.00**	**175.00**
☐	**5** *Emerald cameo of a gentleman, gold, c. early 20th*	**3800.00**	**4000.00**
☐	**6** *Onyx cameo of a gentleman, 14K gold*	**300.00**	**400.00**
☐	**7** *Onyx intaglio of two angels and a butterfly in a sterling and gold mounting, maker: Carl Schon, Baltimore, Maryland, American, c. 1930-50*	**275.00**	**375.00**

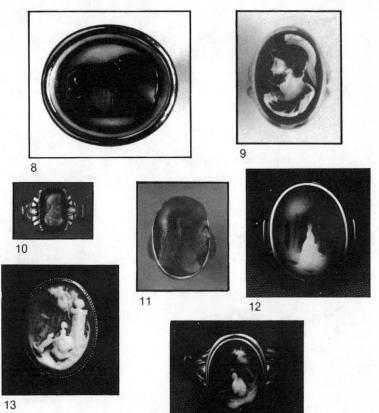

☐	**8**	*Reverse banded agate cameo, brown lion on white background, contemporary mounting, cameo c. late 18th*	**3500.00**	**4000.00**
☐	**9**	*Sardonyx cameo of a Greek warrior, remounted in 22K gold ring, cameo c. early 19th*	**1000.00**	**1200.00**
☐	**10**	*Sardonyx cameo of a lady, gold, c. 1860*	**150.00**	**200.00**
☐	**11**	*Sardonyx cameo of a warrior, 10K gold, American, c. 20th*	**500.00**	**550.00**
☐	**12**	*Shell cameo of Rebecca-at-the-Well, considerably worn, 14K gold, c. 1900*	**50.00**	**80.00**
☐	**13**	*Shell cameo of a lady and dog in garden, 14K gold, c. 1910*	**225.00**	**325.00**
☐	**14**	*Shell cameo of Rebecca-at-the-Well, 14K gold, c. 1880*	**100.00**	**140.00**

CHILD'S · BAND

			PRICE RANGE	
☐	**1**	*"Baby" band, 14K gold, American, c. 1894-95*	**75.00**	**80.00**
☐	**2**	*Fancy engraved band, 14K gold, American, c. 1894-95*	**45.00**	**55.00**
☐	**3**	*Fancy engraved band, 14K gold, American, c. 1894-95*	**60.00**	**70.00**
☐	**4**	*Fancy engraved band, 14K gold, American, c. 1894-95*	**45.00**	**55.00**
☐	**5**	*Fancy engraved band, 14K gold, American, c. 1894-95*	**60.00**	**70.00**
☐	**6**	*Plain band, 14K gold, American, c. 1894-95*	**40.00**	**50.00**

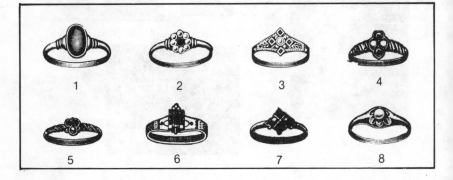

CHILD'S · GEMSTONE

			PRICE RANGE	
☐	**1**	*Cabochon garnet, 14K gold, American, c. 1896* ..	**80.00**	**110.00**
☐	**2**	*Garnet, eight seed pearls, 14K gold, American, c. 1896*	**60.00**	**80.00**
☐	**3**	*Garnets, one seed pearl, 14K gold, American, c. 1896*	**60.00**	**80.00**
☐	**4**	*Garnets, two seed pearls, 14K gold, American, c. 1894-95*	**65.00**	**85.00**
☐	**5**	*Garnets, one seed pearl, 14K gold, American, c. 1894-95*	**50.00**	**70.00**
☐	**6**	*Garnets, 14K gold, American, c. 1894-95*	**80.00**	**100.00**
☐	**7**	*Garnets, two seed pearls, 14K gold, American, c. 1894-95*	**70.00**	**90.00**
☐	**8**	*Moonstone, 14K gold, American, c. 1896*	**45.00**	**65.00**

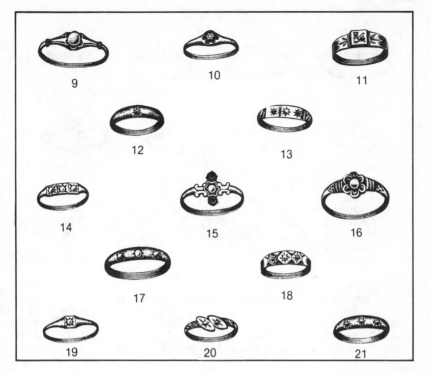

☐	**9**	*Opal, 14K gold, American, c. 1896*	**60.00**	**80.00**
☐	**10**	*Rose diamond, 14K gold, American, c. 1896*	**50.00**	**70.00**
☐	**11**	*Ruby, one turquoise, one seed pearl, 14K gold,*		
		American, c. 1896	**70.00**	**90.00**
☐	**12**	*Ruby, 14K gold, American, c. 1896*	**55.00**	**80.00**
☐	**13**	*Rubies, one seed pearl, 14K gold, American,*		
		c. 1896.	**80.00**	**95.00**
☐	**14**	*Rubies, one seed pearl, 14K gold, American,*		
		c. 1896.	**75.00**	**95.00**
☐	**15**	*Seed pearl, two rubies, 14K gold, American,*		
		c. 1896.	**75.00**	**100.00**
☐	**16**	*Seed pearl, 14K gold, American, c. 1896*	**40.00**	**50.00**
☐	**17**	*Seed pearl, two turquoise, 14K gold, American,*		
		c. 1896.	**50.00**	**70.00**
☐	**18**	*Seed pearl, two turquoise, 14K gold, American,*		
		c. 1896.	**70.00**	**90.00**
☐	**19**	*Seed pearl, 14K gold, American, c. 1896*	**35.00**	**50.00**
☐	**20**	*Seed pearl, turquoise, 14K gold, American, c. 1896*	**40.00**	**60.00**
☐	**21**	*Seed pearl, two turquoise, 14K gold, American,*		
		c. 1896.	**50.00**	**70.00**

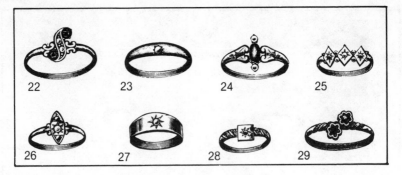

☐	**22**	*Seed pearls, two almondine garnets, 14K gold, American, c. 1896*	80.00	110.00
☐	**23**	*Turquoise, 14K gold, American, c. 1896*	40.00	60.00
☐	**24**	*Turquoise, two seed pearls, 14K gold, American, c. 1896*	60.00	75.00
☐	**25**	*Turquoise, one seed pearl, 14K gold, American, c. 1896*	70.00	90.00
☐	**26**	*Turquoise, one seed pearl, 14K gold, American, c. 1896*	60.00	75.00
☐	**27**	*Turquoise, 14K gold, American, c. 1896*	50.00	60.00
☐	**28**	*Turquoise, 14K gold, American, c. 1896*	50.00	70.00
☐	**29**	*Turquoise, one seed pearl, 14K gold, American, c. 1894-95*	60.00	70.00

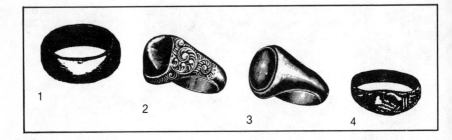

GENTLEMEN'S

			PRICE	RANGE
☐	**1**	*Band motif, coin silver, American, c. 1894-95*	35.00	45.00
☐	**2**	*Carbuncle, engraved shank, 14K gold, American, c. 1896*	325.00	400.00
☐	**3**	*Carbuncle, 14K gold, American, c. 1896*	250.00	300.00
☐	**4**	*Clasped hands motif, coin silver, American, c. 1894-95*	85.00	90.00

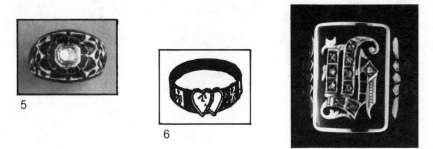

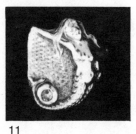

☐	**5**	*Flower and bird motif, translucent enamel, one diamond, gold, Indian, c. 19th*	400.00	500.00
☐	**6**	*Heart motif, coin silver, American, c. 1894-95....*	85.00	90.00
☐	**7**	*Initial motif, gold initial with diamonds on polished black onyx, engraved shank, American, c. 1895....................................*	300.00	400.00
☐		*Similar to above but with diamonds in insignia ..*	225.00	325.00
☐	**8**	*Knights of Pythias motif, polished black onyx, engraved shank, 14K gold, American, c. 1896....*	90.00	135.00
☐	**9**	*Masonic motif, polished black onyx, engraved shank, 14K gold, American, c. 1896 ....*	90.00	135.00
☐	**10**	*Same as above but with diamonds in insignia ...*	250.00	350.00
☐	**11**	*Mermaid motif, one round diamond, 14K gold, Art Nouveau, American, c. 1895 ....*	365.00	425.00
☐	**12**	*Modern Woodmen motif, polished black onyx, engraved shank, 14K gold, American, c. 1896....*	90.00	135.00
☐	**13**	*Odd Fellows motif, polished black onyx, engraved shank, 14K gold, American, c. 1896 ......*	90.00	135.00

14

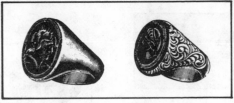

15   16

17   18   19

20   21

☐	**14**	*"Repeal 18th Amendment" motif, sterling silver, American, c. 1930*	**135.00**	**165.00**
☐	**15**	*Sardonyx cameo of a lady, 14K gold, American, c. 1896*	**200.00**	**250.00**
☐	**16**	*Sardonyx cameo of a lady, engraved shank, 14K gold, American, c. 1896*	**300.00**	**350.00**
☐	**17**	*Sardonyx cameo, 14K gold, American, c. 1896* ...	**85.00**	**125.00**
☐	**18**	*Shield initial plaque motif, coin silver, American, c. 1894-95*	**100.00**	**115.00**
☐	**19**	*Shield initial plaque motif, coin silver, American, c. 1894-95*	**110.00**	**120.00**
☐	**20**	*Single stone motif, one old mine diamond approximately 22K gold, English, c. 1894*	**450.00**	**550.00**
☐	**21**	*Skull and crossbones motif, coin silver, American, c. 1894-95*	**85.00**	**100.00**

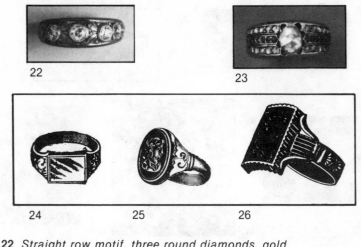

22

23

24 25 26

☐	**22**	Straight row motif, three round diamonds, gold, c. 1890	600.00	750.00
☐	**23**	Straight row motif, center row of rubies, two rows and center rose diamonds, gold, c. late 19th	1800.00	1900.00
☐	**24**	Square initial plaque motif, coin silver, American, c. 1894-95	65.00	85.00
☐	**25**	Tiger eye cameo, 14K gold, American, c. 1896	150.00	200.00
☐	**26**	Tiger eye intaglio, engraved shank, 14K gold, American, c. 1894-95	165.00	225.00

1

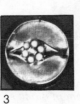

2

3

HUMAN HAIR
All items made from hair referred to throughout this section are of brunette human hair unless stated otherwise.

PRICE RANGE

☐	**1**	Cabochon garnet, white enamel band: "Vivit Post. Funera Virtus. M. W. OBT 13 APR 1729 AET 28," gold, c. 1729	600.00	700.00
☐	**2**	Cluster motif, six cabochon angel skin coral, one seed pearl, reverse: hair locket, c. 1860	140.00	160.00
☐	**3**	Coffin motif, hair under crystal, black enamel band: "I. Saxton. OB. 26 Aug. 1720. AET46," gold, c. 1720	1200.00	1400.00

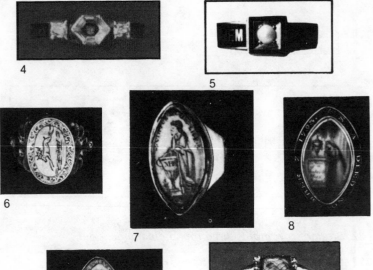

4

5

6

7

8

9

10

☐ **4** *Diamonds: one hexagonal-shape and two fancy-shape diamonds, black enamel band: "Sr. F. Leicester, Bart. OB 30 JUN 1742, AET 68," gold, c. 1742* **1000.00 1200.00**

☐ **5** *Geometric motif, one half pearl in center, black and white enamel, Roman block script "IN MEMORY OF," gold, c. 1880-90* **125.00 150.00**

☐ **6** *Hidden compartment motif, chased and engraved, top plaque with hidden hing, gold, c. 1830-40* **325.00 375.00**

☐ **7** *Lady and urn motif, sepia paint on ivory, c. 1790 .* **350.00 425.00**

☐ **8** *Lady and urn motif, sepia paint and dissolved hair, black and white enamel border: "S A Died November 7 1793," gold, c. 1793* **450.00 500.00**

☐ **9** *Lady sitting weeping by urn with skull and crossbone motif, sepia painted on ivory, gold, inscribed inside: "Ann Allan ob 16 Oct. 1785 AE 68," English, c. 1785* **350.00 450.00**

☐ **10** *Locket motif, chased frame, woven white hair under glass, black enamel band inscribed: "In Memory of," gold, c. 1870* **165.00 200.00**

11

15

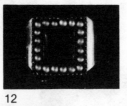

12

16

13

16

14

17

☐ **11** *Locket oval motif, hair under glass, seed pearl
border, gold, c. 1870* **225.00   260.00**

☐ **12** *Locket square motif, hair under glass, seed pearl
border, gold, inscribed inside: "A memory of
Mother," gold, c. 1906* **125.00   150.00**

☐ **13** *Locket with hexagonal crystal motif, portrait under crystal, black enamel scroll band: "A.
Cooper, OB 21 APR 1741 AET 46," gold, c. 1741* .. **900.00 1000.00**

☐ **14** *Locket with hexagonal crystal motif, portrait under crystal, black enamel scroll band: "Rich D.
Tucker, OB 9 APR 1748. AET 72," gold, c. 1748* ... **900.00 1000.00**

☐ **15** *Plaque motif, black enamel, "Tho Lost To Sight
To Memory Dear," chased, gold, c. 1820* **275.00   325.00**

☐ **16** *Sandwich modified motif of inner band with
raised edges holding woven hair, gold, c. 1860* .. **65.00   85.00**

☐ **17** *Sandwich motif of inner band, woven hair and
outer etched band with "MAMIE" cutout, gold,
c. 1880* **150.00   175.00**

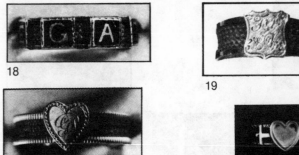

18

19

20

21

23

22

24

☐ **18** *Sandwich motif on inner band, woven hair and outer black and white enamel squares with letters spelling "REGARD," gold, c. 1860* **160.00** **180.00**

☐ **19** *Sandwich motif of inner band with raised edges holding woven hair, shield for monogram covers joining of hair, gold, c. 1860* **125.00** **150.00**

☐ **20** *Sandwich motif of inner band with raised edges holding woven hair, heart for monogram covers joining of hair, gold, c. 1860* **125.00** **150.00**

☐ **21** *Sandwich motif of inner band with raised edges holding woven hair, heart, cross and anchor covers joining of hair, gold, maker: H. H. & S., c. 1860* **150.00** **175.00**

☐ **22** *Sandwich ring of inner band, woven hair and outer engraved and cutout band, gold, c. 1880* ... **100.00** **140.00**

☐ **23** *Sandwich ring of inner band, woven hair and outer engraved and cutout band, third middle band slides to cover openings, gold, c. 1880* **450.00** **550.00**

☐ **24** *Sheaf-of-wheat motif, stalk of strands of hair, wheat grains of dissolved hair, gold, c. 1800* **400.00** **450.00**

25

28

27

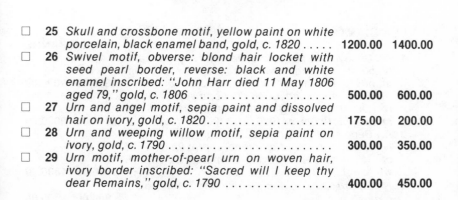

26

29

- [ ] **25** *Skull and crossbone motif, yellow paint on white porcelain, black enamel band, gold, c. 1820* **1200.00 1400.00**
- [ ] **26** *Swivel motif, obverse: blond hair locket with seed pearl border, reverse: black and white enamel inscribed: "John Harr died 11 May 1806 aged 79," gold, c. 1806* **500.00 600.00**
- [ ] **27** *Urn and angel motif, sepia paint and dissolved hair on ivory, gold, c. 1820* **175.00 200.00**
- [ ] **28** *Urn and weeping willow motif, sepia paint on ivory, gold, c. 1790* **300.00 350.00**
- [ ] **29** *Urn motif, mother-of-pearl urn on woven hair, ivory border inscribed: "Sacred will I keep thy dear Remains," gold, c. 1790* **400.00 450.00**

30

31

☐ **30** *Urn motif, shield locket in center, black and white enamel, white enamel signifies death of infant or young child, gold, c. 1790* **300.00   350.00**

☐ **31** *Urn motif, sepia paint and dissolved hair on ivory, gold, c. 1790* **350.00   400.00**

1

2

3

4

5

LADIES · DIAMOND

PRICE RANGE

☐ **1** *Art Deco motif, one round diamond approximately .50 ct., six baguette diamonds, 20 round diamonds, platinum, c. 1930* **1600.00   2000.00**

☐ **2** *Art Deco motif, one round diamond approximately 1.90 cts., six baguette diamonds, round diamonds, platinum, c. 1930* **6000.00   8000.00**

☐ **3** *Art Deco motif, one round diamond approximately .50 ct., one round diamond approximately .25 ct., 16 round diamonds approximately .32 ct., 14K white gold, c. 1935* **1500.00   1800.00**

☐ **4** *Belt motif, three old mine diamonds, 18K gold, c. 1860* **600.00   700.00**

☐ **5** *Belt motif, two diamond chips, English, maker: W. W. Ld., 9K gold* **100.00   150.00**

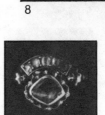

6

7

8

9

10

11

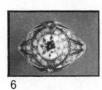

12

13

☐ **6** *Circular motif, one round diamond approximately .90 ct., round diamonds, platinum, c. 1910* **4500.00 5500.00**

☐ **7** *Circular motif, 24 round diamonds approximately 1.0 ct., white gold, c. 1920* **800.00 1000.00**

☐ **8** *Circular and star motif, 46 old mine diamonds approximately 2.50 cts., palladium* **1800.00 2400.00**

☐ **9** *Cluster motif, 11 round diamonds totaling approximately 1.50 cts. in platinum, gold band, c. 1920* **1200.00 1500.00**

☐ **10** *Cross motif, five old mine diamonds approximately .90 ct., gold, c. 1830-40* **1200.00 1400.00**

☐ **11** *Crown motif, five rose diamonds and one enamelled collet set rose diamond in silver gilt, gold band with ladies figures, c. early 19th* **800.00 1000.00**

☐ **12** *Crown motif, 14 old mine diamonds approximately 1.50 cts., c. 1870-80* **1500.00 2000.00**

☐ **13** *Cutout motif, numerous round diamonds, platinum, c. 1890* **900.00 1200.00**

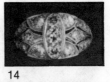

14

15

16

17

18

19

20

☐ **14** *Cutout oval motif, round diamonds approximately 1.75 cts., platinum, c. 1910* **1400.00 1600.00**

☐ **15** *Cutout oval motif, 74 round diamonds approximately 1.50 cts., one round diamond approximately 1.10 cts., platinum, c. 1920* **6000.00 8000.00**

☐ **16** *Diamond-shape motif, nine pavé rose diamonds, 14K gold, c. 1870* **325.00 425.00**

☐ **17** *Domed mount motif, one old mine diamond approximately 1.35 cts., round diamonds, platinum, c. 1910* **3200.00 4200.00**

☐ **18** *Double cluster motif, 14 old mine diamonds approximately .70 ct. in clusters, six rose diamonds in band, 14K gold, c. 1880* **900.00 1200.00**

☐ **19** *Flower motif, rose diamonds, simulated diamond center, silver flower, contemporary gold shank, flower c. 1840* **400.00 500.00**

☐ **20** *Flower motif, one round diamond approximately 1.67 cts., round diamonds, platinum, c. 1900* **4000.00 5000.00**

21

22

23

24

25

26

27

☐ **21** Geometric motif, one round diamond approximately .90 ct., round diamonds, platinum, c. 1920   **2200.00**   **2800.00**

☐ **22** Geometric cutout motif, one round diamond approximately 1.20 cts., round diamond, platinum, c. 1910 . . . . **4500.00**   **5500.00**

☐ **23** Horseshoe motif, seven diamonds totaling approximately .15 ct., 14K gold, c. 1880 . . . . **250.00**   **350.00**

☐ **24** Marquise motif, 15 old mine diamonds, 18K gold, c. 1850 . . . . **750.00**   **950.00**

☐ **25** Marquise openwork motif, round diamonds, one square-shape diamond, two marquise-shape diamonds, calibre cabochon emeralds, platinum, c. 1920 . . . . **1250.00**   **1550.00**

☐ **26** Marquise openwork motif, marquise-shape diamond approximately .15 ct., 20 round diamonds, platinum, c. 1925 . . . . **1600.00**   **2200.00**

☐ **27** Octagonal motif, one round diamond approximately .30 ct., 24 round diamonds approximately 1.68 cts., pavé, 18K white gold, c. 1940 . . . . **2600.00**   **2800.00**

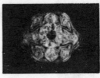

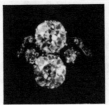

28

29

30

31

32

34

33

☐	**28**	*Open band motif, two round diamonds approximately 1.60 cts., 10 old mine and two rose diamonds, gold, c. 1870*	**2800.00** **3400.00**
☐	**29**	*Open band motif, one old mine diamond diamond approximately 2.75 cts., one old mine diamond approximately 3.0 cts., small old mine diamonds, silver, gold, c. 1875*	**6000.00** **8000.00**
☐	**30**	*Openwork motif, 26 round and marquise diamonds approximately 1.30 cts., calibre emeralds, white gold, c. 1920*	**2000.00** **2400.00**
☐	**31**	*Openwork motif, one round fancy yellow diamond approximately 1.0 cts. in center, round diamonds, platinum, c. 1900*	**3500.00** **4000.00**
☐	**32**	*Openwork motif, round diamonds, four calibre sapphires, platinum, c. 1900*	**500.00** **700.00**
☐	**33**	*Openwork motif, 27 round diamonds, c. 1900*	**2000.00** **2500.00**
☐	**34**	*Openwork motif, round diamonds, grey pearl approximately 6.3MM in center, c. 1890*	**1200.00** **1800.00**

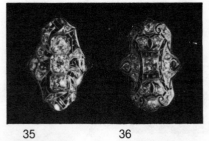

35   36

37

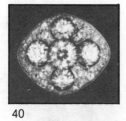

38   39   40

41   42   43

- [ ] **35** Openwork motif, 13 round diamonds approximately 1.50 cts., platinum, c. 1910 . . . . **1000.00 1500.00**
- [ ] **36** Openwork motif, 21 round diamonds approximately 1.50 cts., six square sapphires, platinum, c. 1915 . . . . **1200.00 1600.00**
- [ ] **37** Openwork motif, one round diamond approximately .75 ct. in center, small rose diamonds, platinum, c. 1910 . . . . **1200.00 1500.00**
- [ ] **38** Openwork geometric motif, 26 diamonds approximately .45 ct., one oval diamond approximately 1.15 cts., platinum, c. 1930 . . . . **2400.00 2600.00**
- [ ] **39** Oval motif, 29 rose diamonds, c. 1865 . . . . **550.00   650.00**
- [ ] **40** Oval motif, old mine diamonds, white gold, c. 1890 . . . . **3500.00 4500.00**
- [ ] **41** Pear-shape motif, two pear-shape diamonds approximately 2.50 cts., two old mine diamonds, rose diamonds, gold topped silver, c. 1860 . . . . . . **4500.00 5500.00**
- [ ] **42** Pierced motif, round diamonds, calibre sapphires, platinum, c. 1920 . . . . **350.00   450.00**
- [ ] **43** Rectangular motif, pavé round diamonds, engraved gallery, platinum, c. 1910 . . . . **1500.00 2000.00**

44

45

46

47

48

49

50

☐ **44** Rectangular motif, two round diamonds approximately 1.40 cts., six round diamonds, platinum, c. 1910 . . . . **2000.00 2600.00**

☐ **45** Rosette motif, 21 round diamonds approximately 2.25 cts., gold, c. late 19th **1500.00 1800.00**

☐ **46** Rosette motif, rose diamonds, gold, c. 1860 . . . . . **300.00 400.00**

☐ **47** Rosette motif, 12 old mine diamonds approximately 8.0 cts., 13 old mind and rose diamonds, c. mid 19th **6500.00 8500.00**

☐ **48** Rosette motif, nine old mine diamonds approximately 1.75 cts., gold, c. 1870 . . . . **1600.00 2400.00**

☐ **49** Rosette motif, one old mine diamond approximately .90 ct. in center, old mine diamonds, platinum, c. 1910 . . . . **2000.00 2400.00**

☐ **50** Rosette motif, seven old mine diamonds approximately 3.0 cts., engraved shank, c. 1880 . . . . **2500.00 3500.00**

51

52

53

54

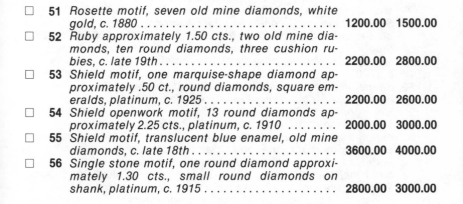

56

55

☐ **51** Rosette motif, seven old mine diamonds, white
gold, c. 1880 .... **1200.00 1500.00**

☐ **52** Ruby approximately 1.50 cts., two old mine diamonds, ten round diamonds, three cushion ru-
bies, c. late 19th........................... **2200.00 2800.00**

☐ **53** Shield motif, one marquise-shape diamond approximately .50 ct., round diamonds, square emeralds, platinum, c. 1925................... **2200.00 2600.00**

☐ **54** Shield openwork motif, 13 round diamonds approximately 2.25 cts., platinum, c. 1910 .... **2000.00 3000.00**

☐ **55** Shield motif, translucent blue enamel, old mine
diamonds, c. late 18th..................... **3600.00 4000.00**

☐ **56** Single stone motif, one round diamond approximately 1.30 cts., small round diamonds on
shank, platinum, c. 1915 .... **2800.00 3000.00**

57

63

58

62

59   61

60

☐ **57** *Single stone motif, one round diamond approximately 1.75 cts., small round diamonds on shank, platinum, c. 1910* **10000.00 12000.00**

☐ **58** *Single stone motif, one old mine diamond approximately 1.0 ct., gold, c. 1860* **800.00 1000.00**

☐ **59** *Single stone motif, one round diamond approximately 2.50 cts., sapphires on shank, platinum, c. 1920* **7000.00 10000.00**

☐ **60** *Single stone motif, one round diamond approximately 1.20 cts., four French-cut sapphires, white gold, c. 1890* **1500.00 1800.00**

☐ **61** *Single stone motif, one round diamond approximately 1.20 cts., round diamonds, c. 1928* **1600.00 2000.00**

☐ **62** *Single stone motif, one round diamond approximately 1.10 cts., round diamonds, engraved band, platinum, c. 1910* **4000.00 5000.00**

☐ **63** *Single stone motif, one round diamond approximately 1.10 cts., six round diamonds, platinum, c. 1920* **3200.00 3600.00**

64

66

65

67

68

69

70

71

☐	**64**	Single stone motif, one round diamond approximately 1.0 ct., 14K gold, American, c. 1895	1000.00	1500.00
☐	**65**	Same as above except diamond approximately 1.0 ct.	1000.00	1500.00
☐	**66**	Same as above except diamond approximately .50 ct.	600.00	800.00
☐	**67**	Same as above except diamond approximately .35 ct.	350.00	500.00
☐	**68**	Same as above except diamond approximately .30 ct.	250.00	300.00
☐	**69**	Same as above except diamond approximately .25 ct.	200.00	250.00
☐	**70**	Same as above except diamond approximately .35 ct.	350.00	475.00
☐	**71**	Same as above except diamond approximately .25 ct.	200.00	250.00

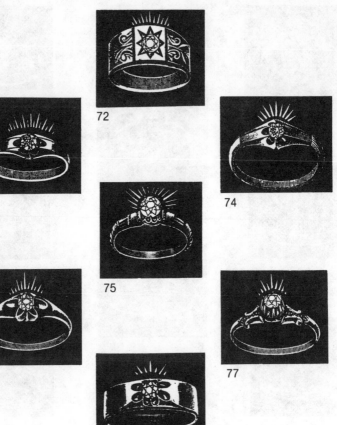

☐	**72** *Same as above except diamond approximately .25 ct.*	250.00	275.00
☐	**73** *Same as above except diamond approximately .12 ct.*	80.00	110.00
☐	**74** *Same as above except diamond approximately .12 ct.*	85.00	110.00
☐	**75** *Same as above except diamond approximately .50 ct.*	600.00	800.00
☐	**76** *Same as above except diamond approximately .25 ct.*	200.00	250.00
☐	**77** *Same as above except diamond approximately .25 ct.*	200.00	275.00
☐	**78** *Same as above except diamond approximately .12 ct.*	100.00	150.00

79

80

81

82

83

84

85

86

☐	79	*Same as above except diamond approximately .12 ct.*	80.00	100.00
☐	80	*Same as above except diamond approximately .34 ct.*	300.00	350.00
☐	81	*Same as above except diamond approximately .12 ct.*	80.00	100.00
☐	82	*Same as above except each diamond approximately .12 ct.*	275.00	325.00
☐	83	*Same as above except diamond approximately .12 ct.*	100.00	150.00
☐	84	*Same as above except diamond approximately .12 ct.*	90.00	110.00
☐	85	*Same as above except diamond approximately .12 ct.*	80.00	100.00
☐	86	*Same as above except diamond approximately .06 ct.*	80.00	90.00

87

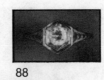
88

89

90

91

92

93

94

☐	**87**	*Single stone motif, one round diamond approximately .80 ct., eight round diamonds in band, 14K gold, c. 1915*	1000.00	1500.00
☐	**88**	*Single stone motif, one round diamond approximately .40 ct., platinum, c. 1925*	600.00	750.00
☐	**89**	*Single stone motif, one round diamond approximately .60 ct., platinum, c. 1910*	800.00	1000.00
☐	**90**	*Single stone motif, one cushion-cut diamond approximately .35 ct., 18K gold, c. late 19th*	350.00	500.00
☐	**91**	*Single stone motif, one cushion-cut diamond approximately .15 ct., 14K gold, c. late 19th*	200.00	250.00
☐	**92**	*Single stone motif, one cushion-cut diamond approximately .20 ct., 14K gold, c. late 19th*	400.00	500.00
☐	**93**	*Single stone motif, one round diamond approximately .15 ct., bead set in star on wide band, English, 15K gold, c. 1875*	275.00	325.00
☐	**94**	*Single stone motif, one round diamond approximately .30 ct., 14K gold, c. late 19th*	350.00	450.00

95

96

97

98

99

100

101

102

☐ **95** *Single stone motif, one round diamond approximately .25 cts., 14K gold, c. 1915* **300.00 400.00**

☐ **96** *Single stone motif, one round diamond approximately .40 ct., 14K gold, c. 1870* **500.00 600.00**

☐ **97** *Snake motif, etched, round diamonds, gold, c. late 19th* **600.00 700.00**

☐ **98** *Split band motif, two round diamonds approximately .20 ct. each, 14K gold, c. 1900* **325.00 425.00**

☐ **99** *Square motif, round diamonds, gold, platinum, c. 1920* **1200.00 1400.00**

☐ **100** *Straight row motif, three round diamonds approximately 2.0 cts., platinum, c. 1920* **4000.00 5000.00**

☐ **101** *Straight row motif, one round diamond approximately 1.50 cts., two round diamonds approximately 1.60 cts., small round diamonds on shank, platinum, c. 1920* **6000.00 8000.00**

☐ **102** *Straight row motif, three round diamonds approximately 3.50 cts., white gold, c. 1890* **6500.00 8500.00**

103

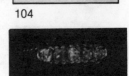
104

105

106

107

108

109

110

112

111

☐	**103** Straight row motif, three round diamonds approximately .90 ct., c. 1900	600.00	750.00
☐	**104** Straight row motif, three round diamonds approximately .45 ct., gold, c. 1930	400.00	500.00
☐	**105** Straight row motif, three round diamonds approximately 1.0 ct., round diamonds, platinum, c. 1910.	650.00	850.00
☐	**106** Straight row motif, five old mine diamonds totaling approximately .25 ct., 18K gold, c. 1880	400.00	500.00
☐	**107** Straight row motif, five old mine diamonds totaling approximately .18 ct., 14K gold, c. 1860	300.00	400.00
☐	**108** Straight row motif, four round diamonds totaling approximately .20 ct., 14K white gold, c. 1930 . . .	200.00	300.00
☐	**109** Straight row motif, seven rose and old mine diamonds totaling approximately .70 ct., collet set, yellow gold shank, inscribed: "N. Biichner 1747"	900.00	1200.00
☐	**110** Straight row motif, three round diamonds approximately 1.25 cts., 14K gold, c. 1925	1200.00	1400.00
☐	**111** Star motif, 21 round diamonds approximately .75 ct., 14K white gold, c. mid 20th	600.00	800.00
☐	**112** Triangular motif, 11 old mine diamonds approximately 1.20 cts., platinum, c. 1910	1200.00	1400.00

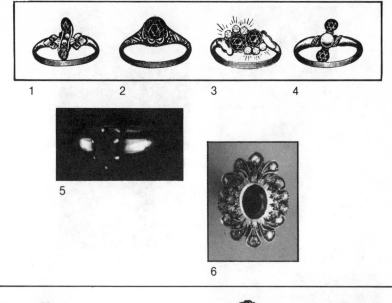

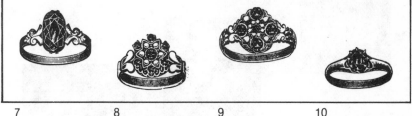

LADIES · DIAMOND and GEMSTONE

PRICE RANGE

☐	1	*Almandine garnets, two pearls, 14K gold, American, c. 1896*	90.00	120.00
☐	2	*Almandine garnet, 14K gold, American, c. 1896*	125.00	165.00
☐	3	*Almandine garnets, six rose diamonds, 14K gold, American, c. 1896*	275.00	325.00
☐	4	*Almandine garnet, one olivine, one pearl, 14K gold, American, c. 1896*	200.00	250.00
☐	5	*Almandine garnet, cabochon, 14K gold*	225.00	250.00
☐	6	*Amethyst, rose diamonds, silver topped 18K gold, c. 1850*	400.00	500.00
☐	7	*Amethyst, 14K gold approximately c. 1896*	150.00	200.00
☐	8	*Amethysts, six pearls, 14K gold, American, c. 1896*	175.00	225.00
☐	9	*Amethyst, 12 pearls, 14K gold, American, c. 1895*	550.00	650.00
☐	10	*Amethyst, 14K gold, American, c. 1895*	100.00	125.00

11

12

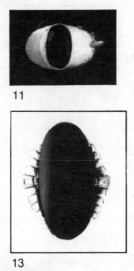

13

14

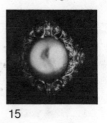

15

16

17

☐	**11**	*Amethyst, 14K gold, c. early 20th*	200.00	300.00
☐	**12**	*Amethyst surrounded by half seed pearls, 14K gold, c. 1870*	600.00	800.00
☐	**13**	*Art Deco motif, oval black onyx center, two round diamonds, 14K gold, c. 1925*	400.00	500.00
☐	**14**	*Baroque pearl, 24 old mine diamonds, platinum topped gold, c. 1890*	1200.00	1500.00
☐	**15**	*Baroque pearl, 80 round diamonds approximately 1.60 cts., platinum, c. 1900*	1400.00	1600.00
☐	**16**	*Black opal, 20 old mine diamonds approximately 1.50 cts., gold topped silver, c. 1890*	2600.00	3000.00
☐	**17**	*Black opal, baguette and rose diamonds, white gold, c. 1910*	3000.00	4000.00

18

19

20

21

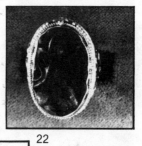

22

23

☐	**18**	*Black opal, eight baguette and round yellow diamonds approximately 1. ct., c. 1910*	3500.00	4500.00
☐	**19**	*Bloodstone, 14K gold, c. early 20th*	80.00	125.00
☐	**20**	*Blue zircon, 10K three color gold mounting, c. 1920*	125.00	225.00
☐	**21**	*Blue zircon, 14K green gold, c. 1900*	200.00	300.00
☐	**22**	*Carved amethyst quartz, seed pearl border, carved leaf motif shank, 14K gold, c. late 19th*	350.00	450.00
☐	**23**	*Chrysoberyl, 18K white and yellow gold, c. 1880*	350.00	450.00

24

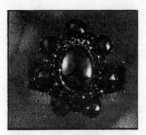

25

26

27

28

29

30

31

☐	**24**	Citrene: rose cut, 14K gold, c. late 19th	65.00	85.00
☐	**25**	Cluster motif, oval cabochon center garnet, rose garnet border, 14K gold, c. 1880	325.00	425.00
☐	**26**	Cluster motif, one ruby approximately .20 ct. in center surrounded by eight old mine diamonds approximately .48 ct., stones in platinum, 14K gold shank, c. early 20th	800.00	1000.00
☐	**27**	Cluster motif, cabochon turquoise in center surrounded by ten old mine diamonds, gold, c. 1870.	650.00	850.00
☐	**28**	Cluster motif, one round ruby in center, eight old mine diamonds approximately 1.20 cts., 14K gold, c. late 19th	1200.00	1400.00
☐	**29**	Coral, gold, c. 1910	150.00	175.00
☐	**30**	Crisscross motif, pink coral, seed pearls, gold, c. 1840.	300.00	350.00
☐	**31**	Cross motif, one pear-shape sapphire, two old mine diamonds, one round sapphire and one round ruby surrounded by old mine diamonds, silver, gold, c. 1840	600.00	800.00

32

33

34

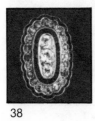

35

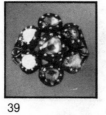

36

37

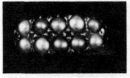

38

39

40

☐	**32**	*Crystal, ruby, 10K white and rose gold, c. 1925* ..	**125.00**	**225.00**
☐	**33**	*Diamond, emeralds, gold, c. 1850*	**500.00**	**700.00**
☐	**34**	*Diamond, four round rubies, gold, c. 1800*.......	**1400.00**	**1600.00**
☐	**35**	*Diamond: old mine approximately 1.30 cts., round diamonds, six calibre French-cut sapphires, platinum, c. 1925*	**4200.00**	**4500.00**
☐	**36**	*Diamond: one round approximately 1.50 cts., six round diamonds, calibre-cut emeralds, all in platinum, gold band, c. 1925*	**5000.00**	**6000.00**
☐	**37**	*Diamonds: 31 round approximately .65 ct., calibre sapphires, white gold, c. 1925*	**1500.00**	**1700.00**
☐	**38**	*Diamonds: 23 old mine approximately 1.50 cts., calibre rubies, platinum, c. 1910*..........	**2500.00**	**3500.00**
☐	**39**	*Diamonds: seven Holland rose, silver topped gold, c. 1840*	**700.00**	**900.00**
☐	**40**	*Double straight row of ten half-seed pearls, 18K gold, London, England, c. 1895*	**140.00**	**180.00**

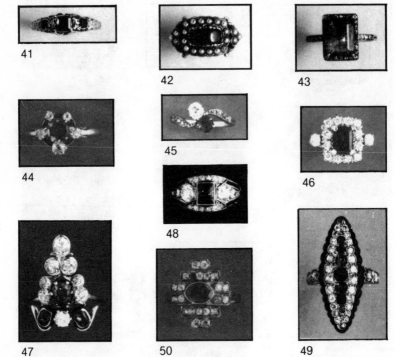

☐	**41**	Emeralds, diamonds, gold, c. 1790	600.00	700.00
☐	**42**	Emerald, half-seed pearls, gold, c. 1860	600.00	800.00
☐	**43**	Emerald: emerald-cut, rose diamonds, gold, platinum, c. 1880	900.00	1200.00
☐	**44**	Emerald: intaglio emerald-cut, five old mine diamonds, 18K gold	1500.00	2000.00
☐	**45**	Emerald: step-cut, one round diamond, rose diamonds, gold, silver, c. 1900.................	600.00	800.00
☐	**46**	Emerald: emerald-cut, 14 round diamonds, 18K gold, c. 1910	1400.00	1600.00
☐	**47**	Emeralds: one emerald-cut and two step-cut, seven old European-cut and one round diamond, gold, platinum, c. 1910	3000.00	3500.00
☐	**48**	Emeralds: one emerald-cut approximately .50 ct. and 12 calibre emeralds, round diamonds approximately 1.0 ct., platinum, c. 1920	2800.00	3200.00
☐	**49**	Emeralds: square-cut in center, round diamonds, black enamelled edges, platinum, c. 1900	3800.00	4200.00
☐	**50**	Emerald: oval faceted, rose diamonds, silver topped gold, c. 1870	1600.00	1800.00

51

52

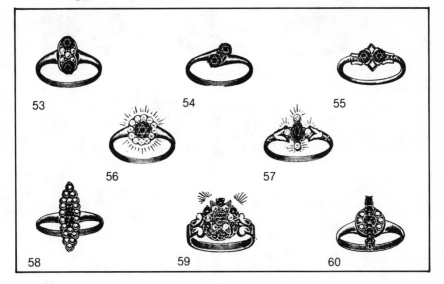

53

54

55

56

57

58

59

60

☐ **51** Emerald: emerald-cut approximately 1.70 cts., nine round diamonds approximately .75 ct., 14K gold, c. mid 20th............................ 3500.00 4500.00

☐ **52** Emerald: emerald-cut approximately 1.35 cts., 14 round diamonds approximately .75 ct., platinum and 18K white gold, c. mid 20th 2600.00 3200.00

☐ **53** Emerald, one ruby, five pearls, 14K gold, American, c. 1896............................... 135.00 175.00

☐ **54** Emerald, one ruby, 14K gold, American, c. 1896.. 125.00 165.00

☐ **55** Emeralds, 14K gold, American, c. 1896 .... 150.00 200.00

☐ **56** Emerald, 12 rose diamonds, 14K gold, American, c. 1896.................................... 340.00 480.00

☐ **57** Emerald, four rose diamonds, 14K gold, American, c. 1896.................................... 275.00 325.00

☐ **58** Emeralds, 20 pearls, 14K gold, American, c. 1895 225.00 265.00

☐ **59** Emeralds, five diamonds, 14K gold, American, c. 1895.................................... 500.00 600.00

☐ **60** Emeralds, two rubies, six pearls, 14K gold, American, c. 1895 .... 250.00 300.00

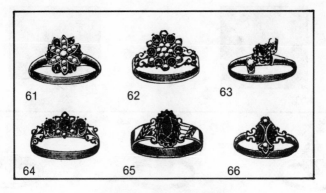

61 62 63

64 65 66

67

68

69

☐	**61**	*Emeralds, three rubies, 13 pearls, 14K gold, American, c. 1895*	275.00	325.00
☐	**62**	*Emeralds, three rubies, 13 pearls, 14K gold, American, c. 1895*	300.00	350.00
☐	**63**	*Emerald, two pearls, 14K gold, American, c. 1895*	125.00	165.00
☐	**64**	*Emeralds, six pearls, 14K gold, American, c. 1895*	250.00	300.00
☐	**65**	*Emerald, 14K gold, American, c. 1895*	900.00	1200.00
☐		*Same as above but garnet*	300.00	350.00
☐	**66**	*Emeralds, two pearls, 14K gold, American, c. 1895*	150.00	200.00
☐	**67**	*Emerald center, two half seed pearls, English, 15K gold, c. 1890*	180.00	225.00
☐	**68**	*Emerald: emerald-cut approximately 1.0 ct., rose diamonds in silver, gold shank, c. 1860*	5000.00	5500.00
☐	**69**	*Emerald: emerald-cut, rose diamonds, platinum, gold, c. 1880-1900*	2500.00	3000.00

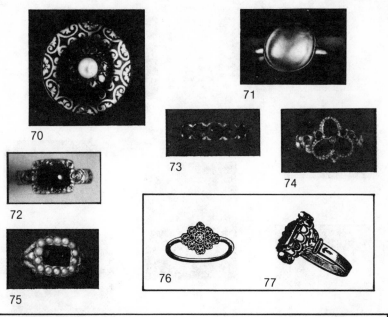

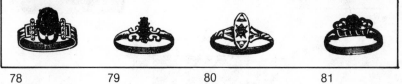

☐	**70**	Flower motif, center cluster of one cultured pearl and rose diamonds, champlevé blue enamel, 14K gold, c. early 20th	400.00	450.00
☐	**71**	Freshwater pearl, earring converted to ring, 14K gold, c. early 20th	40.00	60.00
☐	**72**	Garnet: rectangular, gold, c. 1865	300.00	500.00
☐	**73**	Garnets, gold, c. 1860	200.00	300.00
☐	**74**	Garnets: three oval faceted, three faceted emer- alds, gold, c. 1830	400.00	500.00
☐	**75**	Garnet: square faceted, half seed pearls, En- glish, c. 1840	300.00	400.00
☐	**76**	Garnets, 14K gold, American, c. 1896	110.00	150.00
☐	**77**	Garnet, pearls, 14K gold, American, c. 1895	140.00	180.00
☐	**78**	Garnet, 14K gold, American, c. 1895	300.00	350.00
☐	**79**	Garnet, 14K gold, American, c. 1895	90.00	120.00
☐	**80**	Garnet, two pearls, 14K gold, American, c. 1895 .	90.00	120.00
☐	**81**	Garnet, pearls, 14K gold, American, c. 1895	200.00	250.00

82

83

84

86

85

88

87

89

☐	**82**	*Garnet, 22K gold, Oriental, c. late 19th*	**150.00**	**200.00**
☐	**83**	*Garnet, cabochon foil-backed, gold, c. 1820*	**650.00**	**750.00**
☐	**84**	*Garnets, seed pearls, gold, c. 1830*	**325.00**	**350.00**
☐	**85**	*Green sapphire: oval-cut, rose diamonds and seed pearls set in silver topped gold, gold shank, c. 1920*	**600.00**	**800.00**
☐	**86**	*Half pearls, gold, c. mid 19th*	**340.00**	**380.00**
☐	**87**	*Jade: oblong cabochon, 22K gold, c. 1860*	**800.00**	**1000.00**
☐	**88**	*Jade, two triangular-shape diamonds, 20 round diamonds, platinum, c. 1925*	**2000.00**	**2500.00**
☐	**89**	*Jade, gold, c. 1930*	**1000.00**	**1200.00**

90

91

92

93

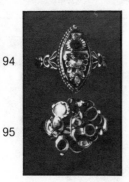

94

95

96

☐	**90**	*Jade, six round diamonds, 14K gold, c. mid 20th* .	1200.00	1500.00
☐	**91**	*Jade, sculptured shank, 14K gold, c. early 20th* . .	800.00	1000.00
☐	**92**	*Loveknot motif with three small turquoise, 14K gold, c. late 19th*	200.00	225.00
☐	**93**	*Marquise motif, oval cabochon banded agate in center surrounded by seed pearls, cabochon banded agate along shank, 14K gold, c. 1850*	250.00	350.00
☐	**94**	*Marquise motif, rose diamonds in silver, blue enamel background, gold shank, c. 1840*	800.00	1000.00
☐	**95**	*Openwork motif, emeralds, ruby, sapphires and diamonds, gold, c. 1750*	900.00	1000.00
☐	**96**	*Marquise motif, three round sapphires, 20 round diamonds, 14K gold, c. 1860*	900.00	1200.00

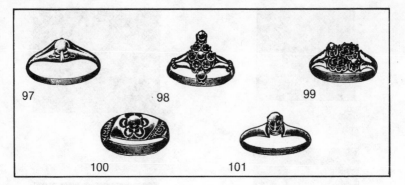

97   98   99

100   101

102

103   104

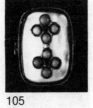

105

106

☐	**97**	*Moonstone, 14K gold, American, c. 1896*	**45.00**	**60.00**
☐	**98**	*Moonstones, six garnets, 14K gold, American, c. 1895*	**175.00**	**225.00**
☐	**99**	*Moonstones, two rubies, 14K gold, American, c. 1895*	**140.00**	**180.00**
☐	**100**	*Moonstone, 14K gold, American, c. 1895*	**70.00**	**90.00**
☐	**101**	*Moonstone, 14K gold, American, c. 1895*	**70.00**	**90.00**
☐	**102**	*Moonstone, 14K gold, c. early 20th*	**70.00**	**90.00**
☐	**103**	*Moonstones, 14K gold, American, c. 1896*	**100.00**	**125.00**
☐	**104**	*Moonstones, 14K gold, American, c. 1896*	**90.00**	**120.00**
☐	**105**	*Mother-of-pearl, eight cabochon turquoise, gold, c. 1915*	**250.00**	**300.00**
☐	**106**	*Octagonal motif, one round tourmaline surrounded by rose diamonds, gold, platinum, c. 1890*	**1000.00**	**1200.00**

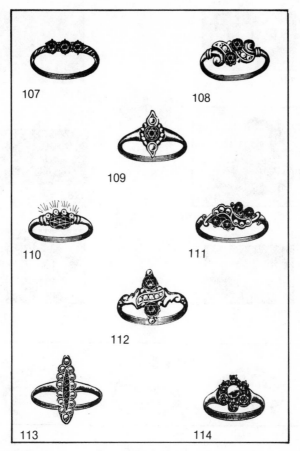

107   108   109   110   111   112   113   114

☐ **107** *Olivines, two almondine garnets, 14K gold, American, c. 1896* 100.00   125.00

☐ **108** *Olivines, four pearls, 14K gold, American, c. 1896*   85.00   100.00

☐ **109** *Olivine, two pearls, 14K gold, American, c. 1896* .   85.00   100.00

☐ **110** *Olivine, four rose diamonds, 14K gold, American, c. 1896* 250.00   300.00

☐ **111** *Olivines, six pearls, 14K gold, American, c. 1896* .   115.00   140.00

☐ **112** *Olivines, seven pearls, 14K gold, American, c. 1896* 140.00   180.00

☐ **113** *Olivines, 14 pearls, 14K gold, American, C. 1895* .   175.00   225.00

☐ **114** *Olivines, moonstone in center, 14K gold, American, c. 1895* 140.00   180.00

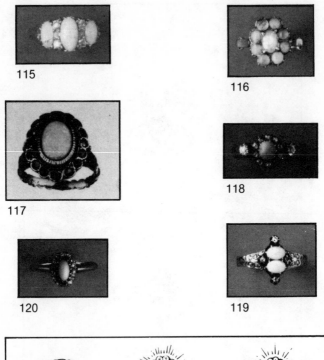

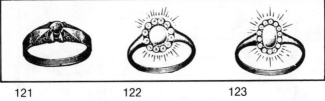

☐	115	Opals, six round diamonds, gold, c. 1860	350.00	450.00
☐	116	Opals, gold, c. 1880	300.00	400.00
☐	117	Opal, rose diamonds, 18K gold, c. 1890	350.00	500.00
☐	118	Opal, rose diamonds, gold, c. 1870	400.00	500.00
☐	119	Opals, four rose diamonds, gold, c. 1860	275.00	350.00
☐	120	Opal, rose diamonds, gold, c. 1870	300.00	400.00
☐	121	Opal, 14K gold, American, c. 1886	85.00	100.00
☐	122	Opal, 12 rose diamonds, 14K gold, American, c. 1896	300.00	350.00
☐	123	Opal, 14 rose diamonds, 14K gold, American, c. 1896	275.00	325.00

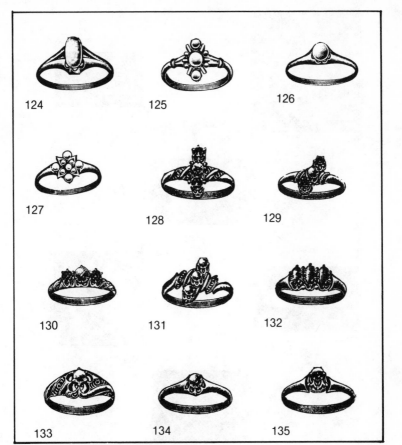

136

137

138

139

140

141

☐ **136** Opal center approximately 2.0 cts. and 13 old mine diamonds approximately 1.30 cts. in platinum, 14K gold shank, c. 1890 .... **1000.00 1500.00**

☐ **137** Opal approximately .75 ct., maker: H W ld., 18K gold, c. early 20th.......................... **100.00 150.00**

☐ **138** Opal, 14K gold, c. early 20th **75.00 100.00**

☐ **139** Opal, 22K gold, c. early 20th **150.00 200.00**

☐ **140** Opal doublet in center, 16 old mine diamonds, silver, gold, c. late 19th **650.00 800.00**

☐ **141** Cross over motif, one oriental pearl approximately 22MM, one old mine diamond approximately .35 ct., eight rose diamonds, all diamonds in platinum, 14K gold shank, c. 1870 .... **500.00 700.00**

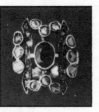

142

143

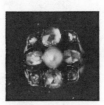

144

145

146

147

148

149

150

☐ **142** Openwork motif, one oval sapphire in center, rose and mine cut diamonds, silver topped gold, c. 1890 . . . .   700.00   900.00

☐ **143** Openwork floral motif, ruby, emerald and cabochon sapphire in silver, gold shank, c. 1750 . . . . .   400.00   500.00

☐ **144** Heart and crown motif, emerald in heart, rose diamonds in crown, gold, c. 1840 . . . .   400.00   500.00

☐ **145** Pear-shape cluster with opal center, border of 14 rose diamonds approximately .30 ct., 14K gold, c. mid 19th 550.00   650.00

☐ **146** Pearls, gold, c. 1860. . . . .   250.00   350.00

☐ **147** Pearl, four Holland rose diamonds, four rose diamonds, gold, silver, c. 1750. . . . .   1200.00   1600.00

☐ **148** Pearls: natural, round diamonds, gold, platinum, c. 1900. . . . .   800.00   1000.00

☐ **149** Pearl, 12 rose diamonds, gold, c. 1880 . . . .   400.00   500.00

☐ **150** Pearls, diamond center, gold, c. 1860 . . . .   275.00   375.00

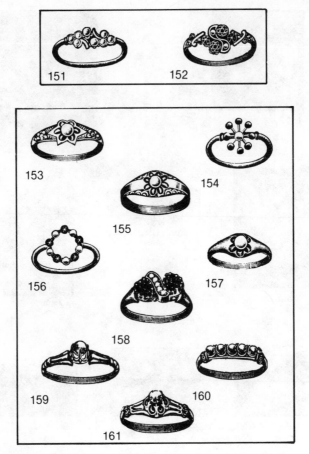

☐	**151**	Pearls, 14K gold, American, c. 1896	85.00	100.00
☐	**152**	Pearls, two rubies, two emeralds, 14K gold, American, c. 1896	175.00	225.00
☐	**153**	Pearl, 14K gold, American, c. 1896	85.00	100.00
☐	**154**	Pearl, eight turquoise, 14K gold, American, c. 1896	135.00	170.00
☐	**155**	Pearls, Garnets, 14K gold, American, c. 1896	70.00	90.00
☐	**156**	Pearl, 14K gold, American, c. 1896	45.00	60.00
☐	**157**	Pearls, two heart rubies, 14K gold, American, c. 1895	300.00	350.00
☐	**158**	Pearl, 14K gold, American, c. 1895	70.00	90.00
☐	**159**	Pearls, 14K gold, American, c. 1895	90.00	120.00
☐	**160**	Pearl, 14K gold, American, c. 1895	70.00	90.00
☐	**161**	Pearl, 14K gold, American, c. 1895	80.00	100.00

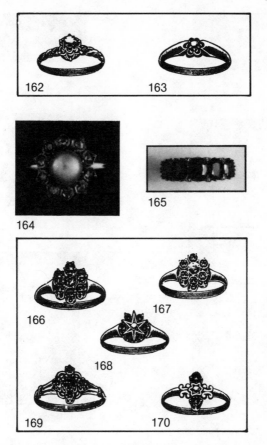

☐	**162**	Pearl, 14K gold, American, c. 1895	65.00	85.00
☐	**163**	Pearl, 14K gold, American, c. 1895	45.00	60.00
☐	**164**	Pearl approximately 5.7MM, rose diamond border, 14K gold	250.00	350.00
☐	**165**	Pink sapphires, rose diamonds, gold, c. 1860....	1200.00	1400.00
☐	**166**	Pink topaz, one olivine in center, 14K gold, American, c. 1895...............................	240.00	280.00
☐	**167**	Pink topaz, pearl in center, 14K gold, American, c. 1895....................................	140.00	180.00
☐	**168**	Pink topaz, pearl in center, 14K gold, American, c. 1895....................................	140.00	180.00
☐	**169**	Pink topaz, olivine in center, 14K gold, American, c. 1895....................................	170.00	210.00
☐	**170**	Pink topaz, one pearl, 14K gold, American, c. 1895	125.00	165.00

171

172

173

174

175

176

177

☐	**171**	Pink tourmaline, gold balls replaced original round diamonds, 14K gold, c. mid 20th	**225.00**	**275.00**
☐	**172**	"Regard" motif, different colored gem stones, gold, c. early 19th.	**200.00**	**250.00**
☐	**173**	Ruby: round, old mine diamonds, c. 1920	**650.00**	**850.00**
☐	**174**	Ruby: round approximately 1.25 cts., old mine diamonds, platinum, c. 1925.	**2200.00**	**2600.00**
☐	**175**	Ruby, old mine diamonds, gold, c. 1850	**800.00**	**1000.00**
☐	**176**	Ruby: oval, old mine and round diamonds, gold topped platinum, c. 1880.	**3000.00**	**3500.00**
☐	**177**	Ruby: oval approximately .90 ct., 27 old European-cut diamonds, gold, silver, c. 1870	**2500.00**	**3500.00**

178

179

180

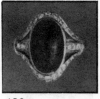

182

181

183   184   185

☐ **178** *Ruby, ten round diamonds, 14K gold, c. 1870 . . . .*   **600.00   800.00**
☐ **179** *Ruby: oval approximately 1.0 ct., rose diamonds,*
          silver topped platinum, c. 1850. . . . . **2800.00   3000.00**
☐ **180** *Rubies: one oval approximately 1.0 ct., calibre*
          rubies, 14 round diamonds, platinum, c. 1920 . . . **3300.00   3500.00**
☐ **181** *Rubies: six square-cut, 23 round diamonds ap-*
          proximately 1.0 ct., platinum, French, Art Deco,
          c. 1925. . . . . **1500.00   1800.00**
☐ **180** *Ruby: oval cabochon approximately 9.75 cts., 32*
          round diamonds approximately .75 ct., platinum,
          c. 1910. . . . . **2600.00   3200.00**
☐ **183** *Rubies, seven pearls, 14K gold, American, c. 1896* **110.00   150.00**
☐ **184** *Rubies, four pearls, 14K gold, American, c. 1896 .* **100.00   125.00**
☐ **185** *Rubies, three pearls, 14K gold, American, c. 1896* **100.00   125.00**

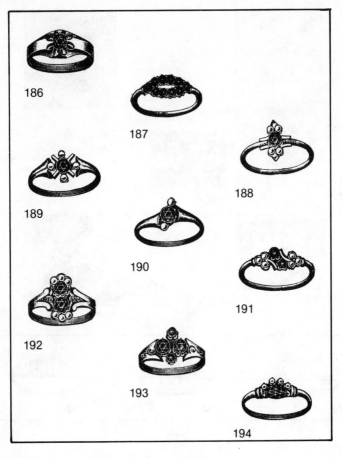

☐	**186**	*Ruby, 14K gold, American, c. 1896*	**110.00**	**150.00**
☐	**187**	*Rubies, 14K gold, American, c. 1896*	**125.00**	**165.00**
☐	**188**	*Ruby, four pearls, 14K gold, American, c. 1896*. . .	**110.00**	**150.00**
☐	**189**	*Ruby, four pearls, 14K gold, American, c. 1896*. . .	**110.00**	**150.00**
☐	**190**	*Ruby, two pearls, 14K gold, American, c. 1896* . . .	**120.00**	**160.00**
☐	**191**	*Rubies, six pearls, 14K gold, American, c. 1896* . .	**100.00**	**125.00**
☐	**192**	*Rubies, six pearls, 14K gold, American, c. 1896* . .	**140.00**	**180.00**
☐	**193**	*Rubies, 14K gold, American, c. 1896*	**170.00**	**210.00**
☐	**194**	*Ruby, four pearls, 14K gold, American, c. 1896*. . .	**110.00**	**150.00**

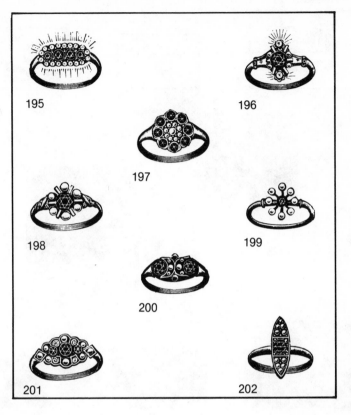

□ **195** *Rubies, 18 rose diamonds, 14K gold, American,*
    c. 1896 . . . . **300.00**   **350.00**
□ **196** *Ruby, two rose diamonds, 14K gold, American,*
    c. 1896 . . . . **400.00**   **450.00**
□ **197** *Rubies, nine pearls, 14K gold, American, c. 1896* . **325.00**   **380.00**
□ **198** *Ruby, six pearls, 14K gold, American, c. 1896* **125.00**   **165.00**
□ **199** *Ruby, eight pearls, 14K gold, American, c. 1896* . . **115.00**   **140.00**
□ **200** *Rubies, six pearls, 14K gold, American, c. 1896* . . **240.00**   **280.00**
□ **201** *Rubies, eight pearls, 14K gold, American, c. 1896* **175.00**   **225.00**
□ **202** *Ruby, ten pearls, 14K gold, American, c. 1895* . . . **180.00**   **240.00**

203

204

205

206

207

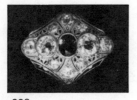
208

209

210

☐	**203**	Ruby, diamond, sapphire, 14K gold, American, c. 1895	**125.00**	**165.00**
☐	**204**	Ruby: oval-cut approximately 1.0 ct., two old mine diamonds approximately .75 ct., rose diamonds, gold, c. 1870	**6000.00**	**6500.00**
☐	**205**	Sapphire, two pearls, rose diamonds, gold, c. 1860	**600.00**	**700.00**
☐	**206**	Sapphires, 24 rose diamonds, silver, gold, c. 1850	**1500.00**	**1800.00**
☐	**207**	Sapphire: cushion, 30 diamonds, gold, silver, c. 1850	**1800.00**	**2200.00**
☐	**208**	Sapphire: oval, calibre sapphires, two round diamonds approximately 1.25 cts., eight one mine diamonds approximately 1.25 cts., platinum, c. 1915	**3000.00**	**4000.00**
☐	**209**	Sapphires: six calibre, one round diamond approximately .70 ct., platinum, c. 1915	**1000.00**	**1400.00**
☐	**210**	Sapphire, two old mine diamonds, gold, c. 1860 .	**2400.00**	**3200.00**

211

212

213

214

215

216

217

☐ **211** *Sapphires: four calibre French-cut, one round diamond approximately .60 ct., platinum, signed: Tiffany & Co., c. 1940* **2000.00 2500.00**
☐ **212** *Sapphire, 18 rose diamonds, 14K gold, c. 1880* ... **500.00 650.00**
☐ **213** *Sapphire, six old mine diamonds, 14K gold, c. 1870* **600.00 800.00**
☐ **214** *Sapphire: oval approximately .90 ct., old mine diamonds, 14K gold, c. 1900* **800.00 1000.00**
☐ **215** *Sapphires: one oval and 12 square, diamonds, gold, silver, c. 1880* **1800.00 2200.00**
☐ **216** *Sapphire: square approximately 2.70 cts., 58 round dimaonds, platinum, c. 1890-1900* **3300.00 3600.00**
☐ **217** *Sapphires, round diamonds, platinum, c. 1930* .. **2000.00 2500.00**

218

219

220

221

222

223

224

☐ **218** *Sapphire: French-cut, 16 round diamonds, c. 1925* 600.00 800.00
☐ **219** *Sapphire: cabochon, three rose diamonds, 14K gold, c. 1890-1900* 300.00 400.00
☐ **220** *Sapphires: square-cut, two rose diamonds, silver, c. 1900* 250.00 350.00
☐ **221** *Sapphire, pearls, gold, c. 1860* 400.00 450.00
☐ **222** *Sapphire: oval cabochon, 54 round diamonds approximately 1.50 cts., platinum, signed: J. E. C. & Co., c. early 20th* 10000.00 12000.00
☐ **223** *Sapphire, 28 old mine diamonds, gold, c. 1890* ... 1200.00 1500.00
☐ **224** *Sapphire: oval approximately 3.25 cts., 48 round diamonds approximately 1.50 cts., platinum, c. 1925*....................................16000.00 18000.00

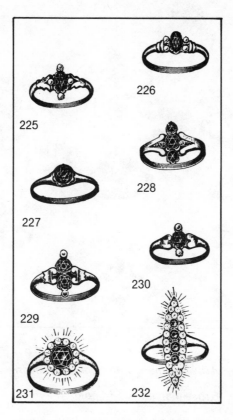

☐ **225** *Sapphire, four pearls, 14K gold, American, c. 1896* **110.00 150.00**
☐ **226** *Sapphire, four pearls, 14K gold, American, c. 1896 .* **85.00 100.00**
☑ **227** *Sapphire, 14K gold, American, c. 1896 . . . .* **100.00 135.00**
☐ **228** *Sapphires, 14K gold, American, c. 1896 . . . .* **150.00 200.00**
☐ **229** *Sapphires, two pearls, 14K gold, American,*
  c. 1896. . . . . **135.00 170.00**
☐ **230** *Sapphire, two pearls, 14K gold, American, c. 1896* **100.00 135.00**
☐ **231** *Sapphire, 12 rose diamonds, 14K gold, American,*
  c. 1896. . . . . **325.00 375.00**
☐ **232** *Sapphires, 22 rose diamonds, 14K gold, Ameri-*
  can, c. 1896. . . . . **400.00 450.00**

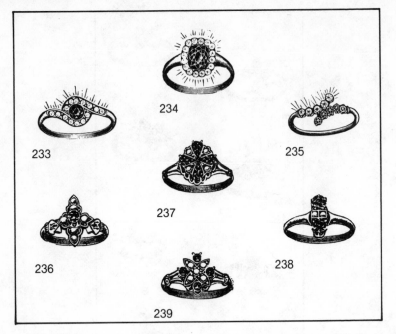

233 *Sapphire, 14 rose diamonds, 14K gold, American, c. 1896*................................... **280.00** **340.00**

☐ **234** *Sapphire, 16 rose diamonds, 14K gold, American, c. 1896*................................... **550.00** **650.00**

☐ **235** *Sapphires, five rose diamonds, 14K gold, American, c. 1896*.............................. **290.00** **340.00**

☐ **236** *Sapphire, six pearls, 14K gold, American, c. 1895* **140.00** **180.00**

☐ **237** *Sapphires, four pearls, 14K gold, American, c. 1895*.................................. **150.00** **200.00**

☐ **238** *Sapphires, two pearls, 14K gold, American, c. 1895*.................................. **110.00** **150.00**

☐ **239** *Sapphires, five pearls, 14K gold, American, c. 1895*.................................. **175.00** **225.00**

240

241

243

242

244

245

246

□ **240** Sapphire: cabochon, round diamonds, silver topped gold, c. 1925 . . . . **3000.00 3300.00**

□ **241** Sapphire, 9K gold, English, c. 20th **150.00 200.00**

□ **242** Sardonyx plaque with four pear-shape diamonds approximately .80 ct., 14K gold, American, c. 1930-40 . . . . **900.00 1200.00**

□ **243** Scarab, sardonyx, 14K gold, c. mid 19th **150.00 200.00**

□ **244** Seed pearl, engraved band, gold, c. 1880 . . . . **90.00 125.00**

□ **245** Seed pearl pavé set, garnet in center, 14K gold, c. late 19th **65.00 100.00**

□ **246** Seed pearls, calibre turquoise, gold, c. 1850 . . . . **115.00 130.00**

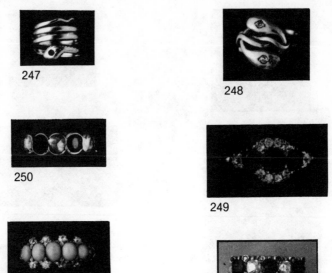

247

248

250

249

251

252

253

☐	**247**	Snake motif, one diamond, gold, c. 20th	**225.00**	**250.00**
☐	**248**	Snake motif, two round diamonds, 14K gold, American, c. 1915	**300.00**	**350.00**
☐	**249**	Straight row motif, three round sapphires approximately .40 ct., ten old mine diamonds approximately .18 ct., 18K gold, Chester, England, c. 1896.	**1200.00**	**1600.00**
☐	**250**	Straight row motif, two garnets, three rose diamonds, collet-set, gold, c. 1850	**800.00**	**1000.00**
☐	**251**	Straight row motif, five cabochon turquoise, rose diamonds, gold, c. 1850	**700.00**	**900.00**
☐	**252**	Straight row motif, three round rubies, two old mine diamonds, small rose diamonds, 18K gold, c. 1870.	**1500.00**	**1600.00**
☐	**253**	Straight row motif, one round diamond approximately 1.70 cts. in center, two round sapphires, two round diamonds approximately .90 ct., gold, c. 1880.	**5000.00**	**5500.00**

254

257

255

258

256

259   260

☐ **254** *Synthetic sapphires, one emerald-cut diamond*
   approximately .60 ct., platinum, c. 1900 . . . .   **1200.00   1600.00**
☐ **255** *Synthetic sapphires: two triangular-shape and*
   numerous calibre-cut, round diamonds, Art
   Deco, c. 1930 . . . .   **500.00   700.00**
☐ **256** *Synthetic coral, sterling, c. 1930* **25.00   50.00**
☐ **257** *Synthetic ruby in center, one round emerald, 18*
   diamond chips, 14K gold, c. 1870 . . . .   **250.00   350.00**
☐ **258** *Synthetic emerald, 14K gold, c. late 19th* **100.00   125.00**
☐ **259** *Topaz, two rose diamonds, 14K gold, American,*
   c. 1896 . . . .   **240.00   280.00**
☐ **260** *Topaz, five pearls, 14K gold, American, c. 1895* . .   **125.00   165.00**

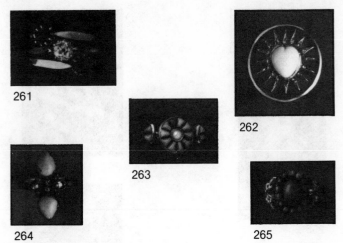

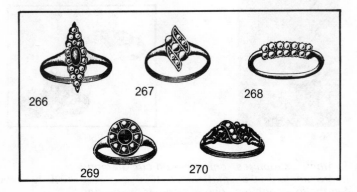

261 *Triple band motif, one round sapphire, one round diamond, one round ruby, each stone approximately .25 ct., 14K gold, American, c. 1930-40* ... **800.00 1200.00**

☐ **262** *Turquoise heart, 16 rose diamonds, gold, c. 1870* **300.00 450.00**

☐ **263** *Turquoise: calibre, pearl, gold, c. 1840* **250.00 350.00**

☐ **264** *Turquoise: pear-shape, diamonds, gold, c. 1860* . **350.00 450.00**

☐ **265** *Turquoise, gold, c. 1850* **300.00 400.00**

☐ **266** *Turquoise, 16 pearls, 14K gold, American, c. 1896* **90.00 120.00**

☐ **267** *Turquoise, four pearls, 14K gold, American, c. 1896* **90.00 120.00**

☐ **268** *Turquoise, seven pearls, 14K gold, American, c. 1896* **140.00 180.00**

☐ **269** *Turquoise, eight pearls, 14K gold, American, c. 1895* **140.00 180.00**

☐ **270** *Turquoise, three pearls, 14K gold, American, c. 1895* **140.00 180.00**

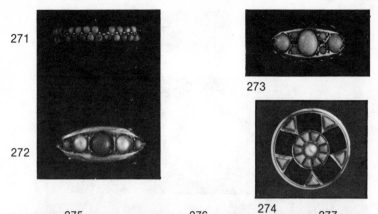

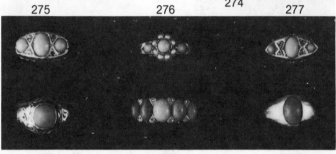

☐ **271** Turquoise pavé set band, 14K gold, c. 1870	200.00	275.00
☐ **272** Turquoise, two half pearls, 9K gold, Birmingham, England, c. early 20th	125.00	150.00
☐ **273** Turquoise, four round corals, maker: C L, 9K gold, Chester, England, c. 1928	135.00	165.00
☐ **274** Turquoise: calibre and triangular-cut, seed pearl center, champlevé black enamel, 15K gold, c. late 19th	500.00	600.00
☐ **275** Turquoise: cabochon, four rose diamonds, 15K gold, English, c. 1910	175.00	200.00
☐ **276** Turquoise: cabochon, seed pearls, 18K gold, Birmingham, English, c. 1887	185.00	225.00
☐ **277** Turquoise: cabochon, four rose diamonds, 18K gold, Birmingham, England, c. 1910	175.00	200.00
☐ **278** Turquoise: cabochon, engraved shank, 18K gold inscribed: "Geo. Wood ob. 12 Mar. 1843 at 65," London, England, c. 1817	200.00	250.00
☐ **279** Turquoise: cabochon, eight rose diamonds, 18K gold, English, c. 1880	300.00	350.00
☐ **280** Turquoise: cabochon, 18K gold, maker: J. S., Birmingham, England, c. 1898.	150.00	200.00

281

282

283

284

□ **281** *Turquoise: cabochon, two pearls, 9K gold, Bir-*
mingham, England, c. 1900 . . . . **100.00** **135.00**
□ **282** *Turquoise: cabochon, two rose diamonds, 18K*
gold, maker: JR, London, England, c. 1900 . . . . . . **225.00** **275.00**
□ **283** *Turquoise: cabochon, four small cabochon coral,*
9K gold, maker: C. L., Chester, England, c. 1928 . . **150.00** **180.00**
□ **284** *White Opal: cabochon, 28 round diamonds ap-*
proximately 1.50 cts., white gold, c. 1925 . . . . **1500.00** **2000.00**

1

2

LADIES · MISCELLANEOUS

PRICE RANGE

□ **1** *Belt motif, maker: W. W., London, England, 22K*
gold, c. 1904 . . . . **300.00** **350.00**
□ **2** *Enamel angel, gold, c. 1870* **350.00** **450.00**

3

4

5

6

7

8

☐	**3**	*Enamel face of Ceres, the goddess of agriculture in Roman mythology, gold, c. 1890*	**400.00**	**500.00**
☐	**4**	*Gold nugget on 14K gold band, c. 1890*	**300.00**	**400.00**
☐	**5**	*Hands holding an oval center of a cabochon garnet and eight diamonds, gold, c. 1880*	**500.00**	**600.00**
☐	**6**	*Hands holding cabochon garnet surrounded by diamonds, modified gimmal ring, gold, c. 1850* ..	**600.00**	**800.00**
☐	**7**	*Hidden compartment, shell cameo of gentleman in cover, gold, c. 1820*	**300.00**	**400.00**
☐	**8**	*Hidden compartment, onyx shield in cover, gold, c. 1860*	**200.00**	**300.00**

9

10

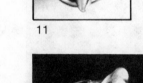

12

13

11

14

15

☐	**9**	Key to jewelry box hinged to fit under plain rectangular plaque for monogram, gold, English, c. 1880	400.00	500.00
☐	**10**	Sculptured childs face, two baroque pearls, two round rubies, Art Nouveau, c. 1890-1910	600.00	700.00
☐	**11**	Snake, five round diamonds, gold	600.00	700.00
☐	**12**	Snake, ruby in head, diamond eyes, gold, c. 1840	250.00	300.00
☐	**13**	Snake, natural fancy color diamond approximately 1.0 ct. in head, rose diamond eyes, gold, c. 1860	2800.00	3200.00
☐	**14**	Snakes, opal and amethyst in heads, maker: A. C. Co., Birmimgham, England, 9K gold	250.00	350.00
☐	**15**	Sphinx carved from garnet, inlaid with gold and two rose diamonds, border of rose diamonds in silver, 18K gold band, c. 1870	5000.00	6000.00

16   17

☐   **16**   *Vinaigrette ring, silver, maker: H.W.D., London,*
         England, c. 1869 . . . .   **400.00**   **500.00**
☐   **17**   *Vinaigrette ring, swivels, carnelian on reverse,*
         gold, c. late 18th **500.00**   **600.00**

1

3

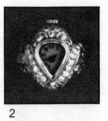

2

WATCH

                                                  PRICE RANGE

☐   **1**   *Watch ring, rose diamonds, enamel dial, steel*
       hands, white gold case, maker: Nomos, c. 1920 . .   **1200.00**   **1500.00**
☐   **2**   *Watch ring, round and fancy-cut diamonds,*
       enamel dial, steel hands, platinum case, c. 1925 .   **5500.00**   **6500.00**
☐   **3**   *Watch ring, oval Art Deco motif, polychrome*
       enamels, white enamel dial, steel hands, 18K
       gold case, c. 1930 . . . .   **1500.00**   **1600.00**

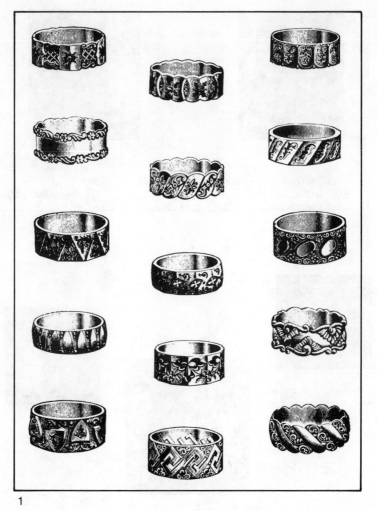

1

WEDDING BAND

PRICE RANGE

☐ **1** *Fancy cutout and shaped motif, engraved and chased, 14K gold, American, c. 1896* **175.00** **325.00**

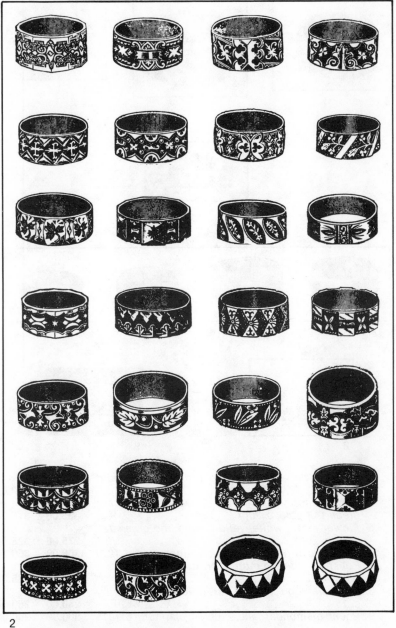

2

□ **2** *Fancy engraved and chased motifs, 14K gold, American, c. 1894-95, each* **150.00** **250.00**

3

4

5

6

7

8

9

☐	**3**	*Bird and flower motif, rose and green 14K gold, c. 20th*	**175.00**	**200.00**
☐	**4**	*Flower motif, round rubies, yellow, rose and green 14K gold, c. 20th*	**325.00**	**375.00**
☐	**5**	*Flower motif, white, yellow, rose and green 14K gold, c. 20th*	**275.00**	**325.00**
☐	**6**	*Heart and arrow motif, black enamel, gold, c. 1900*	**300.00**	**350.00**
☐	**7**	*Polished rounded motif, 14K gold, American, c. 1894-95*	**65.00**	**125.00**
☐	**8**	*Rose diamond, chased 14K gold, American, c. 1896*	**240.00**	**260.00**
☐	**9**	*Round diamonds, calibre rubies, platinum, c. 1915*	**800.00**	**900.00**

Late Victorian photograph of a man and wife with the husband wearing a hair watch chain probably woven from strands of his wife's hair.

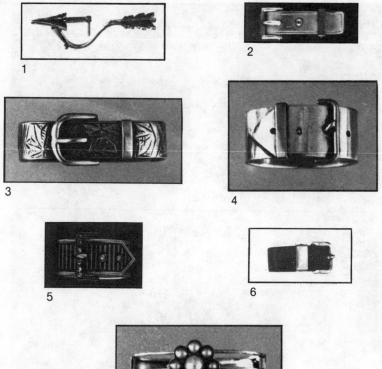

SCARF RINGS and STICKPINS

SCARF RINGS

			PRICE RANGE	
☐	1	Arrow motif, garnets, gold, c. 1900-10	200.00	240.00
☐	2	Belt motif, three old mine diamonds, gold, c. 1900-10	185.00	225.00
☐	3	Belt motif, engraved leaves, sterling silver, c. 1890	95.00	125.00
☐	4	Belt motif, sterling, maker: S.J.R., London, England, c. 1957	80.00	100.00
☐	5	Belt motif, black enamel, half seed pearls, rose diamonds, gold, c. 1890-1900	225.00	240.00
☐	6	Belt motif, tortoise shell, silver, c. 1890-1910	75.00	100.00
☐	7	Cluster motif, pearls, gold, c. 1900-10	175.00	225.00

8

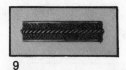

9

10

11

13

12

14

☐ **8** *Etruscan granulation and rope motif, gold,*
c. 1900-10 .... **125.00** **165.00**

☐ **9** *Etruscan granulation and rope motif, 15K gold,*
maker: A & W, English, c. 19th **200.00** **235.00**

☐ **10** *Flower motif, gold, c. late 19th* **650.00** **700.00**

☐ **11** *Flower motif, green, rose and yellow gold,*
c. 1900-10 .... **125.00** **165.00**

☐ **12** *Flower motif, one cushion cut diamond approx.*
.15 ct., gold, registration mark of February 13,
1878 .... **300.00** **350.00**

☐ **13** *Flower motif, six seed pearls, four turquoise,*
gold, c. 1900-10 .... **150.00** **200.00**

☐ **14** *Flower motif, 20K gold, maker: HS, English,*
c. 19th **250.00** **380.00**

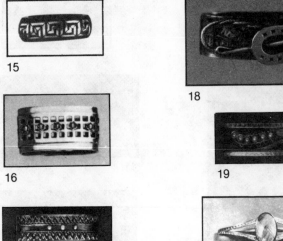

15

18

16

19

17

20

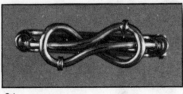

21

	15	Greek key motif, pique: tortoise shell inlaid with gold, c. late 19th	125.00	150.00
	16	Grill motif, five seed pearls, gold, c. 1900-10.....	175.00	225.00
	17	Heart border motif, three seed pearls, gold, c. 1900-10	125.00	165.00
	18	Horseshoe and riding crop motif, engraved sterling silver, c. 1900-10	85.00	115.00
	19	Lily-of-the-valley flower motif, champlevé black enamel, seed pearls, gold, c. 1870	175.00	200.00
	20	Locket motif, hair in basketweave pattern, engraved gold, c. 1880.........................	200.00	235.00
	21	Loveknot motif, gold, c. 1900-10...............	200.00	220.00

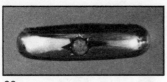

22

23

24

25

26

27

28

☐	**22**	*Single stone motif, opal, gold, c. 1900-10*	**150.00** **175.00**
☐	**23**	*Snake motif, ruby eyes, seven baroque pearls, two wing pearls, gold, c. 1880*.	**300.00** **350.00**
☐	**24**	*Star motif, one faceted garnet, 9K gold, English, c. 1900-10*	**150.00** **175.00**
☐	**25**	*Straight line motif, four garnets, three seed pearls, Etruscan granulation, 9K gold, English, c. 1900-10*	**275.00** **300.00**
☐	**26**	*Straight line motif, three half seed pearls, gold, c. 1900-10*	**160.00** **180.00**
☐	**27**	*Swirl motif, engraved, 15K gold, English, c. 19th* .	**125.00** **150.00**
☐	**28**	*Woven hair motif, gold shield for initials, c. 1840-60*	**85.00** **125.00**

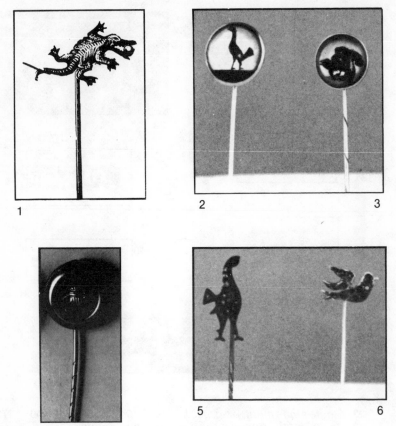

1

2

3

4

5

6

STICKPINS · ANIMALS and BUGS

PRICE RANGE

☐	1	*Alligator, one seed pearl, 14K gold, American, c. 1896*	100.00	125.00
☐	2	*Bird, reverse painting under crystal, gold, c. 19th*	100.00	125.00
☐	3	*Bird, reverse painting under crystal, gold, c. 19th*	100.00	125.00
☐	4	*Beetle, gold, c. 1870*	85.00	135.00
☐	5	*Bird, rose diamonds, silver, gold, c. 1860*	200.00	225.00
☐	6	*Bird, rose diamonds in body, ruby in eye, gold, c. early 20th*	100.00	125.00

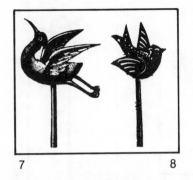

7   8

9

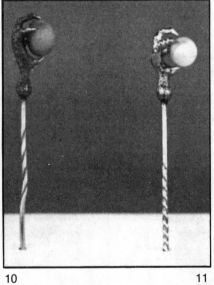

10   11

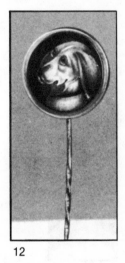

12

☐	**7**	*Bird, 14K rose and yellow gold, American, c. 1894-95*	**90.00**	**100.00**
☐	**8**	*Bird, sterling silver, American, c. 1894-95*	**25.00**	**35.00**
☐	**9**	*Bird head, one seed pearl, 14K green gold, American, c. 1894-95*	**110.00**	**125.00**
☐	**10**	*Bird claw, button-shape coral, gold, c. 1880*	**125.00**	**150.00**
☐	**11**	*Bird claw, pearl, gold, c. 1880*	**125.00**	**150.00**
☐	**12**	*Bloodhound painted on ivory, gold, English, c. 1865*	**265.00**	**315.00**

13

14

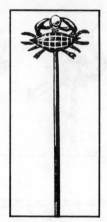

15

16

17

18

	13	Bug, sterling silver, American, c. 1896	30.00	40.00
☐	13	*Bug, sterling silver, American, c. 1896*	30.00	40.00
☐	14	*Butterfly, sterling silver, American, c. 1896*	25.00	35.00
☐	15	*Crab, one seed pearl, 14K gold, American, c. 1896*	65.00	85.00
☐	16	*Deer head, rose diamond eyes, gold, c. early 20th*	100.00	135.00
☐	17	*Dog, carved coral, gold, c. 19th*	120.00	140.00
☐	18	*Dog, carved ivory, gold, c. 19th*	120.00	140.00

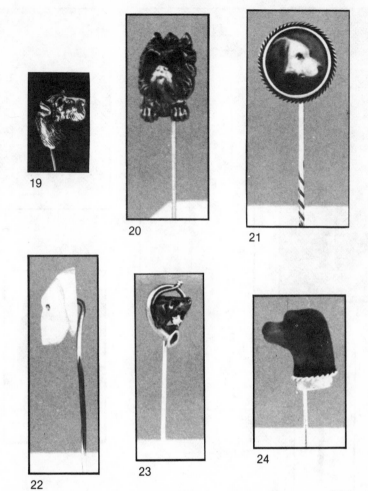

19

20

21

22

23

24

☐	**19**	*Dog head, gold, c. 20th*	65.00	85.00
☐	**20**	*Dog head, glass beads in eyes, gold filled, c. 20th*	35.00	45.00
☐	**21**	*Dog's head painted on porcelain, gold, c. 1865* ..	245.00	285.00
☐	**22**	*Dog head, carved ivory, yellow metal pin, c. 20th* .	45.00	60.00
☐	**23**	*Dog head with horn, translucent brown and gold enamel, one round diamond, gold, c. 1920*	225.00	250.00
☐	**24**	*Dog head, carved amethyst, gold, c. 1915*	500.00	600.00

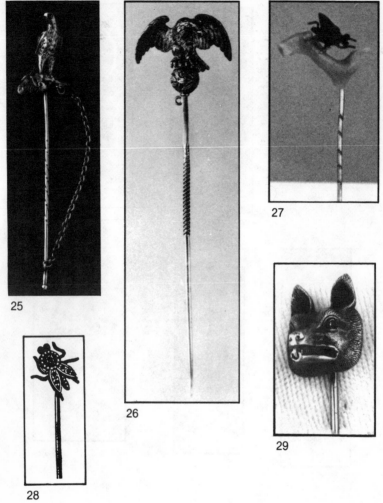

25

26

27

29

28

☐	**25**	*Eagle, carved, rose diamond eyes, gold, c. late 19th*	**1200.00** **1400.00**
☐	**26**	*Eagle, carved, gold, c. 19th*	**1200.00** **1400.00**
☐	**27**	*Fly, carved tortoise shell, branch coral, gold filled pin, c. 19th*	**35.00** **45.00**
☐	**28**	*Fly, garnets, 14K gold, American, c. 1894-95*	**85.00** **95.00**
☐	**29**	*Fox head, rubies in eyes, gold, c. 19th*	**130.00** **160.00**

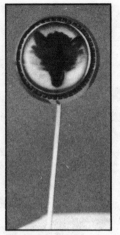

30

31

32

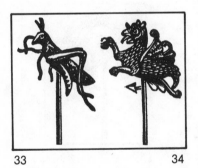

33   34

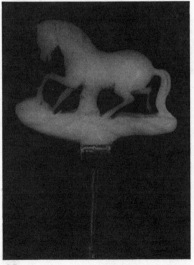

35

☐	**30**	*Fox head, reverse painting under crystal, gold, c. 19th*	300.00 325.00
☐	**31**	*Frog, 14K gold, American, c. 1896*	100.00 125.00
☐	**32**	*Gargoyle, one round diamond, one round cabo-chon jade, gold, c. 1900*	175.00 200.00
☐	**33**	*Grasshopper, 14K gold, American, c. 1894-95* . . .	75.00 95.00
☐	**34**	*Griffin, 14K gold, American, c. 1894-95*	90.00- 100.00
☐		*Same as above but gold filled*	15.00 20.00
☐	**35**	*Horse, carved ivory, gold, c. 19th*	150.00 175.00

36

38   39

37   40

☐	**36**	*Horse, carved tortoise shell, gold pin, c. 1850* . . .	300.00	350.00
☐	**37**	*Horse head painted on porcelain, gold, c. 19th* . .	150.00	165.00
☐	**38**	*Horse and rider, gold, c. 19th*	185.00	200.00
☐	**39**	*Poodle, gold, c. c. 20th*	125.00	145.00
☐	**40**	*Horse head with horseshoe, eight round diamonds, 14K gold, American, c. 1894-95*	225.00	250.00

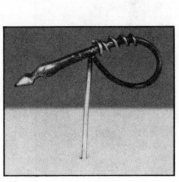

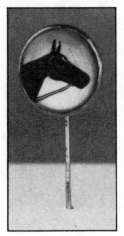

42

41

43

44

45

46

47

48

49

50   51

52

53

☐	**47**	Mouse with trap inscribed "Not For Joseph," gold, c. 20th	**425.00 450.00**
☐	**48**	Mouse with pipe, mouse is bronze, pipe is gold and platinum, c. 19th	**400.00 435.00**
☐	**49**	Mythological animal, one seed pearl, gold, c. 1890	**120.00 140.00**
☐	**50**	Owl, 14K gold, American, c. 1894-95	**50.00 60.00**
☐		Same as above but gold filled	**15.00 20.00**
☐	**51**	Owl, 14K gold, American, c. 1894-95	**50.00 60.00**
☐		Same as above but gold filled	**15.00 20.00**
☐	**52**	Parrot, cabochon turquoise breast, seed pearl wings, cabochon ruby eyes, silver, gold pin, c. 1860	**350.00 400.00**
☐	**53**	Scottish Terrier, reverse painting under crystal, gold, c. 20th	**110.00 125.00**

54

55

56

57

58

59

60

☐	**54** *Snake, one pearl, diamonds, platinum, gold pin, c. 20th*	500.00	550.00
☐	**55** *Snake, cobalt-blue enamel, one pearl, gold, c. 1860*	225.00	250.00
☐	**56** *Snake, woven hair body, ruby eyes, gold, c. mid 19th*	250.00	300.00
☐	**57** *Snake, one round emerald in head, two moonstone balls, 14K gold, American, c. 1894-95*	140.00	160.00
☐	**58** *Snake, one round garnet, 14K gold, American, c. 1894-95*	85.00	110.00
☐	**59** *Spider, silver, c. 19th*	40.00	50.00
☐	**60** *Tiger claw, engraved mountings, gold, c. 1870* ...	225.00	250.00

61

62

63

64

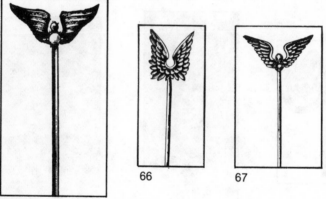

65

66

67

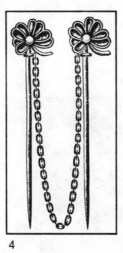

STICKPINS · FLOWERS

		PRICE RANGE	
☐	**1** *Black enamel, one seed pearl, 14K gold, American, c. 1898*	80.00	100.00
☐	**2** *Black onyx, 14K gold, American, c. 1896*	40.00	60.00
☐	**3** *Black onyx, 14K gold, American, c. 1896*	60.00	80.00
☐	**4** *Chain connected pair, two seed pearls, 14K gold, American, c. 1894-95*	150.00	165.00
☐	**5** *Diamond: one round, 14K gold, American, c. 1894-95*	100.00	125.00
☐	**6** *Diamonds: three round, 14K gold, American, c. 1894-95*	200.00	250.00

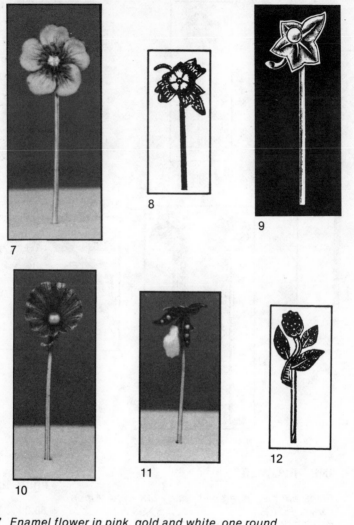

7

8

9

10

11

12

☐ **7** *Enamel flower in pink, gold and white, one round diamond, gold, c. 19th* **225.00** **275.00**

☐ **8** *Enamel flower on leaf, 14K gold, American, c. 1894-95* **50.00** **70.00**

☐ **9** *Enameled leaf, one seed pearl, 14K gold, American, c. 1896* **50.00** **70.00**

☐ **10** *Fan motif flower, engraved, seed pearl, gold, c. 20th* **90.00** **120.00**

☐ **11** *Fresh water pearl flower, seed pearls in leaves, gold, c. 20th* **50.00** **60.00**

☐ **12** *Garnet, 14K gold, American, c. 1894-95* **40.00** **60.00**

13

14

15

16

17

☐	**13**	Gold flower, one round diamond, c. 20th	85.00	125.00
☐	**14**	Hardstone cameo of a flower, buckle motif frame, gold, English, c. 19th	150.00	175.00
☐	**15**	Ivory cameo of a bouquet of flowers, rose gold, c. 19th	150.00	175.00
☐	**16**	Ivory carving of a flower, one round garnet, yellow metal, c. 19th	65.00	85.00
☐	**17**	Ivy leaves, one seed pearl, 14K gold, American, c. 1896	50.00	70.00

18   19

20

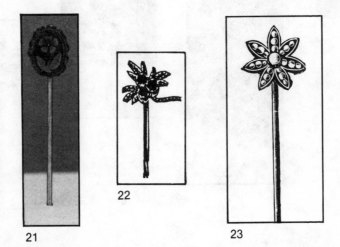

21   22   23

☐	**18**	*Leaf, sterling silver, American, c. 1894-95*	**15.00**	**20.00**
☐	**19**	*Moonstones, 14K gold, American, c. 1894-95*	**50.00**	**65.00**
☐	**20**	*Mosaic, gold, French, c. 19th*	**200.00**	**240.00**
☐	**21**	*Onyx cameo of a flower, gold, c. 20th*	**75.00**	**85.00**
☐	**22**	*Ruby, emerald, sapphire, 14K gold, American,*		
		c. 1894-95	**100.00**	**125.00**
☐	**23**	*Seed pearls, 14K gold, American, c. 1896*	**70.00**	**90.00**

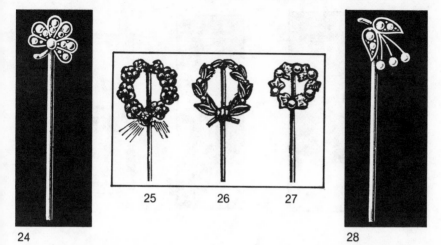

24   28

29   30   31   32   33

☐	24	*Seed pearls, 14K gold, American, c. 1896*	**60.00**	**80.00**
☐	25	*Wreath, one round diamond, 14K gold, American,*		
		c. 1894-95	**70.00**	**90.00**
☐	26	*Wreath, 14K green and yellow gold, American,*		
		c. 1894-95	**40.00**	**60.00**
☐	27	*Wreath, six seed pearls, 14K gold, American,*		
		c. 1894-95	**50.00**	**70.00**
☐	28	*Seed pearls, 14K gold, American, c. 1896*	**50.00**	**70.00**
☐	29	*Seed pearls, one cabochon turquoise, 14K gold,*		
		American, c. 1894-95	**70.00**	**90.00**
☐	30	*Seed pearls, one cabochon turquoise, 14K gold,*		
		American, c. 1894-95	**60.00**	**80.00**
☐	31	*Sheaf of wheat and sickle motif, 14K gold, Ameri-*		
		can, c. 1894-95	**60.00**	**80.00**
☐	32	*Thistle, one round diamond, 14K gold, American,*		
		c. 1894-95	**100.00**	**125.00**
☐	33	*Three-leaf clover, sterling silver, American,*		
		c. 1894-95	**20.00**	**30.00**

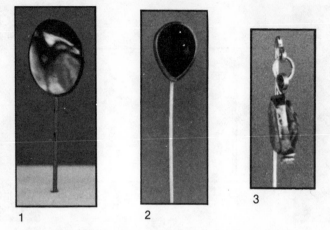

1 2 3

4 5 6 7

STICKPINS · GEMSTONE

			PRICE RANGE	
☐	1	*Abalone, sterling silver, American, c. 20th*	25.00	40.00
☐	2	*Almondine garnet: pear-shape, gold, c. 20th*	165.00	185.00
☐	3	*Ancient scarab, gold, converted to stick pin, c. 20th*	125.00	150.00
☐	4	*Amethyst, 14 old mine diamonds approximately .70 ct., gold, c. 19th*	600.00	650.00
☐	5	*Monkey, one round diamond, 18K gold, c. 20th* ..	240.00	280.00
☐	6	*Bow motif, blue and white enamel, one round diamond, gold, c. 20th*	125.00	145.00
☐	7	*Crystal carved petals, one round diamond, gold c. 20th*	165.00	185.00

8

9

10

11

12

☐	**8**	*Anchor and buoy motif, cabochon turquoise, connecting chain, gold, c. 1830. Pair*	**600.00** **650.00**
☐	**9**	*Aquamarine: square-cut, one seed pearl, 14K gold, c. 20th*	**130.00** **160.00**
☐	**10**	*Aquamarine, Art Nouveau, gold, c. 1880*	**90.00** **120.00**
☐	**11**	*Aquamarine: one pear-shape, one round diamond, 14K white gold, American, c. 1930*	**150.00** **175.00**
☐	**12**	*Baby rattle, coral, silver bells, gold, contemporary pin, c. 19th*	**400.00** **500.00**

14

13

15

16   **17**

☐	**13**	Battle ax motif, sterling silver, American, c. 1894-95	**20.00** **30.00**
☐	**14**	Battle ax motif, two seed pearls, 14K gold, American, c. 1896.	**70.00** **90.00**
☐	**15**	Battle ax motif, blue enamel, 14K gold, American, c. 1896.	**60.00** **80.00**
☐	**16**	Battle ax motif, ten seed pearls, one cabochon turquoise, 14K gold, American, c. 1894-95	**115.00** **145.00**
☐	**17**	Battle ax motif, five seed pearls, 14K gold, American, c. 1894-95	**70.00** **90.00**

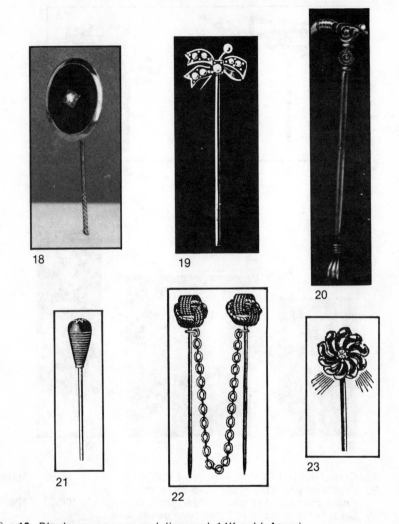

18

19

20

21

22

23

24 25 26 27

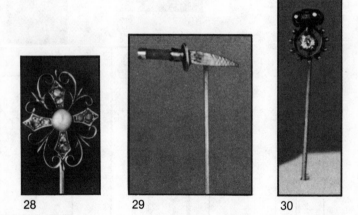

28 29 30

☐	24	Cornet motif, 14K gold, American, c. 1894-95	80.00	100.00
☐	25	Crescent and star motif, five seed pearls, one round diamond, 14K gold, American, c. 1894-95 . .	100.00	125.00
☐	26	Crescent and star motif, five seed pearls, one cabochon turquoise, 14K gold, American, c. 1894-95	60.00	80.00
☐	27	Flower motif, seed pearls, 14K gold, American, c. 1894-95	70.00	90.00
☐	28	Cruciform motif, one pearl, rose diamonds, gold, French, c. 1830	165.00	180.00
☐	29	Dagger motif, coral handle, gold, c. 19th	80.00	100.00
☐	30	Diamond: one round, gold, c. 1860	125.00	150.00

COLORPLATE #1

PRICE RANGE

☐ **1** *Pendant, cabochon garnets, emerald, chryso-beryl, enamel borders, finely engraved back, gold, c. 1860's* 4000.00 4500.00

☐ **2** *Pendant, heart motif, amethyst, seed pearls, gold, c. 19th* 300.00 350.00

☐ **3** *Pendant, amethyst cameo, round diamonds, pearls, platinum, Edwardian, c. 1901-1910* 2500.00 3000.00

☐ **4** *Pendant, heart motif, seed pearls pavé, one round diamond, gold, Victorian* 250.00 300.00

☐ **5** *Pendant or brooch, opals, diamonds, gold, silver, c. 1860's* 3500.00 4000.00

☐ **6** *Brooch, rose motif, diamonds, enamel, gold, Vic-torian* 2500.00 3000.00

☐ **7** *Locket, heart motif, turquoise, diamonds, hinged crystal back, silver, gold, Victorian* 3000.00 3500.00

☐ **8** *Earrings, cultured pearls, diamonds, platinum, c. 1930's* 8000.00 10000.00

☐ **9** *Brooch, pansy motif, carved opal, diamonds, platinum, Edwardian, c. 1901-1910* 1800.00 2200.00

☐ **10** *Locket, heart motif, turquoise, hammered gold, hinged back, Victorian* 150.00 200.00

☐ **11** *Locket, heart motif, seed pearls pavé, diamond, gold, Victorian* 350.00 400.00

☐ **12** *Pendant, heart with Cupid fanning flames of love motif, enamel, gold, French, c. 18th* 600.00 800.00

☐ **13** *Ring, blister pearl, diamonds, gold, platinum, c. 1930's* 800.00 1200.00

☐ **14** *Earrings, natural blue pearls, rose diamonds, Ed-wardian, c. 1901-1910* 1000.00 1200.00

☐ **15** *Earrings, scroll motif, real pearls, round and baguette diamonds, platinum, c. 1920's* 4500.00 5000.00

☐ **16** *Pendant, heart motif, moonstone, seed pearls, gold, Victorian* 250.00 300.00

☐ **17** *Brooch, horseshoe motif, diamonds, jockey with gold cap, moonstone face, citrine vest and sleeves, Victorian* 1500.00 1800.00

☐ **18** *Earrings, blister pearls, diamonds, gold, plati-num, c. 1930's* 1500.00 1800.00

☐ **19** *Brooch, fly motif, natural pearl, ruby, diamonds, silver, gold, c. 1860's* 1400.00 1600.00

COLORPLATE #2

PRICE RANGE

☐ **1** *Locket, double photo compartments, wreath motif, turquoise, natural seed pearls, gold, Victorian* 250.00   300.00

☐ **2** *Brooch or pendant, griffin motif, rose diamonds, 1 round diamond approx. 75 pts., cast and chased gold, French, c. 19th* 2500.00   2800.00

☐ **3** *Pendant, Renaissance motif, diamonds, ruby, natural pearls, gold* 700.00   900.00

☐ **4** *Brooch, honeycomb and mistletoe motif, blue glass, rose diamonds, natural pearls, platinum, Edwardian, c. 1910* 800.00   900.00

☐ **5** *Brooch, diamonds, natural pearls, baby-blue enamel, chased gold, c. 1840* 600.00   800.00

☐ **6** *Brooch, diamonds, demantoid garnets, gold, Victorian* 550.00   650.00

☐ **7** *Brooch, "Rain Cloud & Lightning" motif, round diamonds, pearls, platinum, 14K gold, c. 1900* ... 650.00   750.00

☐ **8** *Brooch, Limoges enamel plaques, rose diamonds, platinum, gold maker: Janesich, Paris* ... 4500.00   5000.00

☐ **9** *Locket, single photo compartment, 1 round diamond, platinum, c. 1920* 1200.00   1500.00

☐ **10** *Pendant, hardstone cameo, gold frame, c. late 18th*   800.00   1000.00

☐ **11** *Brooch, dragon and scroll motif, diamond, natural pearls, cast and chased gold, French, c. 19th* 1400.00   1600.00

☐ **12** *Brooch, enamel miniature of Cupid, rose diamonds, gold, silver, French, c. 18th* 1500.00   1800.00

☐ **13** *Brooch, crescent motif, opals, rose diamonds, gold, Victorian* 650.00   800.00

☐ **14** *Brooch, melon motif, green-stained chalcedony, rose diamonds, gold, silver, c. 1840* 1200.00   1500.00

☐ **15** *Pendant, hardstone cameo of Dionysis, gold frame, c. late 18th* 1500.00   1800.00

COLORPLATE #3

PRICE RANGE

- ☐ 1 Pendant, rubies, natural pearl, translucent enamel, gold center medallion by Leon Bottee titled Cybele of 1892, pendant designed by Eugene Grasset in 1898, Art Nouveau, French 12000.00 15000.00
- ☐ 2 Pendant, opal matrix, seed pearls, freshwater pearl, gold, maker: Myrrle Bennett, Art Nouveau, English, c. 1905 .... 800.00 1000.00
- ☐ 3 Pendant or brooch, Montana sapphires, diamonds, seed pearls, translucent enamel, gold, Art Nouveau, English, c. 1900................. 900.00 1200.00
- ☐ 4 Brooch, clip back, diamonds, sapphires, carved hardstone flowers, gold, Art Deco, c. 1925 ...... 1000.00 1400.00
- ☐ 5 Necklace, opals, demantoid garnets, gold, style of Bernard Cuzner of Birmingham, Art Nouveau, English, c. 1910 .... 8000.00 10000.00

COLORPLATE #4

PRICE RANGE

- ☐ 1 Bar pin, fire opal, rose diamonds, enamel, gold, Edwardian, c. 1900 .... 400.00 450.00
- ☐ 2 Brooch, tortoise motif with moveable head, tail and feet, diamonds, demantoid garnets, gold, Victorian, c. 1860.......................... 1200.00 1500.00
- ☐ 3 Brooch, painted porcelain, rubies, diamonds, gold, French, c. 1850 .... 3500.00 4000.00
- ☐ 4 Brooch, butterfly motif, baroque pearl body, ruby eyes, enamel, gold, c. 1860.................. 550.00 650.00
- ☐ 5 Bar pin, diamonds, demantoid garnets, platinum, Edwardian, c. 1905 .... 2500.00 3000.00
- ☐ 6 Miniature watch, rose diamonds, platinum, Edwardian, c. 1905.......................... 8500.00 10000.00
- ☐ 7 Pendant, carved mother-of-pearl heart motif, pearls, gold, c. 1720........................ 1500.00 1800.00
- ☐ 8 Brooch, painted enamel view of Lake Geneva, gold frame, Swiss, c. 1860 .... 1200.00 1600.00
- ☐ 9 Pendant, carved opal of Minerva's head, pearls, enamel, gold, maker: Child & Child, English, c. 1870.................................. 3500.00 4000.00
- ☐ 10 Pendant, cabochon garnets, rose diamonds, gold, c. 1850 .... 1600.00 1800.00
- ☐ 11 Pendant, carved citrine with a scarab beetle on front and cameo of Leda and the Swan on reverse, rose diamonds, gold, c. 1870 .... 1600.00 1800.00

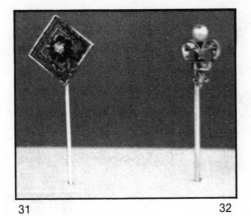

31   32

33

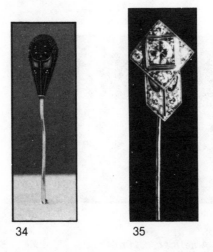

34   35

☐	**31** *Filigree motif, one round diamond, 14K gold, American, c. 1920*	**80.00**	**100.00**
☐	**32** *Fleur-de-lys motif, diamonds, one pearl, platinum, 14K gold, American, c. 1915*	**400.00**	**450.00**
☐	**33** *Fleur-de-lys, white enamel, gold, c. 20th*	**55.00**	**65.00**
☐	**34** *Garnet: one round, Etruscan granulation, gold, c. 1860*.	**80.00**	**90.00**
☐	**35** *Geometric motif, one round diamond approx. .45 ct., six round diamonds approx. .25 ct., platinum, c. 1920*.	**600.00**	**800.00**

37

38

36

39

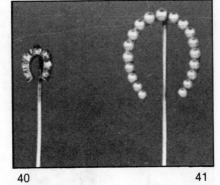

40   41

☐	**36**	Gold dollar, American, c. 20th	300.00	350.00
☐	**37**	Heart motif, one heart-shape opal bordered by rose diamonds, gold, c. 19th.	400.00	450.00
☐	**38**	Heart motif, one round diamond, safety chain and pin, 14K gold, American, c. 1894-95	115.00	145.00
☐	**39**	Horseshoe motif, carved lapis lazuli in center, nine round diamonds approx. 1.75 cts., gold, c. 1910.	1400.00	1600.00
☐	**40**	Horseshoe motif, seven round diamonds approx. .10 pts., 14K gold, American, c. 1910	250.00	275.00
☐	**41**	Horseshoe motif, 19 seed pearls, 14K gold, American, c. 1880	225.00	250.00

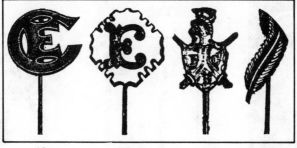

42 43 44 45

46

47

48

☐	**42**	*Initial motif, sterling silver, American, c. 1894-95.*	15.00	20.00
☐	**43**	*Initial motif, carved mother-of-pearl, 14K gold, American, c. 1894-95*	40.00	50.00
☐	**44**	*Knights of Pythias insignia, 14K gold, American, c. 1894-95*	40.00	60.00
☐	**45**	*Leaf motif, 14K gold, American, c. 1894-95*	35.00	50.00
☐		*Same as above but gold filled*	10.00	15.00
☐		*Same as above but sterling silver*	15.00	20.00
☐	**46**	*Lightbulb motif, glass, yellow metal, American, c. 20th*	50.00	75.00
☐	**47**	*Loveknot motif, one seed pearl, 14K gold, American, c. 20th*	50.00	65.00
☐	**48**	*Loveknot motif, one seed pearl, 14K gold, American, c. 1896*	35.00	50.00

49

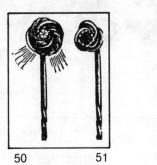

50   51

52

53

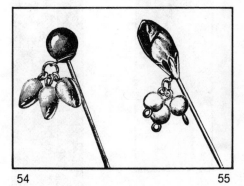

54   55

☐	**49**	*Loveknot motif, 14K gold, American, c. 1896*	**35.00**	**50.00**
☐	**50**	*Loveknot motif, one round diamond, 14K gold, American, c. 1894-95*	**60.00**	**80.00**
☐	**51**	*Loveknot motif, one round ruby, 14K gold, American, c. 1894-95*	**40.00**	**60.00**
☐	**52**	*Masonic insignia, 14K gold, American, c. 1894-95*	**40.00**	**60.00**
☐		*Same as above but gold filled*	**10.00**	**15.00**
☐	**53**	*Natural pearl: approximately 6MM x 7MM, gold, maker: Spaulding & Co., c. 20th*	**200.00**	**250.00**
☐	**54**	*Moonstone ball, three genuine sea shells, 14K gold American, c. 1894-95*	**40.00**	**60.00**
☐	**55**	*Moonstone balls, one genuine sea shell, 14K gold, American, c. 1894-95*	**40.00**	**60.00**

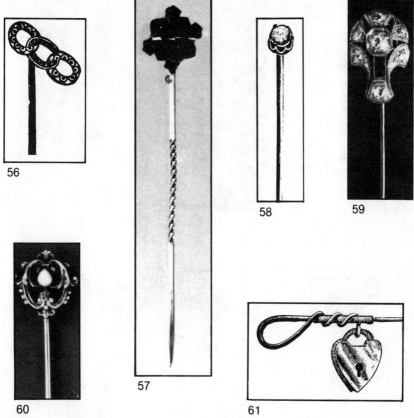

56

58

59

60

57

61

☐	**56**	*Odd Fellows insignia, 14K gold, American,*		
		c. 1894-95	**35.00**	**50.00**
☐		*Same as above but gold filled*	**10.00**	**15.00**
☐	**57**	*Onyx faceted cubes, gold, c. 19th*	**185.00**	**220.00**
☐	**58**	*Opal: cabochon, 14K gold, American, c. 1896....*	**50.00**	**70.00**
☐	**59**	*Openwork motif, seven round diamonds approx.*		
		.75 ct., two square sapphires, platinum, c. 1925..	**375.00**	**450.00**
☐	**60**	*Pearl, gold, French, c. 1870.................*	**65.00**	**85.00**
☐	**61**	*Padlock and riding crop motif, 14K gold, Ameri-*		
		can, c. 1894-95	**70.00**	**90.00**

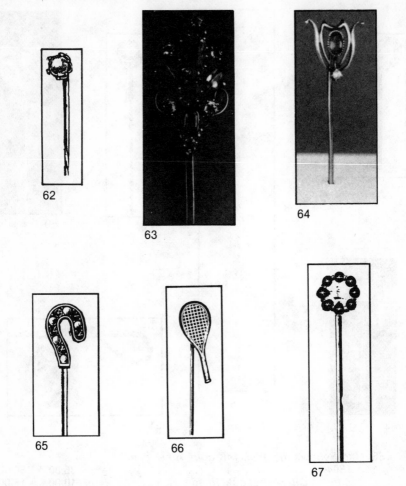

☐	**62**	*Pearl, 14K gold, American, c. 1894-95*	**35.00**	**50.00**
☐	**63**	*Pink tourmaline, silver, c. 19th*	**275.00**	**300.00**
☐	**64**	*Pink tourmaline, diamond, gold, c. 1925*	**85.00**	**100.00**
☐	**65**	*Question mark motif, five seed pearls, five round*		
		rubies, 14K gold, American, c. 1896	**115.00**	**145.00**
☐	**66**	*Racket motif, 14K gold, American, c. 1896*	**40.00**	**60.00**
☐	**67**	*Rubies: eight round, 14K gold, American, c. 1896*	**100.00**	**125.00**

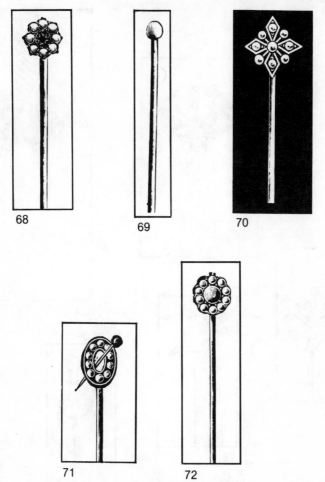

68

69

70

71

72

<table>

☐	**68**	Seed pearls, one round ruby, 14K gold, American, c. 1896	60.00	80.00
☐	**69**	Seed pearl, 14K gold, American, c. 1896	35.00	50.00
☐	**70**	Seed pearls, 14K gold, American, c. 1896	50.00	70.00
☐	**71**	Seed pearls, 14K gold, American, c. 1896	50.00	70.00
☐	**72**	Seed pearls, one cabochon turquoise, 14K gold, American, c. 1896	50.00	70.00

</table>

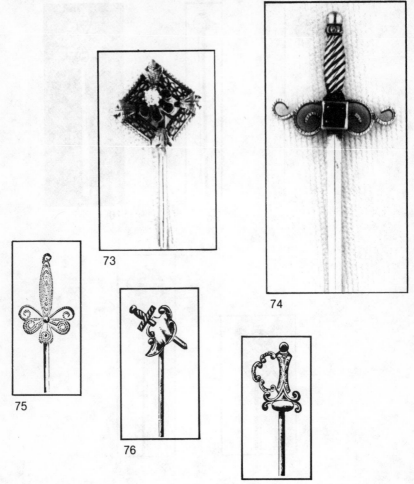

78

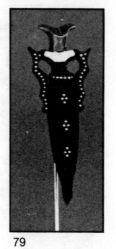

79

80

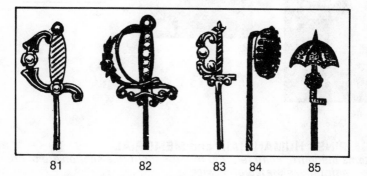

81   82   83 84   85

- ☐ **78** *Sword motif, chain-connected pair, 14K gold, American, c. 1896* **225.00   250.00**
- ☐ **79** *Urn motif, pique: tortoise shell inlaid with gold, gold, c. 1860* **180.00   200.00**
- ☐ **80** *Wishbone motif, one round diamond, 14K gold, American, c. 1894-95* **60.00   80.00**
- ☐ **81** *Sword motif, enamel handle, two seed pearls, 14K gold, American, c. 1894-95* **100.00   125.00**
- ☐ **82** *Sword motif, five seed pearls, 14K gold, American, c. 1894-95* **80.00   100.00**
- ☐ **83** *Sword motif, one seed pearl, 14K gold, American, c. 1894-95* **60.00   80.00**
- ☐ **84** *Topaz, 14K gold, American, c. 1894-95* **50.00   70.00**
- ☐ **85** *Umbrella motif, one round ruby, 14K gold, American, c. 1894-95* **60.00   80.00**

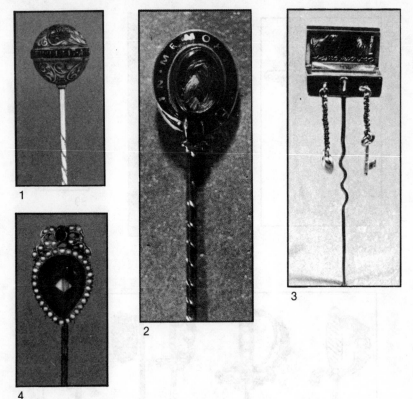

STICK PINS · HUMAN HAIR and MEMORIAL
All items made from hair referred to throughout this section are of brunette human hair unless stated otherwise.

PRICE RANGE

☐ **1** *Ball motif, chased, black enamel band inscribed: "E. D. Davenport Sep. 9, 1847 at 69.," hinge on enamel band with lock of hair under glass inside, gold, English, 1817* **350.00** **400.00**

☐ **2** *Belt motif, black enamel "In Memory Of," basket weave hair under glass, gold, English, c. late 19th* **125.00** **145.00**

☐ **3** *Casket motif, bloodstone top, bottom and sides, heart and key on chains, stalk of hair wrapped with gold wire inside, inscribed: "Chapel Curig Ob. 1813 Absent not Lost," gold, English, c. 1813* **1200.00** **1500.00**

☐ **4** *Heart and bow motif, hair under crystal, seed pearls, one ruby, gold, English, c. 1800* **275.00** **325.00**

6

5

8

7

☐   **5** *Miniature on ivory of initials "NH" and wreath with dissolved hair under glass, gold, English, c. 1790* **250.00**   **300.00**

☐   **6** *Miniature on ivory of gravesite with dissolved hair and sepia paint under glass, black enamel frame "In Memory Of," gold, c. mid 19th* **250.00**   **300.00**

☐   **7** *Miniature of ivory of lamb and tree with sepia paint under glass, signifying the death of a child, gold, c. 1790* **350.00**   **400.00**

☐   **8** *Onyx cameo of a flower, tubular frame filled with woven hair, gold, c. 1860* **125.00**   **150.00**

9

10

11

12

☐	**9**	*Oval motif with shield, woven hair inside oval, gold, c. 1875*	**100.00**	**125.00**
☐	**10**	*Prince of Wales feather motif of white hair and gold thread under glass, chased frame, gold, English, c. 1870*	**150.00**	**175.00**
☐	**11**	*Prince of Wales feather motif of hair with half pearls and gold wire under glass, gold, English, c. 1870*	**100.00**	**125.00**
☐	**12**	*Rope motif, twisted and hollow filled with woven hair, gold, c. 1860*	**125.00**	**150.00**

14

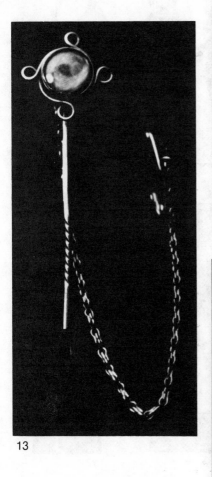

13

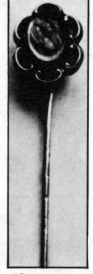

15

16

☐	**13** *Round motif, lock of hair under glass, safety chain, gold, c. 1880*	**65.00**	**85.00**
☐	**14** *Round motif, black enamel "In Memory Of," lock of hair under glass, chased bezel, gold, c. 19th* ..	**85.00**	**100.00**
☐	**15** *Scalloped edge motif, basket weave hair under glass, gold, c. 1880*	**65.00**	**85.00**
☐	**16** *Seed pearl in center, cobalt-blue enamel, reverse: miniature locket with lock of hair, gold, c. 1880*	**200.00**	**250.00**

STICKPINS · PEOPLE and FIGURES

		PRICE RANGE	
☐	**1** *Arm with dumbell motif, 14K gold, American, c. 1894-95*	35.00	50.00
☐	**2** *"Brownie" motif, enameled, silver plate, American, c. 1894-95*	25.00	35.00
☐	**3** *Same as above*	25.00	35.00
☐	**4** *Same as above*	25.00	35.00
☐	**5** *Coral carving of a lady, gold, c. 1860*	150.00	175.00
☐	**6** *Coral carving of Punch, gold, c. 1860*	225.00	275.00
☐	**7** *Cupid, gold, c. 20th*	200.00	225.00

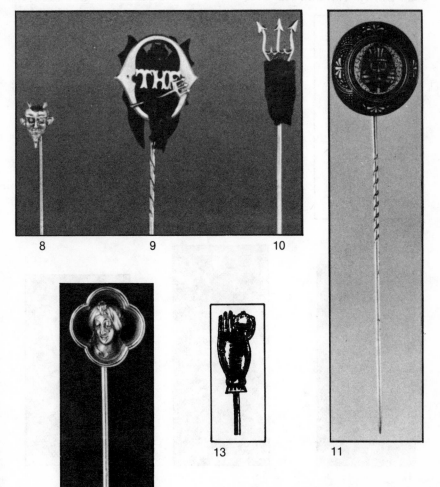

8   9   10

13   11

12

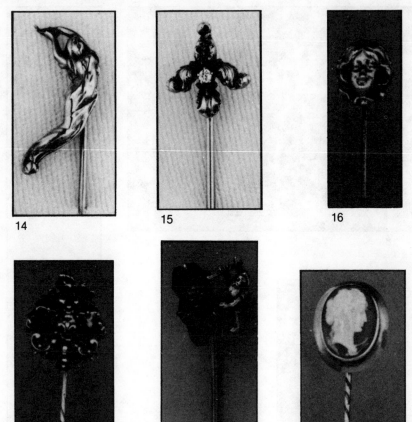

☐	**14**	*Lady, gold, Art Nouveau, c. 1910*	**135.00**	**150.00**
☐	**15**	*Lady motif, one round diamond, Art Nouveau, gold, c. 1890*	**160.00**	**180.00**
☐	**16**	*Lady motif, 14K gold, Art Nouveau, American, c. 1910*.	**125.00**	**140.00**
☐	**17**	*Lady motif, sterling silver, Art Nouveau, American, c. 1910*.	**65.00**	**85.00**
☐	**18**	*Miner, genuine coal lump, silver, gold, English, c. 1876*.	**300.00**	**325.00**
☐	**19**	*Shell cameo of a lady, gold, c. 19th*	**150.00**	**175.00**

20

21

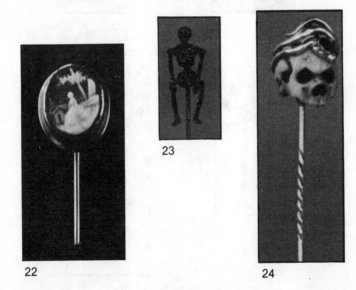

22

23

24

☐	**20**	*Shell cameo of a lady, gold, c. 20th*	**65.00**	**85.00**
☐	**21**	*Shell cameo of a lady, white enamel, yellow metal, c. 20th*	**35.00**	**50.00**
☐	**22**	*Shell cameo of Rebecca-at-the-Well, 14K gold, c. 20th*	**150.00**	**175.00**
☐	**23**	*Skeleton, arms and legs on hinges, silver, c. 20th*	**50.00**	**75.00**
☐	**24**	*Skull with snake, carved ivory, one ruby in snake head, gold, c. 19th*	**500.00**	**600.00**

25

26

27

☐	**25**	*Skull with hinged mask, emerald eyes, silver, gold, c. late 18th*	**800.00**	**900.00**
☐	**26**	*Skull and crossbones motif, 14K gold, American, c. 1894-95*	**75.00**	**85.00**
☐		*Same as above but gold filled*	**10.00**	**15.00**
☐		*Same as above but sterling silver*	**35.00**	**40.00**
☐	**27**	*Winged foot, one round diamond, 14K gold, American, c. 20th*	**325.00**	**350.0**

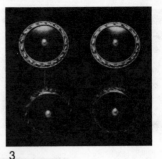

1

2

3

4

5

STUDS AND BUTTONS, CUFF LINKS

CUFF LINKS

			PRICE RANGE	
☐	**1**	*Angel and heart motif, 14K gold, American, c. 1896*	**125.00**	**150.00**
☐		*Same as above but sterling silver*	**75.00**	**85.00**
☐	**2**	*Ball motif, 14K gold, American, c. 1896*	**50.00**	**65.00**
☐	**3**	*Black onyx, four seed pearls, platinum top, gold, maker: Tiffany & Co., c. 1920*	**200.00**	**225.00**
☐	**4**	*Black onyx, four round diamonds, gold, c. 1920*	**500.00**	**550.00**
☐	**5**	*Black onyx, rose diamonds, white gold, cuff links and two studs, c. 1930*	**500.00**	**550.00**

6

7

8

9   10

☐	**6**	*Cabochon oblong opals, chased, gold, c. 1900* ..	**400.00**	**500.00**
☐	**7**	*Cabochon pink and blue star sapphires, gold,*		
		c. 1900.	**575.00**	**625.00**
☐	**8**	*Cabochon turquoise, gold, c. 1840.*	**300.00**	**350.00**
☐	**9**	*Citrines, rose diamonds, gold, c. 1915.*	**400.00**	**425.00**
☐	**10**	*Diamonds: four round, eight fancy-cut sapphires,*		
		platinum top, 14K gold, American, c. 1910	**600.00**	**650.00**

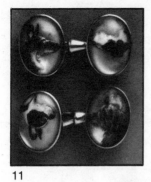

11

12

13

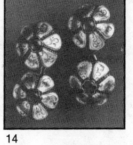

14

15

16

□ **11** *Dog motif, reverse painting under crystal, gold, c. 1870* **500.00 600.00**
□ **12** *Face motif, one with diamonds in eyes and ruby in mouth, one with emeralds in eyes and dia- moand in mouth, gold, c. 1890* **1600.00 1750.00**
□ **13** *Fancy-shape motif, 14K gold, American, c. 1896* . **60.00   70.00**
□   *Same as above but sterling silver* **25.00   35.00**
□ **14** *Flower motif, four cabochon garnets, gold, c. 1820* **300.00 350.00**
□ **15** *Flower motif, 14K gold, American, c. 1896* **60.00   70.00**
□   *Same as above but sterling silver* **25.00   35.00**
□ **16** *Flower motif, 14K gold, American, c. 1896* **75.00   85.00**
□   *Same as above but sterling silver* **30.00   35.00**

17

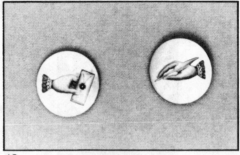

18

19

20

21

☐	**17**	Flower motif, 14K gold, American, c. 1896	**125.00**	**150.00**
☐		Same as above but sterling silver	**75.00**	**85.00**
☐	**18**	Lady hand enameled motif with quill pen and envelope, one round ruby, gold, c. late 19th	**400.00**	**450.00**
☐	**19**	Lever sleeve button, rectangular flower motif, 14K gold, American, c. 1896	**35.00**	**45.00**
☐		Same as above but gold filled	**10.00**	**15.00**
☐	**20**	Lever sleeve button, round engraved motif, 14K gold, American, c. 1896	**35.00**	**45.00**
☐		Same as above but gold filled	**10.00**	**15.00**
☐	**21**	Lever sleeve button, oval flower motif, 14K gold, American, c. 1896	**35.00**	**45.00**
☐		Same as above but gold filled	**10.00**	**15.00**

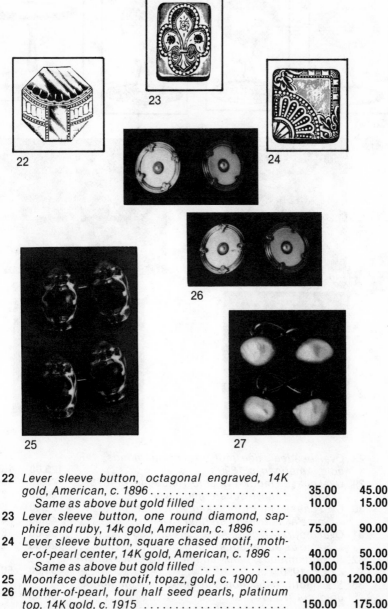

☐	**22**	Lever sleeve button, octagonal engraved, 14K gold, American, c. 1896	35.00	45.00
☐		Same as above but gold filled	10.00	15.00
☐	**23**	Lever sleeve button, one round diamond, sapphire and ruby, 14k gold, American, c. 1896	75.00	90.00
☐	**24**	Lever sleeve button, square chased motif, mother-of-pearl center, 14K gold, American, c. 1896 . .	40.00	50.00
☐		Same as above but gold filled	10.00	15.00
☐	**25**	Moonface double motif, topaz, gold, c. 1900	1000.00	1200.00
☐	**26**	Mother-of-pearl, four half seed pearls, platinum top, 14K gold, c. 1915	150.00	175.00
☐	**27**	Natural baroque pearls, gold, maker: Tiffany & Co., c. 1920	400.00	450.00

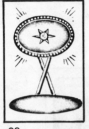

28 29 30 31

32 33

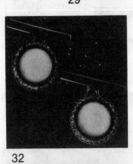
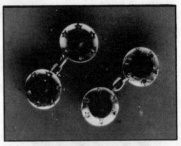

34 35

☐	**28**	Oval beaded edge motif, round diamonds, 14K gold, American, c. 1896	125.00	150.00
☐	**29**	Oval chased motif, 14K gold, American, c. 1896..	75.00	85.00
☐		Same as above but sterling silver	30.00	35.00
☐	**30**	Oval chased motif, 14K gold, American, c. 1896..	75.00	85.00
☐		Same as above but sterling silver	40.00	45.00
☐	**31**	Oval motif, 14K gold, American, c. 1896	50.00	60.00
☐		Same as above but sterling silver	20.00	25.00
☐	**32**	Rose diamonds, black enamel, 14K gold, American, c. 1930	450.00	500.00
☐	**33**	Star motif, cabochon sardonyx, rose diamonds, gold, c. 1875	300.00	350.00
☐	**34**	Tourmaline: square-cut, black enamel, gold, c. 1935	400.00	450.00
☐	**35**	White enamel, four round diamonds, 14K gold, American, c. 1920	225.00	250.00

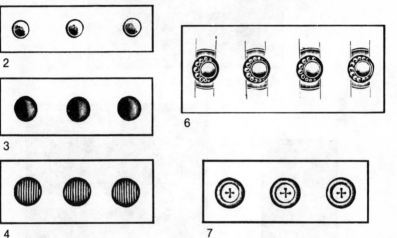

STUDS and BUTTONS

			PRICE RANGE	
☐	1	Angel motif, painted porcelain, gold, buttons, French, c. 1870	450.00	500.00
☐	2	Ball motif, 14K gold, American, c. 1896	50.00	60.00
☐		Same as above but gold filled	10.00	15.00
☐		Same as above but sterling silver	20.00	25.00
☐	3	Ball motif, black onyx, 14K gold, American, c. 1896	20.00	30.00
☐	4	Ball motif, ribbed, 14K gold, American, c. 1896	50.00	60.00
☐		Same as above but gold filled	10.00	15.00
☐		Same as above but sterling silver	20.00	30.00
☐	5	Basket weave hair under glass, gold, c. early 20th	20.00	25.00
☐	6	Beaded motif, 14K gold, American, c. 1896	50.00	60.00
☐		Same as above but gold filled	15.00	20.00
☐		Same as above but sterling silver	30.00	35.00
☐	7	Button motif, mother-of-pearl, 14K gold, American, c. 1896	65.00	75.00

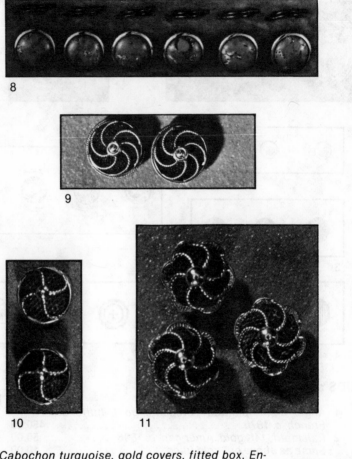

8

9

10   11

☐	**8** Cabochon turquoise, gold covers, fitted box, English, c. 1930	**200.00** **250.00**
☐	**9** Cartwheel motif, woven hair under swirls, gold, c. 1860	**80.00** **100.00**
☐	**10** Cartwheel motif, woven hair under swirls, gold, c. 1860	**60.00** **80.00**
☐	**11** Cartwheel scalloped edge motif, woven hair under swirls, gold, c. 1860	**100.00** **125.00**

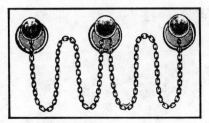

12

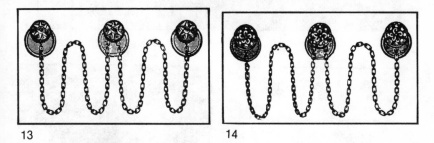

13   14

15   16   17

☐	**12**	*Chain connected button set, plain, 14K gold, American, c. 1894-95*	**40.00**	**50.00**
☐	**13**	*Chain connected button set, cabochon turquoise, 14K gold, American, c. 1894-95*	**80.00**	**90.00**
☐	**14**	*Chain connected button set, chased, 14K gold, American, c. 1894-95*	**65.00**	**75.00**
☐	**15**	*Collar button, engraved, 14K gold, American, c. 1896*	**20.00**	**25.00**
☐		*Same as above but gold filled*	**5.00**	**7.00**
☐	**16**	*Collar button, oblong, 14K gold, American, c. 1896*	**15.00**	**20.00**
☐		*Same as above but gold filled*	**5.00**	**7.00**
☐	**17**	*Collar button, round, 14K gold, American, c. 1896*	**15.00**	**20.00**
☐		*Same as above but gold filled*	**5.00**	**7.00**

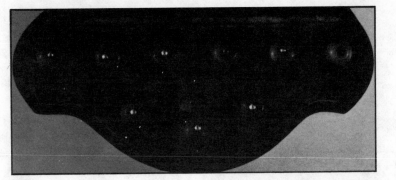

18

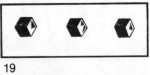

19

20

21

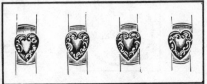

22

☐	**18**	*Coral beads, gold, fitted leather box, English, c. late 19th*	
			325.00 375.00
☐	**19**	*Cube motif, 14K gold, American, c. 1896*	50.00 60.00
☐		*Same as above but gold filled*	10.00 15.00
☐		*Same as above but sterling silver*	20.00 25.00
☐	**20**	*Flower motif, woven hair under gold loops, gold, c. 1870*	
			80.00 100.00
☐	**21**	*Hair woven under white and brown enamel metal frame, buttons, c. mid to late 19th*	
			40.00 50.00
☐	**22**	*Heart motif, chased, 14K gold, American, c. 1896*	65.00 75.00
☐		*Same as above but gold filled*	20.00 25.00
☐		*Same as above but sterling silver*	30.00 35.00

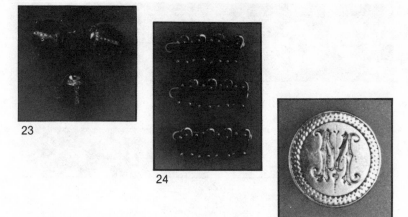

23

24

25

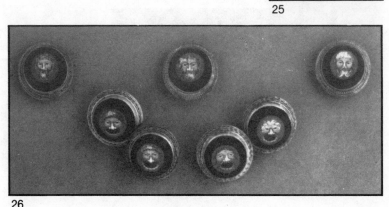

26

☐ **23** Lady-bug motif, translucent purple, yellow and red enamel, seed pearls, gold, fitted leather box, c. 1870 . . . .   500.00   550.00
☐ **24** Leaf motif, carved sapphires, white gold, c. 1900   550.00   600.00
☐ **25** Lovetoken, engraved gold dollar, American, c. late 19th 125.00   150.00
☐ **26** Mosaic face motif, gold, fitted leather box inscribed: Tiffany & Co., studs and cuff links, c. 1880 . . . .   5500.00   6000.00

27

28

29

30

☐ **27** *Mother-of-pearl, cabochon sapphires, platinum top, gold, fitted leather box, maker: Tiffany & Co., buttons, c. 1915* **600.00** **700.00**

☐ **28** *Pearls, 14K gold, American, c. 1896* **50.00** **60.00**

☐ **29** *Plain, 9K gold, fitted leather box, English, c. 1920* **150.00** **175.00**

☐ **30** *Ribbon motif, turquoise-blue enamel, rose diamonds, converted to brooch and earclips, silver topped gold buttons, c. 1750* **1200.00** **1500.00**

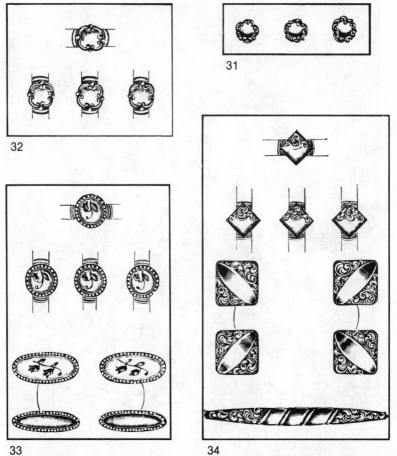

☐	**31** *Scroll plaque motif, 14K gold, American, c. 1896 .*	**50.00**	**60.00**
☐	*Same as above but gold filled*	**15.00**	**20.00**
☐	*Same as above but sterling silver*	**30.00**	**35.00**
☐	**32** *Waist set, chased, sterling silver, American, c. 1896.*	**35.00**	**45.00**
☐	**33** *Waist set, enameled lily-of-the-valley motif, beaded edges, sterling silver, American, c. 1896 .*	**75.00**	**90.00**
☐	**34** *Waist set, square motif, chased, sterling silver, American, c. 1896*	**110.00**	**120.00**

Lovely Victorian lady wears matching hair necklace, brooch and earrings which were woven between 1840-60. The photograph is perhaps as late as 1880. The sentimental attitudes of the era are represented by the figurine of the two lovers and the wistful gaze of the young lady.

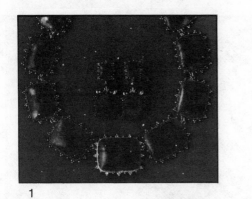

1

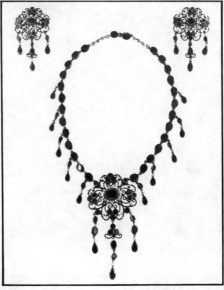

2

SUITES

3

4

☐ **3** *Amethyst cameo of warriors, gold, necklace, bracelet and earrings, c. 1850* **4500.00 4700.00**

☐ **4** *Amethyst centered in scroll plaque with double simple link chain, gold, bracelet and necklace, c. early 20th* **1500.00 2000.00**

5

6

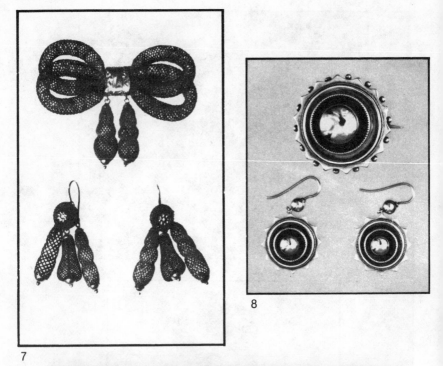

7

8

9

☐ **7** *Bow and pendant motif, woven hair, gold, brooch and earrings, c. 1840-60* **150.00   250.00**

☐ **8** *Circle motif with scalloped edges, silver, brooch and earrings, English, c. 1880.* **250.00   300.00**

☐ **9** *Circular motif, old mine diamond centers, rose diamond borders, silver topped gold, bracelet and earrings, c. 1860* **4500.00   5500.00**

10

☐ **10** *Citrines, faceted ovals, rose, yellow and green gold floral motif mounting, necklace with pendant, brooch, bracelet, earrings, former owner: Empress Eugenia of France, wife to Napoleon III, fitted leather box, c. 1830* **8000.00 10000.00**

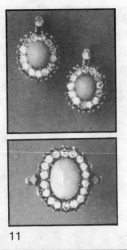

11

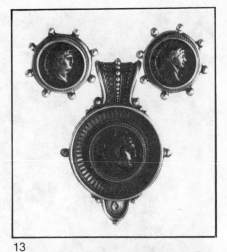

13

12

14

☐ **11** *Cluster motif, oval cabochon turquoise centers surrounded by round diamonds, gold, ring and earrings, c. late 19th* **1500.00 2000.00**

☐ **12** *Cluster motif, ruby centers, rose diamond borders, silver topped gold, ring, earrings and pendant, fitted leather box, c. mid 19th* **2000.00 2500.00**

☐ **13** *Coin motif, Etruscan gold granulation mounts, ancient Greek silver drachma of Alexander the Great, reverse: Zeus with an eagle in center of pendant; ancient Roman silver denaruis of Emperor Nero and one of Trojan in center of each button, signed: Pierret, Roma, Italian, c. 1870* ... **5000.00 6000.00**

☐ **14** *Cross motif, pearls, black enamel, gold, brooch and buttons, French, c. 1850* **400.00 500.00**

☐ **15** *Emeralds: 14 emerald-cut and two pear-shape emeralds, 60 old mine diamonds, cannetille, oval link chain, gold, necklace with detachable cross and earrings, c. 1830* **14000.00 15000.00**

☐ **16** *Rubies: pear-shape and oval rubies, cannetille, gold, necklace and earrings, c. 1830* **10000.00 11500.00**

17

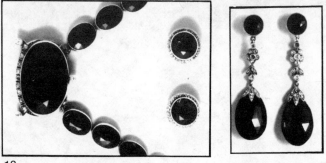

18

☐ **17** *Filigree motif, amethysts, diamonds, 18K gold, necklace, earrings, butterfly brooch or pendant, English, c. 1820-40* **16000.00 20000.00**

☐ **18** *Fire opals, oval and faceted, necklace with detachable brooch with three round diamonds and rose diamonds, stud earrings with rose diamonds, pendant earrings with a small emerald in each and rose diamonds, fitted leather box, c. 1890* **8000.00 9000.00**

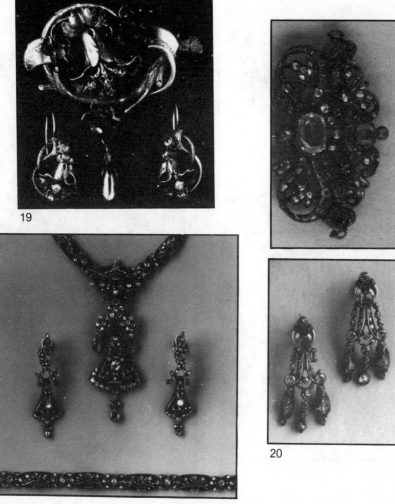

19

20

21

22

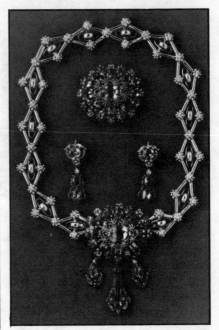

23

24

25

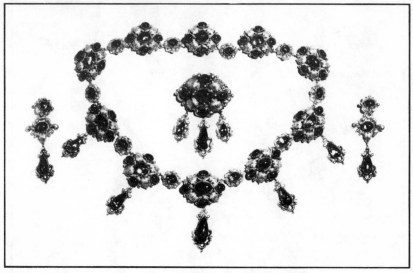

26

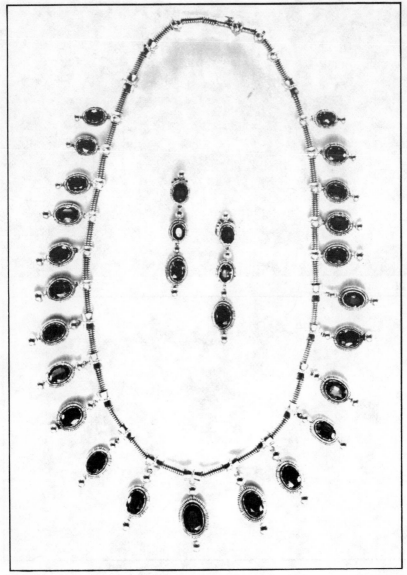

27

28

29

☐ **28** *Greek goddess, tiger and angel motif on painted porcelain plaques, Etruscan gold granulation frames with gold ball pendants, brooch and earrings, c. 1850* **3000.00 3500.00**

☐ **29** *Horseshoe and whip motif, black enamel, seed pearls, three colored gold, brooch and converted earrings, c. 1870* **600.00 800.00**

30

31

32

☐ **30** *Jade and carnelian plaques, pierced and carved,*
14K gold, bracelet and necklace, c. early 20th ... **4000.00 5000.00**
☐ **31** *Leaf motif, woven hair, white hair pendants,*
gold, brooch and earrings, c. 1850-70 .... **400.00   500.00**
☐ **32** *Loveknot motif, woven hair, plaques for initials,*
gold, brooch and earrings, c. 1840-60 .... **200.00   300.00**

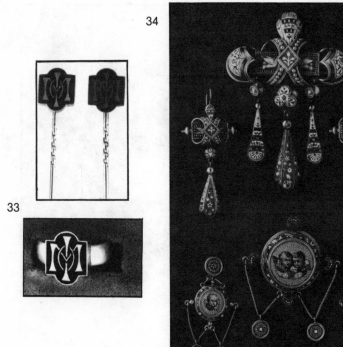

33

34

35

□ **33** *Memorial shields in black and white enamel sig-nifying "In Memory Of," hair locket behind each shield, 18K gold, ring and two detachable stick pins, Birmingham, England, c. 1884* **600.00 800.00**

□ **34** *Mosaic Gothic revival motif, birds and flowers, Etruscan granulation, gold, brooch and earrings, c. 1870* **2800.00 3200.00**

□ **35** *Mosaic motif of angels, gold, brooch and ear-rings, c. 1860* **1600.00 2000.00**

37

36

38

39

40

41

42

43

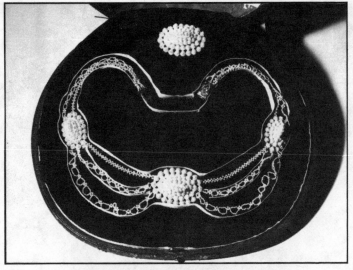

44

45

☐ **44** *Seed pearls on mother-of-pearl templates, gold clasp and pin back, necklace and brooch, fitted leather box, c. 1860* **1000.00 1200.00**

☐ **45** *Shell cameos of Greek gods and butterflies, gold, necklace and earrings, c. mid 19th* **3500.00 3800.00**

46

47

☐ **46** *Shield motif, champlevé blue enamel, seed pearls, Etruscan gold granulation, brooch, earrings and bracelet, c. 1860* **3500.00 4500.00**

☐ **47** *Star motif, half pearls, gold, brooch and earrings, fitted leather box, c. 1850* **500.00 600.00**

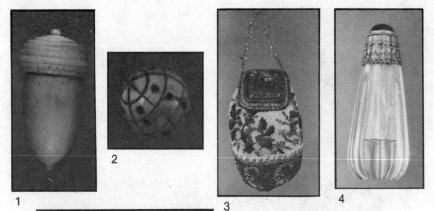

1

2

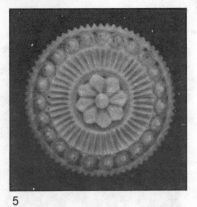

3

4

5

6

VINAIGRETTES

VINAIGRETTES, NUTMEG GRATERS, SNUFF BOXES and SCENT BOTTLES

"NOTE: *Items are vinaigrettes unless stated otherwise.*"

			PRICE RANGE	
☐	1	Acorn motif, grill under top which unscrews, ivory, English, c. 1800	125.00	165.00
☐	2	Ball with geometric motif, holes evenly spaced, ivory, English, c. 1800	125.00	165.00
☐	3	Beaded purse, frame is yellow metal, silver plated, mirror and vinaigrette in lid, six in. long, marked: "Galendrer 1846," French, c. 1846	300.00	350.00
☐	4	Bowed crystal motif, Star of David pierced grill under lid, gold plated inside, sterling silver, French, c. 1880-1900	125.00	150.00
☐	5	Carved round box motif, unscrews with grill inside, ivory, English, c. 1840	125.00	165.00
☐	6	Carved round box motif, unscrews with grill inside, ivory, English, c. 1840	75.00	100.00

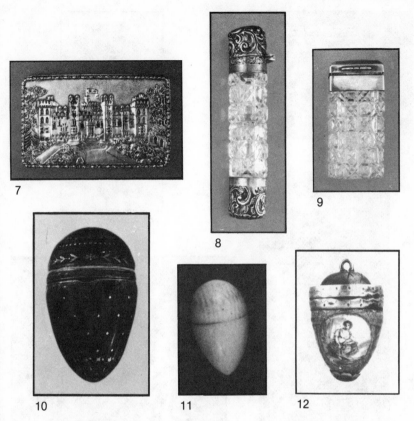

7

8

9

10   11   12

☐ **7** *Castle motif, sterling silver gold plated, maker:*
   Nathaniel Mills, Birmimgham, England, c. 1838.. **600.00   750.00**
☐ **8** *Cut glass motif double scent bottle, repousse,*
   sterling silver, one end on hinge and one end
   screws, maker: DJE, Birmingham, England,
   c. 1890. . . . . **125.00   165.00**
☐ **9** *Cut glass motif, star pierced grill under lid, gold*
   plated inside, sterling silver, American,
   c. 1880-1900 . . . . **100.00   125.00**
☐ **10** *Egg motif, purple, gold and white opaque and*
   translucent enamel, silver, French, c. 19th **800.00 1000.00**
☐ **11** *Egg motif, unscrews with grill inside, ivory, En-*
   glish, c. 1800 . . . . **125.00   165.00**
☐ **12** *Enamel motif of a lady, silver, French, c. 19th . . .* **600.00   700.00**

13

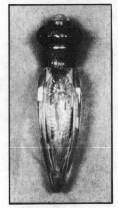

14

15

16

☐ **13** *Fancy-shape motif snuff box, engraved, gold plated inside, sterling silver, colored synthetic stones in lid, maker: K T, French, c. 1830-45* **285.00** **325.00**

☐ **14** *Glass engraved scent bottle, round cabochon opal in cap, 14K gold, American, c. 1910* **400.00** **500.00**

☐ **15** *Glass scent bottle, colored floral enamel, sterling silver, ring chain and cap with gemstones, Hungarian, c. 1840-60* **400.00** **500.00**

☐ **16** *Horn motif, vinaigrette with cutout scroll grill at large end, scent at small end, sterling silver, maker: S. Mordan & Co., London, England, c. 1872* **450.00** **500.00**

17

18

19

20

21

☐ **17** *Horn motif, faceted citrine in lid, finger ring, sterling silver, Scottish, c. 19th* **500.00** **650.00**

☐ **18** *Knight in Armor motif, sterling silver inlaid with gold, cabochon ruby thumbpiece to open hinged helmet, gold pierced grill under helmet, c. 19th* .. **2400.00** **2600.00**

☐ **19** *Lily-of-the-valley flower motif, sterling silver, patent number 1948, American, c. 1893* **200.00** **250.00**

☐ **20** *Locket motif, cutout flower grill, chased edge, gold, American, c. 1850-65* **400.00** **600.00**

☐ **21** *Octagonal motif, Greek key, leaf and monogram engraved, gold plated inside, sterling silver, maker: M. Linwood, Birmingham, England, c. 1800* **285.00** **325.00**

22

25

23

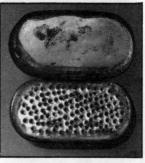

26

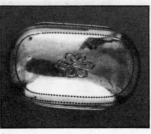

24

27

☐ **22** *Oval motif, engraved edge, gold plated inside, sterling silver, English, c. 1790* **320.00** **370.00**

☐ **23** *Oval motif, engraved, hand-punched grill, sterling silver, maker: Joseph Willmore, Birmingham, England, c. 1809* **375.00** **425.00**

☐ **24** *Oval motif, gold plated inside, sterling silver, maker: Joseph Willmore, Birmingham, England, c. 1793* **340.00** **385.00**

☐ **25** *Oval motif, cut glass bottom, faceted black glass top, sterling silver gold plated grill and frame, English, c. 1880-1900* **175.00** **250.00**

☐ **26** *Oval motif nutmeg grater, black and maroon painted tin, opens both ends, American, c. 1750-1800* **175.00** **225.00**

☐ **27** *Oval motif nutmeg grater, blue tin grill, sterling silver case, maker: J W, Birmingham, England, c. 1806* **250.00** **300.00**

28

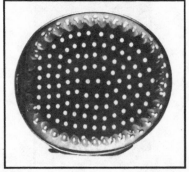

30

29

31

32

☐ **28** *Oval motif nutmeg grater, engraved, opens both ends, gold plated inside, sterling silver, maker: Muirhead & Arthur, Glasgow, Scotland, c. 1881* . .   **225.00   250.00**

☐ **29** *Oval motif nutmeg grater, sterling silver, maker: CR (thought to be mark by C. Reily before he became partner with E. Storer), opens both ends, London, England, c. 1824* **375.00   425.00**

☐ **30** *Oval crystal motif, faceted top, grill and frame are silver gilt, c. 19th* **250.00   300.00**

☐ **31** *Oval fish scale motif, swan cutout grill, gold plated inside, sterling silver, maker: John Shaw, Birmingham, England, c. 1810* **365.00   425.00**

☐ **32** *Oval scalloped edge motif, leaf and monogram engraved, sterling silver, maker: George Unite, Birmingham, England, c. 1890* **275.00   325.00**

33

34

36

37

35

38

39

41

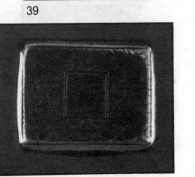
40

42

☐ **38** *Rectangular motif, engraved, sterling silver,*
maker: J. T., Birmingham, England, c. 1844 . . . . . **275.00** **325.00**

☐ **39** *Rectangular motif, geometric engraved, unusual-*
ly thin, gold plated inside, sterling silver, maker:
Lea & Clark, Birmingham, England, c. 1813-14 . . . **275.00** **325.00**

☐ **40** *Rectangular motif, gold plated inside, sterling*
silver, maker: I D, London, England, c. 1808 . . . . . **325.00** **375.00**

☐ **41** *Rectangular motif, engraved top and edges, gold*
plated inside, sterling silver, scroll cutout grill,
Birmingham, England, c. 1811 . . . . **325.00** **390.00**

☐ **42** *Rectangular motif snuff box, engraved, sterling*
silver, maker: Cocks & Bethridge, Birmingham,
England, c. 1812 . . . . **275.00** **325.00**

43

45

46

47

44

☐ **43** *Rectangular motif, engraved, cutout vine grill, unusually spaced grill hinge, gold plated inside, sterling silver, maker: WS, Birmingham, England, c. 1831* 350.00   400.00

☐ **44** *Rectangular bird and flower motif, colored opaque and translucent enamels, reverse is identical, gold, French, c. 19th* 1200.00   1500.00

☐ **45** *Rectangular fish scale motif, gold plated inside, sterling silver, maker: Thomas Shaw, Birmingham, England, c. 1822* 275.00   325.00

☐ **46** *Rectangular flower motif, engraved, sterling silver, maker: Wheeler & Shaw, Birmingham, England, c. 1840* 275.00   300.00

☐ **47** *Rectangular flower motif, engraved, sterling silver, maker: Taylor, London, England, c. 1812* 300.00   350.00

48

51

49

52

50

53

☐ **48** *Rectangular flower repoussé motif, 18K gold, French, c. 1820* **800.00** **900.00**

☐ **49** *Rectangular geometric motif, cutout scroll grill, gold plated inside, sterling silver, maker: T S, Birmingham, England, c. 1827* **375.00** **425.00**

☐ **50** *Rectangular geometric motif snuff box, gold plated inside, sterling silver, maker: Samuel Pemberton, Birmingham, England, c. 1807* **400.00** **450.00**

☐ **51** *Rectangular leaf motif, engraved, cutout flower grill, gold plated inside, sterling silver, maker: S & B, Birmingham, England, c. 1903* **275.00** **325.00**

☐ **52** *Rectangular raised lid motif, engraved, gold plated inside, sterling silver, maker: John Lawrence & Co., Birmingham, England, c. 1825* **285.00** **325.00**

☐ **53** *Rectangular repoussé edge motif, gold plated inside, sterling silver, maker: Thos. Naubold, Birmingham, England, c. 1824* **325.00** **350.00**

54

55

56

57

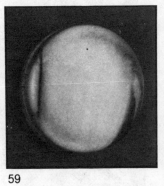

58

59

☐ **54** Rectangular scallop edge motif, engraved, gold plated inside, sterling silver, maker: N & C, Birmingham, England, c. 1859 .... **285.00** **325.00**

☐ **55** Rectangular scalloped motif, engraved, gold plated inside, sterling silver, maker: F M, Birmingham, England, c. 1855 .... **300.00** **335.00**

☐ **56** Rectangular scalloped edge motif, engraved, gold plated inside, sterling silver, maker: JF, Birmingham, England, c. 1858 .... **300.00** **325.00**

☐ **57** Rectangular scalloped edge motif, engraved, flower cutout grill, gold plated inside, sterling silver, maker: Nathaniel Mills, Birmimgham, England, c. 1853 .... **300.00** **350.00**

☐ **58** Rectangular thumbnail motif, engraved, gold plated inside, sterling silver, maker: T N, Birmingham, England, c. 1830 .... **285.00** **340.00**

☐ **59** Round box motif, unscrews with grill inside, ivory, English, c. 1800 .... **125.00** **165.00**

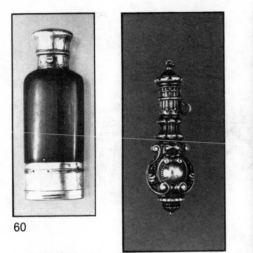

60

61

62

64

63

☐ **60** *Ruby glass scent bottle, gold plated inside, sterling silver, vinaigrette with scroll cutout grill in base, maker: S. Mordan & Co., London, England, c. 1868* **150.00** **225.00**
☐ **61** *Scroll motif, sterling silver, American, c. 1900* ... **125.00** **140.00**
☐ **62** *Shell motif, gold plated inside, sterling silver, c. 1840-60* **375.00** **425.00**
☐ **63** *Shoe motif, 800 silver, French or Dutch, c. 19th* .. **275.00** **350.00**
☐ **64** *Square modified motif, banded agate top and bottom, yellow metal sides, French, c. 1820-30* .. **250.00** **300.00**

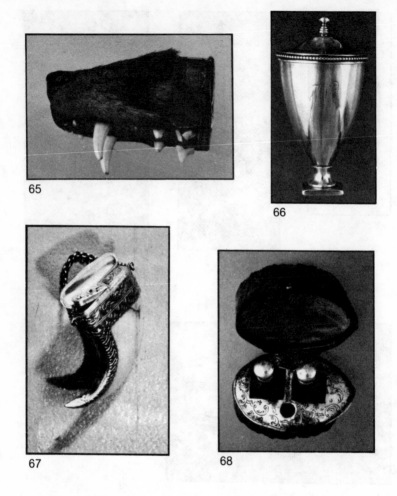

☐ **65** *Stuffed genuine ferret snuff box, engraved flowers on rear lid, silver plated, Scottish, c. early 19th* ... **600.00 650.00**

☐ **66** *Tiger claw motif, engraved, 15K gold, English, c. 1870.* **600.00 800.00**

☐ **67** *Urn motif nutmeg grater, sterling silver, top lifts and front opens with hinge at base, English, c. 1790-1825* **450.00 550.00**

☐ **68** *Walnut box motif, genuine shell, silver interior fittings, two cobalt blue glass scent bottles, English, c. 1860-1900* **300.00 350.00**

69

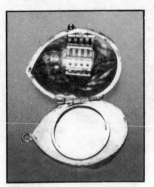

70

71

☐ **69** *Walnut box motif, one glass scent bottle, finger chain, silver plated yellow metal, English, c. 1860-1900* **165.00** **185.00**

☐ **70** *Walnut box motif, one glass scent bottle and picture locket behind mirror, yellow metal, English, c. 1860-1900* **150.00** **165.00**

☐ **71** *Watch, motif, monogram, sterling silver, Norwegian, c. 1900* **225.00** **250.00**

Photograph taken in the early 1900's of a woman wearing a gold link chain attached to a hunting case watch with a shield motif watch pin.

1

2

3

WATCHES

GENTLEMEN'S · POCKET

The movements of all of the watches in this chapter are of average quality unless noted otherwise.

			PRICE RANGE	
☐	**1**	*Bicycle with rider motif, engraved, HC, 14K gold, American, c. 1896*	**750.00**	**900.00**
☐		*Same as above but gold filled*	**200.00**	**250.00**
☐	**2**	*Bird and flower applied motif, three color gold, engraved, HC, 18K gold, American, c. 1900*	**1800.00**	**2000.00**
☐	**3**	*Castle engraved motif, HC, 14K gold, American, c. 1896*	**750.00**	**900.00**
☐		*Same as above but gold filled*	**150.00**	**175.00**

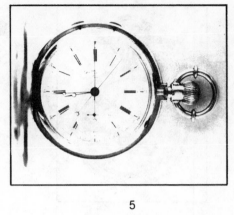

5

4

☐ **4** *Chronograph, 17 jewel, plane case, white porcelain dial, OF, 16 size, gold filled, maker: Waltham,
c. 1900. . . . .* **150.00   200.00**
☐ **5** *Chronograph: jump quarter split second with no
return to zero, 31 jewel, stem wound, lever set,
white porcelain dial, HC, 18K, maker, J. Higuenin* **3500.00 3800.00**

6

7

8

☐ **6** *Engine turned motif, patented bow setting mechanism, highest grade movement number 10792, HC, 18K gold, 42MM, maker: Jules Jurgensen, Copenhagen, with original certifical, c. 1867* 2000.00 2200.00

☐ **7** *Figural mandolin watch, polychrome cobalt-blue and black enamel, seed pearls, glazed window exposing balance, enamel dial, steel hands, verge escapement, opens to reveal watch, gold, maker: Johann Jär in Wien, c. 1815* 6000.00 8000.00

☐ **8** *Figural oriental harp motif, pierced and engraved, enamel dial, steel hands, verge escapement, opens to reveal watch, silver gilt, signed: "Ruegger a Geneva," c. 1790* 3500.00 4000.00

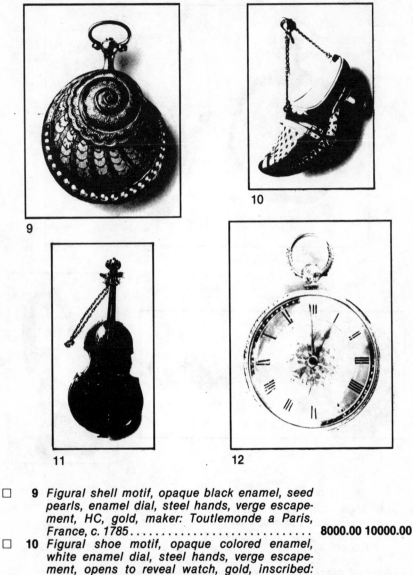

9

10

11

12

13

14

15

16

☐ **13** *Flower motif, champlevé opaque black enamel with colored enamel flowers, silver dial, gold Breguet hands, cylinder escapement, OF, gold, with matching chain and key, Paris, France, c. 1815* .. **3000.00 3500.00**

☐ **14** *Flower motif with engraved lake scene, HC, 14K gold, American, c. 1896* **600.00 750.00**

☐ **15** *Flower carved motif, rose diamonds, enamel dial, gold hands, cylinder escapement, HC, gold, Geneva, Art Nouveau, c. 1900* **1200.00 1400.00**

☐ **16** *Flower engraved motif, seven jewel, white porcelain dial, HC, 16 size, 14K gold, maker: Waltham, c. 1900* **450.00 550.00**

17

18

19

20

	17	Flower engraved motif, seven jewel, white porcelain dial, HC, 23 size, 14K gold, maker: Elgin, c. 1900	500.00	600.00
	18	Flower engraved motif, 17 jewel, case number 742015, movement number 21828106, HC, 14K gold, maker: Elgin, c. 1918	500.00	600.00
	19	Flower and initial shield motif, engraved, HC, 14K gold, American, c. 1896	600.00	750.00
		Same as above but gold filled	140.00	180.00
	20	Flower and scalloped edge motif with engraved lake scene, HC, 14K gold, American, c. 1896	1000.00	1200.00
		Same as above but gold filled	225.00	250.00

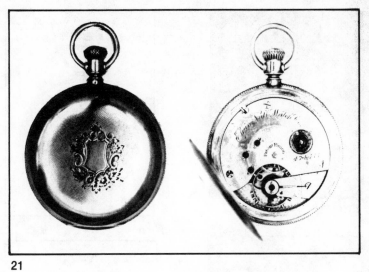

21

22

□ **21** *Flower wreath and initial shield motif, 15 jewels, grade 46 nickel movement, keywind, HC, 18K gold, 14 size, maker: Elgin, c. 1876* **600.00** **650.00**

□ **22** *Greek key motif in opaque black enamel, enamel dial, gold hands, cylinder escapement with double enamel slide fox-tail link chain and key, HC, gold, signed: "Mercier á Genéve," c. 1830* **3000.00** **3500.00**

□ *Same as above but chain only* **450.00** **500.00**

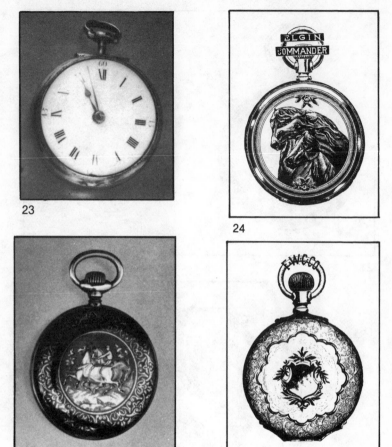

23

24

25

26

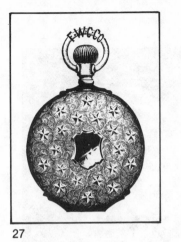

27

28

29   30

☐ **27** *Initial shield and star motif, peacock engraving,*
HC, 14K gold, American, c. 1896 . . . . **600.00   750.00**
☐   *Same as above but gold filled* **140.00   180.00**
☐ **28** *Initial shield motif with deep wavy engraving, 21*
jewel, model 993, white porcelain dial, HC, 14K
gold, 16 size, maker: Hamilton, c. 1900 . . . . **1000.00 1200.00**
☐ **29** *Leaf motif, opaque black enamel, rose dia-*
monds, silver-plated lever movement, ruby end-
stones, compensation balance, HC, 18K gold,
maker: Ch. Suchy & Fils, c. 1880 . . . . **2500.00 3000.00**
☐ **30** *Lion engraved motif, HC, 14K gold, American,*
c. 1896. . . . . **1100.00 1300.00**
☐   *Same as above but gold filled* **200.00   225.00**

31

32

33

34

- ☐ **31** Masonic motif, 17 jewel, high grade movement, white porcelain dial, OF, silver, maker: Alpina, Swiss, c. 1900............................ **700.00 800.00**
- ☐ **32** Octagonal motif, 108 round diamonds approximately 2.0 cts., OF, platinum, maker: Waltham, American, c. 1915 .... **1600.00 1800.00**
- ☐ **33** Open back motif, 23 jewel, highest quality railroad grade movement, OF, gold filled, maker: E. Howard Watch Co., Boston, U.S.A., c. 1910-20 ... **350.00 400.00**
- ☐ **34** Plain motif, HC, 14K gold, American, c. 1896 .... **450.00 500.00**
- ☐   Same as above but gold filled **125.00 150.00**

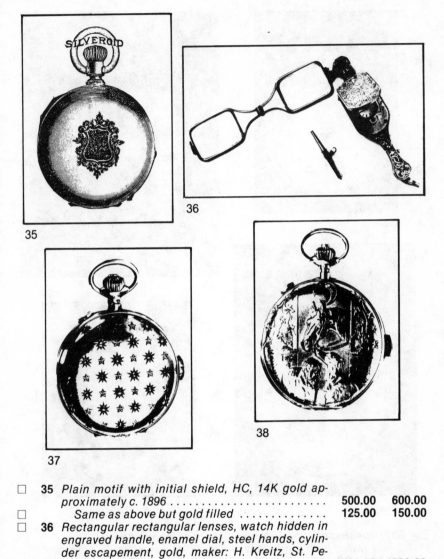

☐ **35** *Plain motif with initial shield, HC, 14K gold approximately c. 1896* 500.00 600.00

☐ *Same as above but gold filled* 125.00 150.00

☐ **36** *Rectangular rectangular lenses, watch hidden in engraved handle, enamel dial, steel hands, cylinder escapement, gold, maker: H. Kreitz, St. Petersbourg, c. 19th* 3500.00 4000.00

☐ **37** *Repeater: minute with chronograph, star motif, rose diamonds, glazed movement with lever escapement, enamel dial, gilt hands, HC, 5.8CM, inscribed: Invicta Chronographe, Geneva, c. 1900* . 6000.00 8000.00

☐ **38** *Repeater: minute with chronograph, horse, dog and crescent motif, rose diamonds, glazed movement with lever escapement, enamel dial, gilt hands, HC, 6CM, 18K gold, Liége, c. 1906* 6000.00 8000.00

39

40

41

☐ **39** *Repeater: minute with split second chronograph, 21 jewel, high grade movement, white porcelain face, OF, 14K gold, maker: Patek, Philippe & Co., Geneva, Switzerland, c. 1900* **8000.00 10000.00**

☐ **40** *Repeater: quarter hour, Jaquemar, standard better grade movement, gold hands, OF, gold, maker: Vacheron, Swiss, c. 1900* **3500.00 4000.00**

☐ **41** *Repeater: quarter hour, verge movement, three color gold, miniature enamel of lady and angels, white enamel dot border, OF, gold, Geneva, Switzerland, c. 1794* **4000.00 5000.00**

42

43

☐ **42** *Reversible motif, engraved, 15 jewels, white por-*
celain dial, J series nickel movement #501154,
HC or OF, 18K gold, 12 size, maker: E. Howard &
Co., c. 1887 . . . . **3500.00 3800.00**

☐ **43** *Scalloped edge with applied three color gold*
flower motif, one round diamond, case number
6366717, movement number 15174777, 15 jewels,
HC, 15K gold, maker: Waltham, American, c. 1892 **2000.00 2500.00**

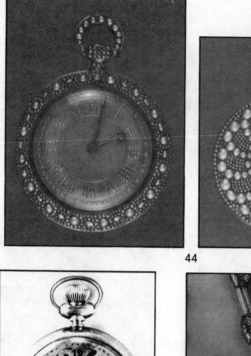
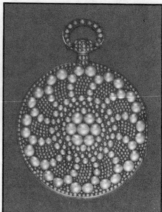

44

45

46

☐ **44** *Seed pearls pavé, high grade lever movement,*
fusee, jeweled, OF, gold, English, c. 1830-60 .... **13000.00 14000.00**
☐ **45** *Skeleton motif, New England skeleton duplex es-*
capement, seven jewel, OF, 16 size, silveroid,
c. early 20th **300.00 350.00**
☐ **46** *Square opaque enamel watch, rose diamonds,*
white porcelain face, OF, matching oval plaque
chatelaine top, two slides, seal and key, fox-tail
chain, gold, c. 1850 .... **5000.00 5500.00**
☐ *Same as above but chain only* **800.00 900.00**

47   48   50

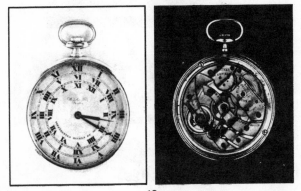

49

☐ **47** *Stag and scalloped edged motif, engraved, HC,*
14K gold, American, c. 1896 .... **1000.00 1200.00**
☐   *Same as above but gold filled* **200.00 215.00**
☐ **48** *Tiger head and carved flower motif, rose dia-*
monds, enamel dial, cylinder escapement, HC,
gold, inscribed: Invicta, maker: Chaux-de-Fonds,
Art Nouveau, c. 1900 .... **1200.00 1400.00**
☐ **49** *Time zone motif for three time zones, 18 jewel,*
adjusted eight, OF, 12 size, 18K gold, maker: un-
signed Ekegrin, c. 1900 .... **800.00 1000.00**
☐ **50** *Train and flower engraved motif, HC, 14K gold,*
American, c. 1896 .... **1000.00 1200.00**
☐   *Same as above but gold filled* **175.00 200.00**

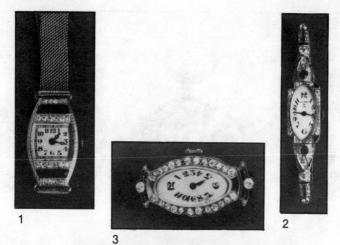

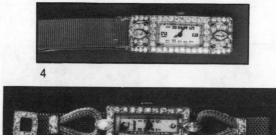

LADIES · DIAMOND WRISTWATCHES

PRICE RANGE

☐ **1** Cushion-shape geometric motif, 32 round diamonds approx. .50 ct., two calibre French-cut black onyx, platinum, Art Deco, c. 1920 .... 800.00 1000.00

☐ **2** Oval geometric motif, round diamonds, calibre and round sapphires, platinum, Art Deco, signed: Tiffany & Co., c. 1920 .... 2000.00 2400.00

☐ **3** Oval geometric motif, round diamonds, gold, maker: Patek Philippe, c. 1920 .... 1600.00 1900.00

☐ **4** Rectangular geometric motif, 66 round and two marquise-shape diamonds approx. 2.25 cts., fancy-shape cabochon black onyx, platinum, Art Deco, c. 1920 .... 1500.00 1800.00

☐ **5** Rectangular geometric motif, two marquise-shape diamonds and round diamonds approx. .70 ct., platinum, Art Deco, maker: Nicolet, c. 1910 ... 800.00 1000.00

6

7

8

9

☐ **6** *Rectangular geometric motif, four French-cut diamonds, and round diamonds approx. 5.25 cts., platinum, Art Deco, c. 1910* **3800.00 4200.00**

☐ **7** *Rectangular geometric motif, diamonds, 14K gold, Art Deco, c. 1930* **1200.00 1500.00**

☐ **8** *Rectangular geometric motif, 29 square-cut diamonds approx. 5.25 cts., 112 round diamonds approx. 2.75 cts., 18 French-cut diamonds, platinum, Art Deco, c. 1925* **7500.00 8500.00**

☐ **9** *Round flower motif, 125 round diamonds approx. 3.0 cts., platinum, movement: Meylan, signed: Tiffany & Co., c. 1915* **3200.00 3600.00**

10

11

☐ **10** *Round geometric motif, four round diamonds, 24 rose diamonds, platinum, maker: Agassiz, c. 1920* **1600.00 1800.00**

☐ **11** *Square geometric motif, 64 round diamonds approx. 1.26 cts., 20 baguette diamonds approx. 1.06 cts., 14K white gold, maker: Hamilton, 22 jewels, Art Deco, c. 1930* **2800.00 3000.00**

1

LADIES · PENDANT

PRICE RANGE

☐ **1** *Angel motif, chased, OF, 14K gold, Art Nouveau, with Jack-in-the-Pulpit flower motif brooch with watch loop, one fresh water pearl, 14K gold, Art Nouveau, c. 1895* **900.00 1200.00**

☐ *Same as above but watch brooch only* **125.00 150.00**

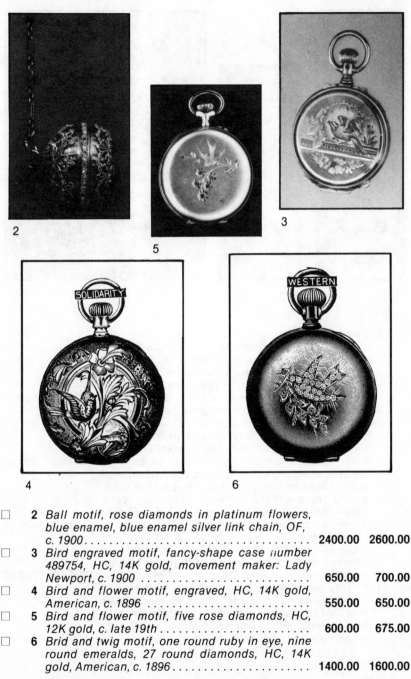

2

3

5

4

6

- □ **2** *Ball motif, rose diamonds in platinum flowers, blue enamel, blue enamel silver link chain, OF, c. 1900* **2400.00 2600.00**
- □ **3** *Bird engraved motif, fancy-shape case number 489754, HC, 14K gold, movement maker: Lady Newport, c. 1900* **650.00   700.00**
- □ **4** *Bird and flower motif, engraved, HC, 14K gold, American, c. 1896* **550.00   650.00**
- □ **5** *Bird and flower motif, five rose diamonds, HC, 12K gold, c. late 19th* **600.00   675.00**
- □ **6** *Brid and twig motif, one round ruby in eye, nine round emeralds, 27 round diamonds, HC, 14K gold, American, c. 1896* **1400.00 1600.00**

7   8   9   10   11

12

13

14

☐ **12** Chain and watch, watch is guilloche green
enamel with diamonds in platinum, white enamel
dial, chain is trace links spaced with guilloche
green enamel baton links and seed pearls, OF,
18K gold, Swiss, c. 1880 . . . . **2000.00   2200.00**

☐ **13** Crescent and star motif, six round diamonds,
HC, 14K gold, American, c. 1896 . . . .   **750.00   850.00**

☐ **14** Diamond geometric motif, one round diamond
approximately .70 ct., 167 round and eight baguette diamonds approximately 5.0 cts., OF, plati-
num, maker: Huguenin, c. 1925 . . . . **4000.00   4500.00**

15

17

16

□ **15** *Diamond motif, two round diamonds approx. 2.20 cts., 32 round diamonds, OF, gold, platinum, maker: Tiffany & Co., with rose diamond and fancy-cut black onyx bow motif brooch with watch loop, gold, platinum, c. 1900* **7500.00 8000.00**

□ **16** *Engraved edge motif, HC, 14K gold, American, c. 1896.* **450.00 550.00**

□ *Same as above but OF and gold filled* **100.00 125.00**

□ **17** *Fleur-de-lys rose diamond motif, translucent blue enamel, HC, 14K gold, with fleur-de-lys dia- mond motif brooch with watch loop, 14K gold, c. early 20th* **2000.00 2200.00**

□ *Same as above but watch brooch only* **600.00 700.00**

19

18

20

☐	**18**	*Flower basket motif, chased, OF, 18K gold, with flower motif brooch with watch loop, 18K gold, c. 1860.*	1200.00	1400.00
☐		*Same as above but watch brooch only*	185.00	225.00
☐	**19**	*Flower engraved motif, HC, 14K gold, American, c. 1896.*	550.00	650.00
☐		*Same as above but OF and gold filled*	85.00	110.00
☐		*Same as above but gold filled*	140.00	180.00
☐	**20**	*Flower motif, two round rubies, ten round emeralds, 14 round diamonds, HC, 14K gold, American, c. 1896.*	1500.00	1800.00

21

22

23

☐ **21** *Flower motif, chased, OF, 18K gold, two round diamonds, lever escapement, 19 jewel, white porcelain face, Art Nouveau, Swiss, with carved flower motif brooch with watch loop, 18K gold, Art Nouveau, c. 1890* **1800.00 2000.00**

☐ *Same as above but watch brooch only* **200.00   250.00**

☐ **22** *Flower motif, guilloche translucent cobalt blue and black enamel, rose diamonds, keywind, HC, 18K gold, maker: Patek, c. 1860, with cobalt blue enamel brooch with watch loop, rose diamonds, 14K gold* **1600.00 2000.00**

☐ *Same as above but watch brooch only* **300.00   350.00**

☐ **23** *Flower motif, chased, OF, 14K gold, with peacock motif translucent enamel brooch with watch loop, 14K gold, Art Nouveau, c. 1900* **3600.00 3800.00**

☐ *Same as above but watch brooch only* **3000.00 3200.00**

24

25

26

27

☐ **24** *Flower motif, guilloche blue enamel, gold and silver wire overlaid, seven rose diamonds, OF, gold, maker: Schumann's Sons, New York, c. early 20th*   **1200.00**   **1400.00**

☐ **25** *Flower motif in gold and silver, guilloche green enamel face and rear cover, OF, silver gilt, Swiss, with wreath motif brooch with watch loop, gold, c. 1880* **400.00**   **425.00**

    Same as above but watch brooch only **75.00**   **100.00**

☐ **26** *Flower motif, multi-colored enamel, OF, 18K gold, maker: Henri Capt, c. late 19th* **1200.00**   **1500.00**

☐ **27** *Flower diamond motif, guilloche lavender enamel, OF, gold, c. 1900* **1500.00**   **1700.00**

28

29

30

- ☐ **28** Flower lily-of-the-valley motif, six round dia-
  monds, HC, 14K gold, American, c. 1896 . . . .   **750.00**   **850.00**
- ☐ **29** Flower with peacock engraved motif, HC, 14K
  gold, American, c. 1896 . . . .   **550.00**   **650.00**
- ☐   Same as above but gold filled **150.00**   **175.00**
- ☐ **30** Flower and scalloped edge motif, guilloche
  translucent blue enamel, rose diamonds, OF,
  gold, maker: R. F., with guilloche translucent
  blue enamel fleur-de-lys motif brooch with watch
  loop, c. 1880 . . . . **1000.00** **1200.00**

31

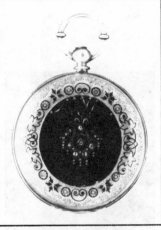

32

33

34

☐ **31** *Flower wreath of opaque black enamel, engraved mountain scene, case number 14210, HC, 14K rose gold, maker: H. Montandon, Locle, Switzerland, c. 1900* **750.00   850.00**

☐ **32** *Flower wreath motif, translucent and opaque blue and black enamel on both covers, rose diamonds, white enamel face, keywind, HC, gold, maker: F. G. Jacob, c. 1860* **1200.00   1400.00**

☐ **33** *Garland motif, OF, gold, c. late 19th* **350.00   375.00**

☐ **34** *Guilloche blue enamel face and case, OF, gold, Swiss, c. 1880* **600.00   650.00**

36

35

37

☐	**35**	*Half-hunter motif, black enamel Roman numerals, white enamel dial, 18K gold, c. late 19th*	**400.00**	**450.00**
☐	**36**	*Initial shield engraved motif, HC, 14K gold, American, c. 1896*	**450.00**	**550.00**
☐		*Same as above but OF and gold filled*	**85.00**	**110.00**
☐		*Same as above but gold filled*	**125.00**	**150.00**
☐	**37**	*Miniature champlevé enamel of a lady, white enamel dial, three rose diamonds, OF, gold, marked: SG, c. mid 19th*	**650.00**	**700.00**

40

38

39

☐	**38** *Miniature enamel of a lady with a gold enamel wreath and guilloche translucent red enamel background, seed pearl border, OF, silver, with matching guilloche translucent red enamel bow motif brooch with watch loop, silver, c. early 20th*	**800.00** **850.00**
☐	*Same as above but watch brooch only . . . .*	**75.00** **100.00**
☐	**39** *Miniature enamel of a lady and gentleman, rose diamonds, OF, gold, maker: Plojoux, Geneve, with engraved ribbon motif brooch with watch loop, gold, c. 1870 . . . .*	**3200.00** **3500.00**
☐	*Same as above but watch brooch only . . . .*	**225.00** **250.00**
☐	**40** *Miniature enamel of a lady, guilloche translucent green enamel, HC, gold, with Art Nouveau motif brooch with watch loop, one round peridot, gold, c. 1880 . . . .*	**1200.00** **1500.00**
☐	*Same as above but watch brooch only . . . .*	**225.00** **250.00**

41

43

42

☐ **41** *Miniature enamel of an angel, guilloche green enamel, rose diamonds, OF, 14K gold, with guilloche green enamel fluer-de-lys motif brooch with watch loop, nine rose diamonds, 14K gold, c. 1895.* **2200.00 2400.00**

☐   *Same as above but watch brooch only* **300.00 350.00**

☐ **42** *Miniature enamel of a lady and lamb on one side and miniature enamel of lovers on other side, seed pearl border, HC, gold, case is French, medium grade cylinder movement is Swiss, c. 1860* . **3000.00 3500.00**

☐ **43** *Miniature enamel of a swan and tiger lily flower, rose diamonds, three seed pearls, OF, gold, Swiss, c. 1900.* **1200.00 1300.00**

44

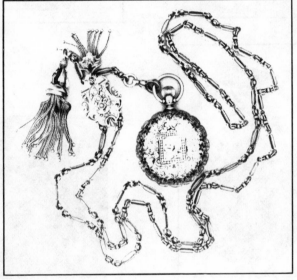

45

☐ **44** *Miniature engraved head of a lady, opaque black enamel, keywind, patent lever movement number 20567, 15 jewels, HC, 14K gold, maker: James Tissot, c. 1860* **800.00** **900.00**

☐ **45** *Miniature outdoor scene and scalloped edge motif, 15 jewels, HC, 14K gold, maker: Illinois, American, with fancy link chain with slide and tassel, 14K gold, c. 1890* **2500.00** **3000.00**

☐   *Same as above but chain only* **1000.00** **1500.00**

46

48

49

51

50

52

53

☐	**50**	*Rose diamond border, white porcelain face, case number 13051, OF, 14K gold, c. 1900*	**450.00**	**500.00**
☐	**51**	*Scalloped edge motif, three color gold applied flowers, one round diamond, HC, 14K gold, American, c. 1896*	**1600.00**	**1800.00**
☐	**52**	*Scalloped edge and engraved flower motif, HC, 14K gold, American, c. 1896*	**750.00**	**850.00**
☐		*Same as above but gold filled*	**175.00**	**200.00**
☐	**53**	*Seed pearls pavé, HC, 18K gold, c. 1900*	**2000.00**	**2500.00**

54

55

56

☐ **54** *Snake motif, OF, gold, maker: M. Patek, Geneva,*
   c. 1869 . . . . **3000.00 3500.00**
☐ **55** *Star motif, rose diamonds, seed pearl border,*
   OF, 18K gold, French, c. 1870 . . . . **850.00 900.00**
☐ **56** *Star motif, one round diamond, HC, 14K gold,*
   American, c. 1896 . . . . **750.00 850.00**

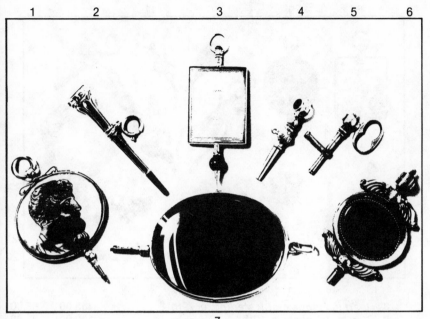

7

WATCH KEYS

PRICE RANGE

☐	**1** *Cameo of a gentleman, carved mother-of-pearl, gold, c. 19th*	**225.00**	**260.00**
☐	**2** *Hardstone seal, chased, gold, c. 19th*	**110.00**	**125.00**
☐	**3** *Plaque motif, guilloche enamel, hardstone ball, gold, c. 19th*	**200.00**	**225.00**
☐	**4** *Chased motif, gold, c. 19th*	**100.00**	**120.00**
☐	**5** *Key motif, gold, c. 19th*	**140.00**	**160.00**
☐	**6** *Medallion motif, lapis lazuli, gold, c. 19th*	**220.00**	**240.00**
☐	**7** *Medallion motif, oval cabochon banded agate, gold, c. 19th*	**175.00**	**200.00**

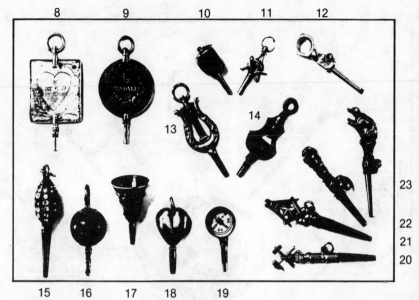

☐	8	Heart in plaque motif, sterling, c. 19th	65.00	85.00
☐	9	Coin motif, silver, c. 19th....................	110.00	125.00
☐	10	Mallet motif, hardstone, gold, c. 19th	75.00	90.00
☐	11	Loveknot motif, gold, c. 19th	110.00	125.00
☐	12	Hexagonal cutout motif, gold, c. 19th	90.00	100.00
☐	13	Lyre motif, gold, c. 19th.....................	140.00	180.00
☐	14	Shield cutout motif, gold, c. 19th	90.00	100.00
☐	15	Paste, gold filled, French, early 19th	110.00	125.00
☐	16	Ball motif, agate, gold, c. 19th	125.00	140.00
☐	17	Funnel motif, gold, c. 19th	110.00	125.00
☐	18	Heart motif, gold, c. 19th	110.00	125.00
☐	19	Compass motif, gold, c. 19th	125.00	140.00
☐	20	Mallet motif, gold, c. 19th...................	140.00	180.00
☐	21	Masonic and star motif, gold, c. 19th	125.00	150.00
☐	22	Chased motif, gold, c. 19th..................	90.00	100.00
☐	23	Dog on branch, sterling, c. 19th	125.00	150.00

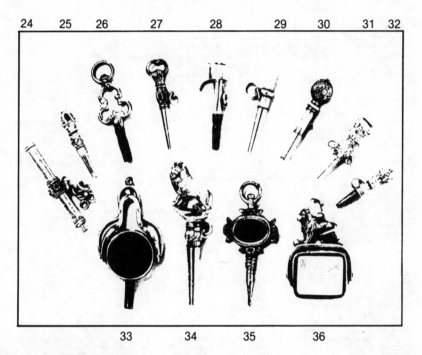

	24	Retractable pencil motif, four garnets, gold, c. 1840	175.00	200.00
☐	24	Retractable pencil motif, four garnets, gold, c. 1840....................................	175.00	200.00
☐	25	Chased motif, gold, c. 19th...................	85.00	100.00
☐	26	Shield openwork motif, gold, c. 19th..........	90.00	110.00
☐	27	Chased motif, gold, c. 19th...................	85.00	100.00
☐	28	Ax motif, gold, c. 19th......................	140.00	180.00
☐	29	Ribbed motif, gold, c. 19th..................	65.00	85.00
☐		Same as above but gold filled	25.00	35.00
☐	30	Ball motif, enamel, gold, c. 19th..............	140.00	180.00
☐	31	Chase motif, gold, c. 19th...................	165.00	185.00
☐	32	Chased motif, turquoise, gold, c. 19th.........	165.00	185.00
☐	33	Hardstone swivel seal, gold, c. 19th	185.00	200.00
☐	34	Lion motif, gold, c. 19th	300.00	375.00
☐	35	Flower motif, oval faceted garnet, gold, c. 1860..	250.00	300.00
☐	36	Lion motif, swivel hardstone seal, gold, c. 19th ..	225.00	260.00

INDEX

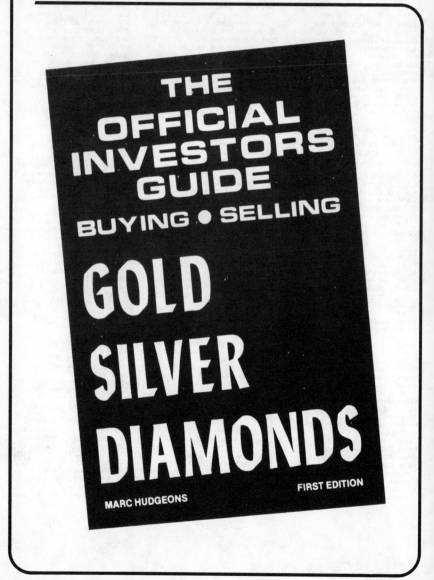

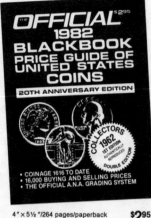